Research Methodology for Management

Research Methodology for Management

Dr. N.K. Mandal

CENTRUM PRESS
NEW DELHI-110002 (INDIA)

CENTRUM PRESS
H.O.: 4360/4, Ansari Road, Daryaganj,
New Delhi-110002 (India)
Tel: 23278000, 23261597, 23255577, 23286875
B.O.: No. 1015, Ist Main Road, BSK IIIrd Stage,
IIIrd Phase, IIIrd Block, Bengaluru-560085 (INDIA)
Tel: 080-41723429
Email: centrumpress@gmail.com
Visit us at: www.centrumpress.com

Research Methodology for Management

First Edition, 2013

ISBN 978-93-81938-25-6

PRINTED IN INDIA

Printed at Tarun Offset, Delhi

Contents

Preface

One important methodological option in conducting management research is the use of qualitative methods for data collection and analysis. Qualitative research, with its emphasis on understanding complex, interrelated and/or changing phenomena, is particularly relevant to the challenges of conducting management research. Qualitative methods combined with quantitative ones can provide particularly rich and robust inquiries. Either alone or in combination, qualitative research must be conducted with methodological rigor. This section does not attempt to provide a primer on qualitative methods. The role, benefits and appropriate use of qualitative research have been discussed extensively in the literature. Several references to excellent articles can be found in the references section and links to references.

Qualitative research methods are valuable in providing rich descriptions of complex phenomena; tracking unique or unexpected events, illuminating the experience and interpretation of events by actors with widely differing stakes and roles; giving voice to those whose views are rarely heard; conducting initial explorations to develop theories; and to generate and test hypotheses; and moving toward explanations.

Behavioural research is conducted by scientists who are interested in understanding the behaviour of human beings and animals. These scientists believe that knowledge gained through personal intuition or the claims of others is not a sufficient basis for drawing conclusions about behaviour. They demand that knowledge be gained through the accumulation of empirical data, as prescribed by the scientific method. Behavioural scientists understand that the scientific approach is not perfect, but it is better than any other known way of drawing conclusions about behaviour.

Although science is designed to create a collection of facts, it is not entirely free of values. The values of scientists influence how they interpret their data, what and whom they study, and how they report their research. For instance, some scientists conduct basic research, whereas others conduct applied research. One of the important goals of the scientific method is to make clear to others which aspects of the research process are based on facts and which are based on values. There are three major research designs in behavioural research. There are advantages and disadvantages to each of the approaches, and each provides an essential avenue of scientific investigation. Descriptive research, such as surveys and naturalistic observation, is designed to provide a snapshot of the current state of affairs.

This work would be useful for teachers, students and others who have much respect for Research Methodology and Management.

—*Editor*

1

Introduction to Research

Research can be defined as the search for knowledge, or as any systematic investigation, to establish novel facts, solve new or existing problems, prove new ideas, or develop new theories, usually using a scientific method.

The primary purpose for basic research (as opposed to applied research) is discovering, interpreting, and the development of methods and systems for the advancement of human knowledge on a wide variety of scientific matters of our world and the universe.

Scientific research relies on the application of the scientific method, a harnessing of curiosity. This research provides scientific information and theories for the explanation of the nature and the properties of the world around us. It makes practical applications possible. Scientific research is funded by public authorities, by charitable organizations and by private groups, including many companies. Scientific research can be subdivided into different classifications according to their academic and application disciplines.

Artistic research, also seen as 'practice-based research', can take form when creative works are considered both the research and the object of research itself. It is the debatable body of thought which offers an alternative to purely scientific methods in research in its search for knowledge and truth. Historical research is embodied in the historical method. Historians use primary sources and other evidence to systematically investigate a topic, and then to write histories in the form of accounts of the past. The phrase *my research* is also used loosely to describe a person's entire collection of information about a particular subject.

Etymology

As per the Merriam-Webster Online Dictionary, the word *research* is derived from the Middle French *"recerche"*, which means "to go about seeking", the term itself being derived from the Old French term *"recerchier"* a compound word from "re-" + "cerchier", or "sercher", meaning 'search'. The earliest recorded use of the term was in 1577.

Definitions

Research has been defined in a number of different ways. A broad definitior of research is given by Martin Shuttleworth- "In the broadest sense of the word, the definition of research includes any gathering of data, information and facts for the advancement of knowledge."

The Merriam-Webster Online Dictionary defines research in more detail as "a studious inquiry or examination; especially : investigation or experimentation aimed at the discovery and interpretation of facts, revision of accepted theories or laws in the light of new facts, or practical application of such new or revised theories or laws".

Scientific Research

Generally, research is understood to follow a certain structural process. Though step order may vary depending on the subject matter and researcher, the following steps are usually part of most formal research, both basic and applied:

1. Observations and Formation of the topic
2. Hypothesis
3. Conceptual definitions
4. Operational definition
5. Gathering of data
6. Analysis of data
7. Test, revising of hypothesis
8. Conclusion, reiteration if necessary.

A common misunderstanding is that by this method a hypothesis could be proven or tested. Generally a hypothesis is used to make predictions that can be tested by observing the outcome of an experiment. If the outcome is inconsistent with the hypothesis, then the hypothesis is rejected. However, if the outcome is consistent with the hypothesis, the experiment is said to support the hypothesis. This careful language is used because researchers recognize that alternative hypotheses may also be consistent with the observations. In this sense, a hypothesis can never be proven, but rather only supported by surviving rounds of scientific testing and, eventually, becoming widely thought of as true. A useful hypothesis allows prediction and within the accuracy of observation of the time, the prediction will be verified. As the accuracy of observation improves with time, the hypothesis may no longer provide an accurate prediction. In this case a new hypothesis will arise to challenge the old, and to the extent that the new hypothesis makes more accurate predictions than the old, the new will supplant it.

Historical Method

The historical method comprises the techniques and guidelines by which historians use historical sources and other evidence to research and then to write history. There are various history guidelines commonly used by historians in their work, under the headings of external criticism, internal criticism, and synthesis. This includes lower criticism and sensual criticism. Though items may vary depending on the subject matter and researcher, the following concepts are usually part of most formal historical research:

- Identification of origin date
- Evidence of localization
- Recognition of authorship
- Analysis of data
- Identification of integrity
- Attribution of credibility.

Research Methods

The goal of the research process is to produce new knowledge. This process takes three main forms:

- Exploratory research, which structures and identifies new problems

- Constructive research, which develops solutions to a problem
- Empirical research, which tests the feasibility of a solution using empirical evidence.

Research can also fall into two distinct types:

- Primary research (collection of data that does not exist yet)
- Secondary research (summary, collation and/or synthesis of existing research).

In social sciences and later in other disciplines, the following two research methods can be applied, depending on the properties of the subject matter and on the objective of the research:

- Qualitative research (understanding of human behaviour and the reasons that govern such behaviour)
- Quantitative research (systematic empirical investigation of quantitative properties and phenomena and their relationships).

Research is often conducted using the hourglass model Structure of Research. The hourglass model starts with a broad spectrum for research, focusing in on the required information through the methodology of the project.

Publishing

Academic publishing describes a system that is necessary in order for academic scholars to peer review the work and make it available for a wider audience. The 'system', which is probably disorganized enough not to merit the title, varies widely by field, and is also always changing, if often slowly. Most academic work is published in journal article or book form. In publishing, STM publishing is an abbreviation for academic publications in science, technology, and medicine.

Most established academic fields have their own journals and other outlets for publication, though many academic journals are somewhat interdisciplinary, and publish work from several distinct fields or subfields. The kinds of publications that are accepted as contributions of knowledge or research vary greatly between fields; from the print to the electronic format. Business models are different in the electronic environment. Since about the early 1990s, licensing of electronic resources, particularly journals, has been very common. Presently, a major trend, particularly with respect to scholarly journals, is open access. There are two main forms of open access: open access publishing, in which the articles or the whole journal is freely available from the time of publication, and self-archiving, where the author makes a copy of their own work freely available on the web.

Research Funding

Most funding for scientific research comes from two major sources: Corporate research and development departments; and government research councils such as the National Institutes of Health in the USA and the Medical Research Council in the UK. These are managed primarily through universities and in some cases through military contractors Many senior researchers (such as group leaders) spend a significant amount of their time applying for grants for research funds. These grants are necessary not only for researchers to carry out their research, but also as a source of merit.

Original Research

Original research is research that is not exclusively based on a summary, review or synthesis of earlier publications on the subject of research. This material is of a primary source character. The purpose of the original research is to produce new knowledge, rather than to present the existing knowledge in a new form (*e.g.*, summarized or classified).

Different Forms

Original research can take a number of forms, depending on the discipline it pertains to. In experimental work, it typically involves direct or indirect observation of the researched subject, e.g., in the laboratory or in the field, documents the methodology, results, and conclusions of an experiment or set of experiments, or offers a novel interpretation of previous results. In analytical work, there are typically some new (for example) mathematical results produced, or a new way of approaching an existing problem. In some subjects which do not typically carry out experimentation or analysis of this kind, the originality is in the particular way existing understanding is changed or reinterpreted based on the outcome of the work of the researcher. The degree of originality of the research is among major criteria for articles to be published in academic journals and usually established by means of peer review. Graduate students are commonly required to perform original research as part of a dissertation.

Artistic Research

The controversial trend of artistic teaching becoming more academics-oriented is leading to artistic research being accepted as the primary mode of enquiry in art as in the case of other disciplines. One of the characteristics of artistic research is that it must accept subjectivity as opposed to the classical scientific methods. As such, it is similar to the social sciences in using qualitative research and intersubjectivity as tools to apply measurement and critical analysis. Artistic research has been defined by Dans och Cirkushögskolan (the University of Dance and Circus), Stockholm in the following manner-"Artistic research is to investigate and test with the purpose of gaining knowledge within and for our artistic disciplines. It is based on artistic practices, methods and criticality. Through presented documentation, the insights gained shall be placed in a context."

THE IMPORTANCE OF RESEARCH

The purpose of research is to inform action. Thus, your study should seek to contextualize its findings within the larger body of research. Research must always be high quality in order to produce knowledge that is applicable outside of the research setting with implications that go beyond the group that has participated in the research. Furthermore, the results of your study should have implications for policy and project implementation.

One problem that often plagues progress in global health is the slow translation of research into practice. Oftentimes, a disconnect exists between those who create the evidence base and those who are positioned to implement the research findings. The underlying problem is in "the way in which the production of evidence is organized institutionally with highly centralized mechanisms, whereas the application of that science is highly decentralized. This social distance prevails because scientists are more oriented to the international audiences of other scientists for which they publish than to the needs of practitioners, policy makers, or the local public." Thus, as researchers, it is imperative to take steps to overcome this barrier. Publishing your study may be one initial step to make your research known to the global community. Other proactive measures can be taken to encourage the uptake of evidence-based interventions. For example, you can present your research findings at various venues such as the Unite for Sight sponsored Global Health and Innovation Conference. Furthermore, you can send the results of your study to local officials, policy-makers, and community leaders.

Goals of Research

There are relatively few published studies about eye care in developing countries, and Unite For Sight encourages all volunteers to consider developing a research study to contribute important knowledge to the eye care community on a global scale. Pursuing a research project will be a challenging and rewarding experience, and this opportunity enables you to pursue an in-depth original study about a topic of interest.

Well-conducted research is vital to the success of global heath endeavours. Not only does research form the foundation of program development and policies all over the world, but it can also be translated into effective global health programs. Research draws its power from the fact that it is empirical: rather than merely theorizing about what *might* be effective or what *could* work, researchers go out into the field and design studies that give policymakers hard data on which they can base their decisions. Furthermore, good research produces results that are examinable by peers, methodologies that can be replicated, and knowledge that can be applied to real-world situations. Researchers work as a team to enhance our knowledge of how to best address the world's problems.

The "Iterative" Process of Research

Ultimately, the key to a successful research project lies in iteration: the process of returning again and again to the research questions, methods, and data, which leads to new ideas, revisions and improvements. It is easy to think of research as a step-by-step "1,2,3" process, but it is important to be fluid and open to change. Oftentimes, by discussing the research project with advisers and peers one will find that new research questions need to be added, variables need to be omitted, and other changes made. As a proposed study is examined and re-examined from different perspectives, it may begin to transform and take a different shape. This is to be expected and is a component of a good research study. In addition, it is important to examine study methods and data from different viewpoints to ensure a comprehensive approach to the research question. In conclusion, there is no one formula for developing a successful research study, but it is important to realize that the research process is cyclical and iterative.

RESEARCH VALUE

We can trace the roots of Oriental medicine back thousands of years. Historians can look back to the *Huang Di Neijing* (*The Yellow Emperor's Internal Classic*) more than 2,300 years ago and find that the Chinese performed autopsies to determine the cause of death. This may not be the first type of research related to the practice of Oriental medicine, but it would be a very good place to start.

Why did the Chinese perform these procedures? To demonstrate, on a consistent basis, what happens to the human body and why. Today, the key to any health profession is how it performes in clinical practice. The true test of a profession's credibility and growth is the ability of a clinician to get consistent results (what happens and why) in the treatment of patients.

How does a clinician achieve consistent, predictable and reliable results in treatment after treatment, patient after patient? The answer is research. All professions grow, change, build credibility and improve based on the research they conduct and produce. Millions of Oriental medicine treatments have been delivered. Patients have benefited and moved to new levels of health and wellness. Today, we are experiencing a meeting of Eastern and Western forms of care. Western medicine, with its voluminous masses of empirical data, is now looking to Eastern medicine, which has produced remarkable results in a large percentage of patients. The question is, can these results be reproduced reliably and consistently? Oriental medicine is in a stage of growth and development in which a research paradigm must be established and properly conducted. Credible studies must be undertaken, and their results must be verified to validate the physiological aspects of Oriental medicine.

A number of questions come to mind when asking about research:

1. What type of research is going to be conducted?
2. Where will it be conducted?
3. How will the results of the research impact our profession?
4. Who's going to pay for it?

In Western medicine, the gold standard for determining the effectiveness of a product or technique remains the randomized controlled trial (RCT). While the validity of the RCT has come under fire recently, it's still one of the biggest factors that insurance providers, health plans and managed care groups use to determine whether they'll provide coverage. If we want to be included in these groups' plans, we'll need to start publishing large-scale, *bona fide* research, and the RCT may be the best place to start.

Many of today's studies are conducted at universities and other institutions. We already have a good foundation, with more than fourdozen acupuncture colleges in the U.S. and dozens more overseases — not to mention the Society for Acupuncture Research in Maryland. Many of these schools already have small, but growing, research departments. With the advent of the Internet and other forms of communication, there's no reason they can't work together to produce a large, multi-site study. Research helps build the respect and credibility our profession needs to achieve national licensing. Increased research improves our chances of achieving licensing in all 50 states, based on standards of competency that will be due — at least in part — to research. Positive research backed by large, controlled studies can also play a role in the profession's getting state and national legislation passed that would be favourable to Oriental medicine practitioners and their patients.

Research findings also help protect the public; they can begin to understand what acupuncture is, how it works, and what it can do for them. If everyone benefits from research, it only seems fair that everyone should contribute. Support comes in many forms. The most obvious is financial, but there are other ways of helping further Oriental medicine. In other professions, alumni associations help support ongoing research. Research grants are slowly beginning to surface around the country. More schools are looking toward conducting research or opening research departments.

Still, much more work needs to be done. Recently, an acupuncturist was sitting in front of a hospital credentialing committee composed of seven medical doctors. When they asked the acupuncturist what happened to a neuron when an acupuncture needle was inserted, the acupuncturist froze: he wasn't able to explain the effects to the doctors in a way that made sense to them scientifically.

Research will help the profession bridge that gap in communication. It will not only support and explain procedures, it will lead to better treatment and functional outcomes. For new patients "sitting on the fence," it will give them reason to give acupuncture and Oriental medicine a try. For those who already believe in acupuncture, it will help persuade them to refer more of their friends for care. And for providers of Oriental medicine, research will prove to the world that what they do has scientific merit, and it will help them experience the rewards they rightly deserve.

RESEARCH AND DEVELOPMENT

The phrase research and development (also R and D or, more often, R&D), according to the Organization for Economic Co-operation and Development, refers to "creative work undertaken on a systematic basis in order to increase the stock of knowledge, including knowledge of man, culture and society, and the use of this stock of knowledge to devise new applications". Research and development is often scientific or towards developing particular technologies and is frequently carried out as corporate or governmental activity.

New product design and development is more often than not a crucial factor in the survival of a company. In an industry that is changing fast, firms must continually revise their design and range of products. This is necessary due to continuous technology change and development as well as other competitors and the changing preference of customers. Without an R&D program, a firm must rely on strategic alliances, acquisitions, and networks to tap into the innovations of others.

A system driven by marketing is one that puts the customer needs first, and only produces goods that are known to sell. Market research is carried out, which establishes what is needed. If the development is technology driven then it is a matter of selling what it is possible to make. The product range is developed so that production processes are as efficient as possible and the products are technically superior, hence possessing a natural advantage in the market place. The top eight spenders in terms of percentage of GDP were Israel (4.53%), Sweden (3.73%), Finland (3.45%) Japan (3.39%), South Korea (3.23%), Switzerland (2.9%), Iceland (2.78%) and United States (2.62%). The Commitment to Development Index ranks these countries, rewarding them for research and development that support the creation and dissemination of innovations of value to developing countries.

In general, R&D activities are conducted by specialized units or centres belonging to companies, universities and state agencies. In the context of commerce, "research and development" normally refers to future-oriented, longer-term activities in science or technology, using similar techniques to scientific research without predetermined outcomes and with broad forecasts of commercial yield.

Statistics on organizations devoted to "R&D" may express the state of an industry, the degree of competition or the lure of progress. Some common measures include: budgets, numbers of patents or on rates of peer-reviewed publications. Bank ratios are one of the best measures, because they are continuously maintained, public and reflect risk.

In the U.S., a typical ratio of research and development for an industrial company is about 3.5% of revenues. A high technology company such as a computer manufacturer might spend 7%. Although Allergan (a biotech company) tops the spending table with 43.4% investment, anything over 15% is remarkable and usually gains a reputation for being a high technology company. Companies in this category include pharmaceutical companies such as Merck & Co. (14.1%) or

Novartis (15.1%), and engineering companies like Ericsson (24.9%). Such companies are often seen as credit risks because their spending ratios are so unusual.

Generally such firms prosper only in markets whose customers have extreme needs, such as medicine, scientific instruments, safety-critical mechanisms (aircraft) or high technology military armaments. The extreme needs justify the high risk of failure and consequently high gross margins from 60% to 90% of revenues. That is, gross profits will be as much as 90% of the sales cost, with manufacturing costing only 10% of the product price, because so many individual projects yield no exploitable product. Most industrial companies get only 40% revenues.

On a technical level, high tech organizations explore ways to re-purpose and repackage advanced technologies as a way of amortizing the high overhead. They often reuse advanced manufacturing processes, expensive safety certifications, specialized embedded software, computer-aided design software, electronic designs and mechanical subsystems. Research has shown that firms with a persistent R&D strategy outperform those with an irregular or no R&D investment programme.

Pharmaceuticals

Research often refers to basic experimental research; development refers to the exploitation of discoveries. Research involves the identification of possible chemical compounds or theoretical mechanisms. In the United States, universities are the main provider of research level products. In the United States, corporations buy licences from universities or hire scientists directly when economically solid research level products emerge and the development phase of drug delivery is almost entirely managed by private enterprise. Development is concerned with proof of concept, safety testing, and determining ideal levels and delivery mechanisms. Development often occurs in phases that are defined by drug safety regulators in the country of interest. In the United States, the development phase can cost between $10 to $200 million and approximately one in ten compounds identified by basic research pass all development phases and reach market. Pharmaceuticals market, however are extremely complex in many respects.

Large public sector investment in biomedical R & D influence private companies' choices about what to work and how intensively to invest in research and development. The returns on private sector R & D are attractive, on average but they vary considerably from one drug to the next. Consumer demand for prescription drug is often indirect, mediated by doctors and health insurers. New drug must undergo costly and time consuming testing before they sold.

Business

Research and development is nowadays of great importance in business as the level of competition, production processes and methods are rapidly increasing. It is of special importance in the field of marketing where companies keep an eagle eye on competitors and customers in order to keep pace with modern trends and analyse the needs, demands and desires of their customers. Unfortunately, research and development are very difficult to manage, since the defining feature of research is that the researchers do not know in advance exactly how to accomplish the desired result. As a result, higher R&D spending does not guarantee "more creativity, higher profit or a greater market share".

R&D Alliance

An R&D alliance is a mutually beneficial formal relationship between two or more parties to pursue a set of agreed goals while remaining independent organisations, where acquiring new knowledge is a goal by itself. The different parties agree to combine their knowledge to create new innovative products. Thanks to funding from government organizations, like the European Union's Seventh Framework Programme (FP7), and modern advances in technology, R&D alliances have now become more efficient. Every company has their own research and develop department.

R&D Reorientation

Industrial sector is transforming from vertical integration to horizontal structure. So far this transformation has taken place in manufacturing, but now it's the turn for R&D to make a paradigm shift. The restructuring trends of manufacturing predict the future of R&D to be focused, financially independent, universally expanded and distributed. In 2003 on July the 25th with their article titled Reorienting R&D for a Horizontal Future Downey, Greenberg and Kapur illustrated that a horizontal structure of development in all industrial disciplines is required because of emerging markets, cost cutting needs and globalization. Collaborative networks in a decentralized environment are producing better results because of flexibility and cost reduction. R&D is spreading across the globe for faster development and unique innovations. Building block structure is getting popular in R&D because it is more manageable and focused.

In a challenging market environment after manufacturing now companies are eyeing to reduce the development cost where R&D needs to justify its existence as an independent profit centre with increased productivity and reduced operational costs. This can only be achieved through collaboration and trade-offs. Formation of horizontal collaborative network is challenging because it incorporates the issues of adaptability, security, cultural differences, varying standards, trust and ownership. Globalization is pushing R&D to concentrate on global design approach with the design flexibility where products can be tailored as per different geographic markets.

Innovating products in response to market requirements will keep organizations in business whereas knowing their own productivity and capacity will enable them to operate more effectively. Firms can make better investment decisions if they can predict their development cost. This will directly add to the bottom line of the business. In a race to improve the productivity, lower the cost and save time, firms should not forget to retain the expertise of their core competencies. The proper synchronization of global resources must be addressed in order to save time and money. Companies must support the development of innovation management system for future growth.

Companies are decentralizing their R&D units across the globe to extract the time and diversity benefits. Customer centric orientation is most profitable approach for any firm to operate in a competitive environment. R&D is an area where 'The World is Flat' theory applies perfectly. World is shrinking with the increasing pace of information technology, and the same time decentralization is making our days longer. In this fast pace environment managing intellectual property is more critical for businesses to keep themselves in the race. Never ending attempts should be made to optimize the development with minimal resources. Flattening the innovation process will result in technological development with greater profits and efficiency.

TYPES OF RESEARCH

Research can be classified by purpose or by method. If we categorise it by purpose, it would fall into two major categories: Basic Research and Applied Research, while in case of method, it would be deductive research and inductive research.

Also called Pure or fundamental Research, it is undertaken for increase in knowledge. There is no direct benefit as it is a research for the sake of research. It is conducted to satisfy any curiosity such as: (a) what makes things happen, (b) why society changes and (c) why social relations are in a certain way. In fact, it is the source of most new theories, principles and ideas. Basic research rarely helps anyone directly. It only stimulates new ways of thinking. The main motivation is to *expand man's knowledge*. There is absolutely no commercial value to the discoveries resulting from such research.

However, in the long run, it forms the basis of applied research or development commercial products. If basic work is done first, then applied spin-offs often eventually result from this research. As Dr. George Smoot of LBNL says, "People cannot foresee the future well enough to predict what's going to develop from basic research. If we only did "applied research", we would still be making better spears."

Applied Research

It is use of basic research or past theories, knowledge and methods for solving an existing problem. It deals with practical problems. It is opposed to pure research which is not problem-oriented but for the increase in knowledge which may or may not be used in future. In the present world situation, more emphasis is being given to applied research to solve problems arising out of overpopulation and scarcity of natural resources. Applied research should not be treated the same as Research

& Development (R&D) which is involved in developing products demanded by the existing clients.

Applied Research, on the other hand, focuses on uncovering what needs are not being met and use that information in designing products or services that would create their own demand. Thus, applied research brings in new customers and also provides better products and services to the existing customers. In old days, the mobile phone was expensive, bulky and had a short range. Applied Research foresaw that this product would have a limited market and stressed on cost-cutting, reduced weight and long-distance communication. Such measures caused a heavy demand.

Methods or Approaches

In research, conclusions are based two methods known as the *deduction* and *induction*. Both are widely used in research projects. This helps the researchers to understand, explain, or predict business phenomena. Deduction follows an approach which is "top-down" or "from general to specific." On the other hand, induction is "bottom-up" in nature or from specific to general. In deduction, we start from a theory and try to prove it right with the help of available information. In induction, we observe some happening, deduct a pattern and draw conclusion.

Example of Deduction

1. All men are mortal. (General and no specific to one man)
2. Socrates is a man
3. (Therefore,) Socrates is mortal (specific).

Example of Induction

This ice is cold. (Specific, based on a direct observation.)

All ice is cold. (General, can be applied to any ice).

Take another example: 3 + 5 = 8 and eight is an even number. Therefore, an odd number added to another odd number will result in an even number.

Example of Both Deduction and Induction

1. You push the light switch and find no light
2. You ask the question, Why no light? (induction)

3. You infer a conclusion (hypotheses) to answer the question and explain the fact that the bulb is burned out. (deduction)
4. You use this hypothesis to conclude (deduce) that the light will not go on when we push the switch. We know from experience that burned-out bulb will not light.

Package and Product Testing

We do product and package testing to estimate consumer and market response for a new product going to market. On the basis of the data captured from this testing, our clients can design more effective product launches taking into consideration the various product attributes and market zones.

We can also test vis-à-vis competitors how the product will fare in terms of product attributes. Do you need to obtain specific information regarding your organization and areas for best practice implementation? AbsolutData's Best Practices Surveys can help you measure your target audience's opinions about their needs and aspirations. We can help you assess the effectiveness of:

- Sales Strategy and Customer Management-the impact of your strategy formulation and communication process across your sales organization
- Sales Talent management-Effectiveness of your hiring processes and cultivation of employees/manpower
- Sales Process Design and Productivity – sales process and the support provided for its execution
- Metrics and Rewards – Monitor and measure performance as well as the rewards system in place at your organization.

These surveys consist of agree/disagree types of radio button questions and are ideal for Managers, Representatives or Operational Managers.)

Employee Skill Assessment Studies

In order to accurately identify where the various organizations can target their skill improvements, we program surveys for organizational Sales Skill Analysis. These types of surveys are known as Upskilling Surveys. These projects provide a valuable opportunity for the employees to tell the organization what they must do in order to succeed.

Usually, a particular sales team is nominated by the manager(s) to participate in the Assessment for the project. To gain an understanding of current capabilities, the team members in the focus roles will first be asked to do a self-assessment of the skill model. Then, the direct manager will perform an assessment, using team members' initial feedback as a starting point. These surveys ask the team members to consider their capabilities across a broad range of skills, some of which are core requirements of their current position, and some of which will increase in importance as the business evolves.

Usually, the survey consists of agree/disagree types of radio button questions. They may be for the Managers, representatives or operational managers. Also, these surveys require complex mapping. For example:

- The login page may direct the manager to assess various employees using the link inserted
- The manager can view the responses of their employees
- The manager can view the names of the employee etc.

Employee Productivity Surveys

Our main offering in Employee Productivity Surveys is Time and Productivity Survey (TPA Surveys). This type of survey is typically conducted for the sales processes. It offers the team member the opportunity to provide confidential feedback directly to the leadership on how the executive team can help them work more effectively. Specifically, questions are asked about the amount of time for trade off between selling versus administrative activities, the effectiveness of the various sales tools/resources available, and the team member's personal sales process.

This survey contain following major sections:

- Sales Activity Section-This section focuses on how they spend their time
- Sales Process & Strategy Section-This section will focus on the various processes and strategies they employ in the role

- Sales Resources Section-This section will focus on the sales resources and tools that are available for them in their role
- Other section – this section asks the demography etc.

These surveys are for both Managers and representatives.

Customer Satisfaction

This type of survey is used for organizations to identify skills that are critical for meeting the needs of their customers. Once these skills are identified the organization intends to dedicate training and development resources to these key focus areas. As part of this survey, we target a select group of customers whose feedback is strongly valued by the organization. The type of questions asked is mixed, including:

- Background and history of the customer relationship
- Customer rating for the organization's skills.

Ad/Copy Testing

This type of survey is done to track the audience mindset about the client's product. Estimate if they are well informed about your product or not, if the ad is working or not, if the ad is converting into sales. We can also make product attribute matrixes based on client requirements to test where the ad fits on the matrix.

Competitor Research and Analysis: Estimate how competitors are faring on similar products. Estimate market share, calculate and compare market standing vis-à-vis competition.

Tracking and Market Performance: We can conduct a time based analysis over different periods of time, to understand:

- Customer churn out over a period of time and emergence of new customers
- Product performance in market
- The benchmarking of your product/services against the overall market, comparable business models, and other competitive models by geographical region. These contribute significantly in validating existing business initiatives and developing more effective business strategies.

Brand and Corporate Image Research

Across multiple countries, multi lingual, maxdiff conjoint is used to analyse the brand image and how consumers align to the concepts of the brand. We also assess whether consumers prefer personal use or corporate use of the product/brand. This type of surveys is specifically relevant in cases where sales are based on the brand's image and not the product in particular. We measure the product's brand equity in the market as well as the brand perception vis-à-vis competition.

Website Testing

This is used for ecommerce businesses, and specifically companies that do a lot of online trading. This study evaluates the speed, accessibility, performance, product presentation and the look and feel of your website. The look and feel includes layout, organization, colour, images, quality of images, download sizes etc.

DEDUCTIVE METHOD

Like Sherlock Holmes, the starting point is a given situation and moving to a specific conclusion. All relevant information is assembled, studies to solve the mystery. Aristotle, a Greek philosopher, described deduction as "drawing conclusions by applying rules or principles; logically moving from a general rule or principle to a specific solution". It is the process of reaching a conclusion that is guaranteed to follow, if the evidence provided is true and the reasoning used to reach the conclusion is correct. An investigator is distracted with the noise and thinks that "noise adversely affects mental problem solving." It can be turned into a research question like "would it be more conducive to solve mental puzzle when there is no noise."

In order to test it, two puzzles are given to the same group, one in noiseless conditions and other in a blaring noise. If the results of test conducted under noisy-environment are poor it can be deduced or concluded that controlling the aversive noise is helpful in solving mental puzzles. (Someone may say "why research, it is apparent?" It is logical to say it but it had been previously proved and awareness has been created of the noise pollution. In fact, noise can be measure in term of decibel (dB) and by research, it has been established how much noise is tolerable under what conditions. Zero dB describes perfect silence while 140 dB would reflect a gunshot.

In deductive method, the premises (basis or evidence) provide a guarantee of the true conclusion. Consider the following example:

1. There are 32 books on the top-shelf of the book case,
2. There are 12 books on the lower-shelf of the book case.
3. There are no books anywhere on the bookcase.

Also known as Inductive reasoning or logic, this methods involves moving from a specific situation to a general conclusion This is a way of "theory-building", whereby "specific facts are used to create a theory that explains relationships between the facts and allows prediction of future knowledge". This method is more open-ended and exploratory. This does not give 100% guarantee of truth but probability of being true.

Here is an example:

1. Socrates was Greek. (premise)
2. Most Greeks eat fish. (premise)
3. Socrates ate fish. (conclusion).

While the premises were true, it is possible that conclusion was false. Maybe Socrates was allergic to fish, for example. It can be said that inductive approach is weaker than deductive approach as there is possibility of arriving at false conclusion. However, it is not entirely true. This hub states categories of research. If one wants to classify the research by purpose, it would be basic research and applied research. While basic research is done for the sake of gaining knowledge or exploration or invention, the applied research uses the knowledge gained through basic research for solving problem. While discovery of laser was through basic research, its subsequent use in remote-control pointer or surgery is a result of applied research. Another classification is deductive research and inductive research. In deduction, we move from general to specific while in induction, it is the other way round. Both methods are used in research.

THE BASIC TYPES OF RESEARCH

Research is an academic activity and as such the term should be used in a technical sense. According to Clifford woody research companies defining and redefining problems, formulating hypothesis or suggested solutions; collecting, organizing and evaluating data; making deductions and reaching conclusions; and at last carefully testing the conclusions to determine whether they fit the formulating hypothesis. Research is, thus, an original contribution to the existing stock of knowledge making for its advancement. It is the persuit of truth with the help of study, observation, comparison and experiment.

The basic types of research are as follows:

Descriptive vs. Analytical: Descriptive research includes surveys and fact-finding enquiries of different kinds. The major purpose of descriptive research is description of the state of affairs as it exists at present. In social science and business research we quite often use the term Ex post facto research for descriptive research studies. The main characteristic of this method is that the researcher has no control over the variables; he can only report what has happened or what is happening. Most ex post facto research projects are used for descriptive studies in which the researcher seeks to measure such items as, for example, frequency of shopping, preferences of people, or similar data. Ex post facto studies also include attempts by researchers to discover causes even when they cannot control the variables. The methods of research utilized in descriptive research are survey methods of all kinds, including comparative and correlational methods. In analytical research, on the other hand, the researcher has to use facts or information already available, and analyse these to make a critical evaluation of the material.

Applied vs. Fundamental: Research can either be applied (or action) research or fundamental (to basic or pure) research. Applied research aims at finding a solution for an immediate problem facing a society or an industrial/business organisation, whereas fundamental research is mainly concerned with generalisations and with the formulation of a theory. "Gathering knowledge for knowledge's sake is termed 'pure' or 'basic' research." Research concerning some natural phenomenon or relating to pure mathematics are examples of fundamental research. Similarly, research studies, concerning human behaviour carried on with view to make generalizations about human behaviour, are also examples of fundamental research, but research aimed at certain conclusions facing a concrete social or business problem is an example of applied research. Research to identify social, economic or political trends that may effect a particular institution or copy research or the marketing research are examples of applied research. Thus, the central aim of applied research is to discover a solution for some pressing practical problems. Whereas basic research is directed towards finding information that has a broad base of applications and thus, adds to the already existing organized body of scientific knowledge.

Quantitative vs. Qualitative: Quantitative research is based on the measurement of quantity or amount. It is applicable to phenomena that can be expressed in terms of quantity. Qualitative research, on the other hand, is concerned with qualitative phenomenon, i.e., phenomena relating to or involving quality or kind. For instance, when we are interested in investigating the reasons for human behaviour, we quite often talk of 'Motivation Research', an important type of qualitative research. This type of research aims at discovering the underlying motives and desires, using in depth interviews for the purpose. Other techniques of such research are word association tests, sentence completion tests, story completion tests and similar other projective techniques. Attitude or opinion research, i.e., research designed to find out how people feel or what they think about a particular subject or institution is also qualitative research. Qualitative research is specially important in the behavioural sciences where the aim is to discover the underlying motives of human behaviour. Through such research we can analyse the various factors which motivate people to behave in a particular manner or which make people like or dislike a particular thing. It may be stated, however, that to apply qualitative research in practice is relatively a difficult job and therefore, while doing such research, one should seek guidance from experimental psychologists.

Conceptual vs. Empirical: Conceptual research is that related to some abstract idea(s) or theory. It is generally used by philosophers and thinkers to develop new concepts or to reinterpret existing ones. On the other hand, empirical research relies an experience or observation alone, often without due regard for system and theory. It is data based research, coming up with conclusions which arc capable of being verified by observation or experiment. We can also call it as experimental type of research, in such a research it is necessary to get at facts firsthand, at their source, and actively to go about doing certain things to stimulate the production of desired information. In such I research, die researcher must first provide himself with a working hypothesis or guess as to the probable results. He then works to get enough facts (data) to prove or disprove his hypothesis.

He then sets up experimental designs which he thinks will manipulate the persons or the materials concerned so as to bring forth the desired information. Such research is thus characterised by the experimenter's control over the variables under study and his deliberate manipulation of one of them to study its effects. Empirical research is appropriate when proof is sought that certain variables affect other variables in some way. Evidence gathered through experiments or empirical studies is today considered to be the most powerful support possible for a given hypothesis.

Some Other Types of Research: All other types of research are variations of one or more of the above stated approaches, based on either the purpose of research, or the time required to accomplish research, on the environment in which research is done, or on the basis of some other similar factor. Form the point of view of time, we can think of research either as one-time research or longitudinal research. In the former case the research is confined to a single time-period, whereas in the latter case the research is carried on over several time-periods. Research can be field-setting research or laboratory research or simulation research, depending upon the environment in which it is to be carried out. Research can as well be understood as clinical or diagnostic research. Such research follow case-study methods or indepth approaches to reach the basic causal relations. Such studies usually go deep into the causes of things or events that interest us, using very small samples and very deep probing data gathering devices. The research may be exploratory or it may be formalized. The objective of exploratory research is the development of hypotheses rather than their testing, whereas formalized research studies are those with substantial structure and with specific hypotheses to be tested. Historical research is that which utilizes historical sources like documents, remains, etc. to study events or ideas of the past, including the philosophy of persons and groups at any remote point of time. Research can also be classified as conclusion-oriented and decision oriented. While doing conclusion oriented research, a researcher is free to pick up a problem, redesign the enquiry as he proceeds and is prepared to conceptualize as he wishes. Decision-oriented research is always for the need of a decision maker and the researcher in this case is not free to embark upon research according to his own inclination. Operations research is an example of decision oriented research since it is a scientific method of providing executive departments with a quantitative basis for decisions regarding operations under their control.

PRIMARY STAGES OF RESEARCH PROCESS

Research is a source which can be draw upon to make a substantial contribution to the body of the knowledge; research should be followed by some sort of original contribution. The primary stage of any research process includes:

- Observation: Research start with observation, which leads to curiosity to learn more about what has been observed. Observation can either be unaided visual observation or guided and controlled observation. Sometimes a casual or associated observation leading to substantial research and a great invention. Deliberate and guided observation can also form the basis for research. While observation leads to research, research results in elaborate observation and convulsions; or even further research observation can either be subjective or objective. These are participant observation, on –participant observation, controlled observation and non-controlled observation.
- Interest: The observation of certain occurrences creates an interest and inquisitiveness in the mind of the researcher to study it further. This is the basis of interest to study the subject matter of observation. It may be self-interest or group interest. The interest is the guiding force behind any research.

- Crystallization: Crystallization is the process of designing the definite form of Research to be undertaken for the purpose of studying the subject matter. It is the formulation of the research project, a defining its objectives, rationale, scope, methodology, limitations, including financial commitments and sources. It is at this stage that the research project is given a concrete shape and structure, forming a basis of further investigation.
- Formulation of hypothesis: At this stage the hypothesis is formed on the basis of observation. Hypothesis is apart of the scientific method, and has been dealt with in detail in the chapter on "scientific method and hypothesis"
- Primary synopsis: Synopsis is a summary/outline/brief of any subject. It is not a complete subject still formalization of a subject/replica of a subject. It saves time. It will give an idea of time required for presentation of the main subject. Once the subject is decided you can arrange titles likes like main headings, paragraph heading-elaborate the paragraph with important of main issues.
- Conceptual clarity: Any researcher should have in-depth background knowledge of the topic of his study. He can gain such basic knowledge only be an extensive reading of text books, specialized books and publications on the topic in addition to articles and research papers published in journals and periodicals, reports of the past studies, etc. he can also gain knowledge with the people concerned and by his own observation. However it is imperative for a researcher to gain a deep knowledge form any reliable source prior to actually plunging himself into a research, so theta he may have clear knowledge of the concepts which would be of value to him in his task.
- Documentation: The documentary sources are important sources of information for a researcher. A document is anything in writing – a record, files or diaries, published or unpublished-which can be extracted and used in research. It is very valuable source of information for

research either in management or in social science. It may comprises office files, business and legal papers, biographies, official and unofficial records, letters, proceedings of any courts, committees, societies, assemblies and parliaments, enactments, constitution, reports of surveys or research of commissions, official statistics, newspapers editorials, special articles, company news, cases or company directors reports etc. documentation is the process of collecting and extracting the documents which relevant research. Documents may be classified into personal documents, Company documents, Consultants report and published materials and Public documents

- Bibliography: At the end of any research report a bibliography is generally added. This is the list of books publication, periodicals, journals, reports, etc. which are used by researcher in the connection with the study. It is a description of books, their authorship, editions, publishers, year of publication, place of publication etc. in ordinary circumstance, a researcher reads, and makes notes form, many books and publications at the primary stage of researcher in order to gain conceptual clarity. He prepares a list of such publications are reports then and there, which helps him in the course of his research. On the contrary a bibliography contains and is composed of the details of publications that the researcher has used in connection with his study. These facilities any further reference to the matter either by the researcher himself or anybody who goes through the researcher report.

Defining a Research Problem

Defining a research problem is the fuel that drives the scientific process, and is the foundation of any research method and experimental design, from true experiment to case study. It is one of the first statements made in any research paper and, as well as defining the research area, should include a quick synopsis of how the hypothesis was arrived at.

Operationalization is then used to give some indication of the exact definitions of the variables, and the type of scientific measurements used. This will lead to the proposal of a viable hypothesis. As an aside, when scientists are putting forward proposals for research funds, the quality of their research problem often makes the difference between success and failure.

Structuring the Research Problem

Look at any scientific paper, and you will see the research problem, written almost like a statement of intent. Defining a research problem is crucial in defining the quality of the answers, and determines the exact research method used. A quantitative experimental design uses deductive reasoning to arrive at a testable hypothesis. Qualitative research designs use inductive reasoning to propose a research statement.

Defining a Research Problem

Formulating the research problem begins during the first steps of the scientific process. As an example, a literature review and a study of previous experiments, and research, might throw up some vague areas of interest.

Many scientific researchers look at an area where a previous researcher generated some interesting results, but never followed up. It could be an interesting area of research, which nobody else has fully explored.

A scientist may even review a successful experiment, disagree with the results, the tests used, or the methodology, and decide to refine the research process, retesting the hypothesis.

This is called the conceptual definition, and is an overall view of the problem. A science report will generally begin with an overview of the previous research and real-world observations. The researcher will then state how this led to defining a research problem.

The Operational Definitions

The operational definition is the determining the scalar properties of the variables. For example, temperature, weight and time are usually well known and defined, with only the exact scale used needing definition. If a researcher is measuring abstract concepts, such as intelligence, emotions, and subjective responses, then a system of measuring numerically needs to be established, allowing statistical analysis and replication. For example, intelligence may be measured with IQ and human responses could be measured with a questionnaire from '1-strongly disagree', to '5 – strongly agree'. Behavioural biologists and social scientists might design an ordinal scale for measuring and rating behaviour. These measurements are always subjective, but allow statistics and replication of the whole research method. This is all an essential part of defining a research problem.

Examples of Defining a Research Problem

An anthropologist might find references to a relatively unknown tribe in Papua New Guinea. Through inductive reasoning, she arrives at the research problem and asks, 'How do these people live and how does their culture relate to nearby tribes?' She has found a gap in knowledge, and she seeks to fill it, using a qualitative case study, without a hypothesis. The Bandura Bobo Doll Experiment is a good example of using deductive reasoning to arrive at a research problem and hypothesis. Anecdotal evidence showed that violent behaviour amongst children was increasing. Bandura believed that higher levels of violent adult role models on television, was a contributor to this rise. This was expanded into a hypothesis, and operationalization of the variables, and scientific measurement scale, led to a robust experimental design.

REFERENCES

- Babbie, E.R.: *Survey Research Methods*. Belmont, CA: Wadsworth, 1973.
- Bajpai, R B : *Research Methodology : Data Presentation*, APH, 2007.
- Dasgupta, Manas: *Research Methodology in Economics : Problems and Issues*, Deep and Deep, 2007.
- Sudhir Gupta: *Workshop on Research Methodology*, Centrum Press, 2011.

2

Research Methodology

The system of collecting data for research projects is known as research methodology. The data may be collected for either theoretical or practical research for example management research may be strategically conceptualized along with operational planning methods and change management. Some important factors in research methodology include validity of research data, Ethics and the reliability of measures most of your work is finished by the time you finish the analysis of your data.

Formulating of research questions along with sampling weather probable or non probable is followed by measurement that includes surveys and scaling. This is followed by research design, which may be either experimental or quasi-experimental. The last two stages are data analysis and finally writing the research paper, which is organised carefully into graphs and tables so that only important relevant data is shown.

Types of Research Methods:

- Qualitative
- Quantitaive
- Mixed
- Critical and action oriented.

Data Collection

Data collection depends on the research design (quantitative or qualitative design). Tutors India helps in a survey tool validation and also online and face to face data collection process.

We help you to conduct surveys [in person Interviews: Formal to informal; structured to unstructured, observations, self-administered questionnaire, diaries, citizen report cards, Delphi techniques, expert judgement, online surveys, secondary sources such as journals, newspaper articles, annual reports, government sources such as census, budgets, policies, procedures, etc.

Quantitative Consulting

The preparation of a successful dissertation involves conducting effective research, analysing data and results presentation all which require a high level of statistical expertise. We at statswork provides solution from formulating methodology to the results presentation. You can approach statswork with any or all of the following steps:

- Framing your Research Methodology
- Study design
- Sample size calculation and justification
- Development of questionnaire
- Statistical techniques.

Appropriate selection of statistical tools (parametric and non-parametric) depends on the study design and sample size. The following are some of the statistical tools used by our expertise..

- Exlportary data analysis
- T-test, ANOVA, ANCOVA
- Chi-square
- Linear regression
- Dichotomous logistic regression
- Ordinal logistic regression
- Multinomial logistic regression
- Quantile regression
- Poisson regression
- Survival analysis
- LogLinear models
- Factor analysis
- Principal component analysis

- Multidimensional scaling
- Forecasting
- Decision Tree
- Neural Network
- Cluster analysis
- Multiple imputation
- An extensive array of graphical procedures.

RELIABILITY AND VALIDITY OF RESULTS

Understanding some aspects of social life and its methods through text rather than numbers, as data for analysis. Although there are criticism for such methodology, you need such methodology that the survey can't answer very well.

Some common criticism include:

- Findings lack rigour
- Small sample size
- Not necessarily representative of the broader population

METHODOLOGICAL CHALLENGE

Qualitative research methods are valuable in providing rich descriptions of complex phenomena; tracking unique or unexpected events, illuminating the experience and interpretation of events by actors with widely differing stakes and roles; giving voice to those whose views are rarely heard; conducting initial explorations to develop theories; and to generate and test hypotheses; and moving toward explanations.

Using Qualitative Research Methods

One important methodological option in conducting management research is the use of qualitative methods for data collection and analysis. Qualitative research, with its emphasis on understanding complex, interrelated and/or changing phenomena, is particularly relevant to the challenges of conducting management research. Qualitative methods combined with quantitative ones can provide particularly rich and robust inquiries. Either alone or in combination, qualitative research must be conducted with methodological rigor.

This section does not attempt to provide a primer on qualitative methods. The role, benefits and appropriate use of qualitative research have been discussed extensively in the literature. Several references to excellent articles can be found in the references section and links to references.

Our more limited aims here are:

- To offer, for those who are not familiar with qualitative methods, a brief overview of how they are used and what value they offer, drawing heavily from articles by Shoshanna Sofaer.
- To propose the use of qualitative methods in hypothesis testing. Qualitative methods are often used inductively, for exploration, theory building and description. Less attention has been given to their use in deductive hypothesis testing. The white paper, prepared by Brian Mittman discussed in this section explores those potential uses.

Specially this section addresses four questions:

- What are the uses and value of qualitative research?
- What are the methodological challenges in qualitative research?
- What are some key qualitative research methods?
- What is the role of qualitative research in hypothesis testing?

What are the uses and value of qualitative research? Qualitative research is characterized by an emphasis on describing, understanding, and explaining complex phenomena-on studying, for example, the relationships, patterns and configurations among factors; or the context in which activities occur. The focus is on understanding the full multi-dimensional, dynamic picture of the subject of study.

Its approaches contrast with quantitative methods that aim to divide phenomena into manageable, clearly defined pieces, or variables. Quantification is good for separating phenomena into distinct and workable elements of a well-defined conceptual framework. But when we focus research on what we already know how to quantify, (e.g., what can be reliably quantified), we may miss factors that are key to a real understanding of the phenomena being studied. The downside of quantification is that it does not always support (as well as qualitative methods) understanding of complex, dynamic, and multi-dimensional wholes.

Qualitative methods are useful, not only in providing rich descriptions of complex phenomena, but in constructing or developing theories or conceptual frameworks, and in generating hypotheses to explain those phenomena.

What are the methodological challenges in qualitative research techniques? Key challenges to conducting rigorous qualitative research range from instrument development through data collection to data analysis. In addition, results need to be documented and reported using formal accepted methods.

For example, typical deficiencies are unfocused instrument development and lack of supporting theory. Rigor related to instrument protocol development requires attention to validity, intrusiveness (the Hawthorne effect) and triangulation. In addition, attention must be paid to distinguishing between collecting subjective and objective data, information on the formal vs. the informal organizational structures and processes and the differences between collecting facts vs. opinions vs. interpretations.

Planned, systematic, comprehensive data collection requires variable definitions and measures, document coding form protocols, administrative database specifications and survey instrument question libraries. In the data collection phase, problems can be minimized through pilot-testing and pretesting, validity/quality checks, triangulation and monitored flexibility. Sole reliance on subjective data, self-reports, etc. can reduce validity. Some tips to insure rigor in data collection management include training of all data collection staff and conducting immediate post-collection coding for time/memory sensitive data. Other methods to ensure the validity of data include tape recording interviews, performing real time data entry and editing, using paired interviewers, and implementing quality assurance for each instrument. And, to avoid further problems, incomplete, missing or unusable data should be corrected immediately.

Pitfalls related to data analysis include using ad hoc, emergent, exploratory, informal analyses that may lead to inappropriate conclusions and unpublishable results. Rigorous analysis requires an *a priori* theoretical model and hypothesis, a formal framework guiding data collection and analysis and adherence to the formal framework and research best practices.

Finally, reporting requires results structured by hypotheses and an analysis plan. Reports need to include data syntheses and summaries with a focused analysis of the data. Conclusions must have a documented basis and systematic formal analysis methods, and validity must be documented.

What are some key qualitative research methods? A wide range of tested qualitative research methods are available to address these challenges. The selection of method, or combination of methods, will be tailored to the questions being studied and the setting for research. Typical methods include:

- Naturalistic inquiry and participant observation
- Case study research
- Structured observations of meetings and events
- Content analysis of documents
- Collection and analysis of other archival, administrative and performance data
- Focus groups
- Cognitive interviews
- Mail and telephone surveys.

Naturalistic inquiry, or ethnography, has its roots in anthropology and sociology and involves long-term exposure to a setting or a group of people. Extensive use of unstructured observations and conversations documented by detailed field notes form the basis for this type of research, often considered the purest form of qualitative research. Naturalistic inquiry is used when situations are unique or complex, when the level of uncertainty about the questions to ask is high and when there is little or no theory to direct the investigator.

A subset of this type of inquiry involves participant observation in which the investigator becomes a part of the setting or the process being studied. (Sofaer) reports that she was able to learn more from attending a few group meetings in a particular setting than she could have by using more structured qualitative methods such as interviews or surveys.

Case studies are the preferred strategy when 'how' or 'why' questions are being posed, when the investigator has little control over events, and when the focus is on a contemporary phenomenon within some real-life context. The case study is especially appropriate when the boundaries between phenomenon and context are not clearly evident. The case study copes with the technically distinctive situation in which there will be many more variables of interest than data points, and as one result relies on multiple sources of evidence, with data needing to converge in a triangulating fashion.

The case study approach can involve a single event or multiple cases and can be short or long term. However, rather than requiring total immersion in the setting or culture, sampling of sites, experiences and/or informants is typical. The methods used in case study research is similar to those of naturalistic inquiry. However the data collection is often more structured, using key informant interviews, structured observations of events and interactions and the collection and content analysis of relevant documents (e.g., to help establish the facts, the assumptions, values and priorities, or to illuminate differences in perceptions). Case studies often also include quantitative data for background or to help generate questions to ask informants (e.g., data on demographics, heath status, utilization, finances, etc.).

Structured Observations of Meetings

This involves attending meetings of the group that you wish to research. This can also be extended to observation of individuals in their daily work routine or on special tasks. The purpose of observing is to learn what is going on at the meeting and witness the group dynamic in process. This can be a rich information source as it can give researchers insight into the group.

Content Analysis of Documents

This is a non-intrusive form of research. This involves reviewing documents, memos or other pieces of written information for content and themes. By examining written word, the researcher is studying one type of communication that occurs in the selected sample.

This method also is non-intrusive. Information that has been previously collected, or secondary data, is reviewed to gain a better understanding into the topic. This information is part of the organization's history and can be a valuable key to understanding the past.

Focus groups usually explore specific issues. The focus group brings together individuals chosen to meet a specific profile. They may be homogenous along some dimensions and heterogeneous along others and a structured, yet informal, setting is used to explore a limited number of questions. Focus groups, unlike individual interviews, provide the added dimension of the interactions among members. Focus groups are often combined with more quantitative approaches such as surveys that can be administered at different points in the group discussion and even used as grist for additional discussion.

Cognitive interviews are typically used in survey development. One-to-one interviews are conducted (with people meeting the criteria for completing a particular survey) as the individuals complete the instrument being tested. This method helps investigators understand how people perceive and interpret language and their own experiences as they refine the survey instruments.

Mail and telephone surveys are a method of collecting information by sending surveys via email or postal mail. Participants return completed forms to the researcher or an outside vendor. Surveys may ask respondents to rate items on a scale (e.g., Likert scale of 1-5). Some surveys also allow respondents to write their feelings or attitudes about a particular event or to elaborate in more detail on an item, or to express suggestions, etc.

What is the role of qualitative research in hypothesis testing? The origins and development of qualitative research methods and their close association with inductive, interpretive and historical research have led many researchers to associate these methods exclusively with these forms of research and to fail to recognize their value in conventional deductive empirical research.

Some investigators, however, contend that hypothesis-testing, deductive research can benefit from the use of qualitative research methods-and that these methods can be used in a manner consistent with accepted standards of rigor and validity. In particular they believe that the acknowledged strength and unique contribution of qualitative methods in developing insights into actors' values, beliefs, understandings and interpretations of events and other phenomena, or in explaining historical occurrences, can enhance "conventional" forms of empirical research.

SURVEY METHODOLOGY

Mailed, self-administered questionnaires are a common data collection method used in family practice research. However, little guidance exists in the medical literature about survey methodology specifically designed for family practitioners. As a result, primary care physicians sometimes struggle with questionnaire design and interpretation. Our goal was to synthesize general survey methodology guidelines (from other disciplines as well as our own) in a manner that would be meaningful to novice family practice researchers.

Research using self-developed questionnaires is a popular study design in family practice and is frequently used for gathering data on knowledge, beliefs, attitudes, and behaviours. A Medline literature search from 1966 to 2000 identified 53,101 articles related to questionnaires, of which 2088 were directly related to family practice.

Despite the large number of questionnaire-related articles, however, only 2 in the general medical literature and 1 in the family practice literature were directly related to research methodology.

To obtain guidance on survey research methodology, novice family practice researchers often must go through volumes of information by specialists in other disciplines. For example, a search of a psychology database (PsychInfo) from 1966 to 2000 produced 45 articles about questionnaire methodology. The goal of this chapter is to synthesize pertinent survey research methodology tenets-from other disciplines as well as from family practice-in a manner that is meaningful to novice family practice researchers as well as to research consumers. This chapter is not aimed at answering all questions, but rather is meant to serve as a general guideline for those with little formal research training who seek guidance in developing and administering questionnaires.

Avoiding Common Pitfalls in Survey Research

Although constructing a questionnaire is not exceedingly complex, simple mistakes can be avoided by following some basic rules and guidelines. For conducting a survey research project that combines guidelines and suggestions from published survey research literature, and the cumulative experience of the authors. Two of the authors (M.J.D. and K.C.O.) are experienced survey researchers who have published, in peer-reviewed journals, numerous studies that used questionnaires. One of the authors (MJD) has been teaching research to residents and junior faculty for over a decade, and has been an advisor on scores of resident, student, and faculty research projects. The perspective of the novice researcher is represented by 1 author (C.R.W.).

Getting Started

The "quick and dirty" approach is perhaps the most common pitfall in survey research. Because of the ease of administration and the relatively low cost of survey research, questionnaires can be developed and administered quickly. The researcher, however, should be sure to consider whether or not a survey is the most appropriate method to answer a research question. Adequate time must be given to thoroughly searching the relevant literature, developing and focusing on an appropriate research question, and defining the target population for the study. Large, multisite surveys are more likely to be generalizeable and to be published in peer-reviewed journals.

One way to avoid undertaking a project too rapidly and giving inadequate attention to the survey research process is for novice researchers to avoid independent research. Those with little or no experience must realize that researchers in both family practice and other fields perform research in teams, with the various participants bringing specific skills to the process. Oversights, mistakes, and biases in the design of questionnaires can always occur, whether a researcher is working independently or as a member of a team. It seems reasonable to assume, however, that significant problems are much less likely to occur when a multidisciplinary team approach is involved rather than an individual researcher undertaking a study independently.

Ideally, a research team should include a statistician, a professional with experience in the content areas of the study, and a senior investigator. The desirable area of expertise, however, is often not readily available to family physicians, especially those in community-based settings. Individuals with some training in research who are interested in being involved can usually be found in colleges and universities, hospitals, and at the local public health department.

Psychologists, sociologists, health services researchers, public health epidemiologists, and nursing educators are all potential resources and possible collaborators. Establishing the necessary relationships to form an ad hoc research team is certainly more time and labour intensive than undertaking research independently, but generally results in the collection of more useful information.

Novices should consult survey methodology books before and during the study. Excellent resources are available that provide a comprehensive overview of survey methods, means for improving response rates, and methods for constructing relatively brief but thorough survey questions. Academic family practice fellowships often provide training in survey methodology. In addition, many family practice researchers respond favourably to requests for information or advice requested by telephone or email contact. The novice author of this chapter reports excellent success in contacting experts in this manner. With the advent of the Internet, a "cyberspace" team comprised of experts in the topic and the methodology is a reasonable and helpful option for the novice.

Survey Content and Structure

Novice researchers often assume that developing a questionnaire is an intuitive process attainable by virtually anyone, regardless of their level of research training. While it is true that questionnaires are relatively simple to construct, developing an instrument that is valid and reliable is not intuitive. An instrument is valid if it actually measures what we think it is measuring, and it is reliable if it measures the phenomenon consistently in repeated applications. By following a few basic guidelines, those with limited research training can develop survey instruments capable of producing valid and reliable information. The 3 primary concerns for developing appropriate questions (items) are: (1) response format; (2) content; and (3) wording and placement.

Format

Questionnaires generally use a closed-ended format rather than an open-ended format. Closed formats spell out response options instead of asking study subjects to respond in their own words. Although there are many reasons for using closed formats, their primary advantages over open formats is that they are more specific and provide the same frame of reference to all respondents, and they allow quantitative analysis. A disadvantage is that they limit the possible range of responses envisioned by the investigators. Questionnaires with closed formats are therefore not as helpful as qualitative methods in the early, exploratory phases of a research project.

Closed-ended items can be formatted into several different categories (classes) of measurement, based on the relationship of the response categories to one another. Nominal measurements are responses that are sorted into unordered categories, such as demographic variables (i.e., sex, ethnicity). Ordinal measurements are similar to nominal, except that there is a definite order to the categories. For example, ordinal items may ask respondents to rank their preferences among a list of options from the least desirable to the most desirable.

Survey items that ask for respondents (delete apostrophe) to rank order preferences are often a more useful than items that state, "check all that apply." While checking all relevant responses may be necessary for certain items, such questions often lose valuable information as they can only supply raw percentages without supplying any comparison between responses.

Two additional tools used on questionnaires are continuous variables and scales. Continuous variables can be simple counts (e.g., the number of times something occurred) or physical attributes (e.g., age or weight). A general rule when collecting information on continuous variables is to avoid obtaining the information in ranges of categories unless absolutely necessary. Response categories that reflect ranges of responses can always be constructed after the information is gathered, but if the information is gathered in ranges from the start, it cannot later be expanded to reflect specific values.

Scales are used by survey researchers to assess the intensity of respondents' attitudes about a specific issue or issues. Likert scales are probably the best known and most widely used for measuring attitudes. These scales typically present respondents with a statement and ask them to indicate whether they "strongly agree," "agree," "neither agree nor disagree," "disagree," or "strongly disagree." The wording of the response categories can be changed to reflect other concepts (e.g., approval or disapproval), and the standard 5-response format can be expanded or abbreviated if necessary.

There are no hard and fast rules for determining the number of response categories to use for scaled items, or whether to use a neutral category or one that reflects uncertainty. Research indicates that the reliability of respondents' ratings declines when using more than 9 rating scale points. However, the reliability of a scale increases when the number of rating scale points is increased, with maximum benefit achieved with 5 or 7 scale points. Since the objective of using scales is to gauge respondent's preferences, it is sometimes argued that a middle point or category of uncertainty category should not be used. Odd-numbered rating scales, however, conform better with the underlying tenets of many statistical tests, suggesting the need for including this category. As the number of rating scale points increases, respondents' use of the midpoint category decreases substantially. Thus, based on the available literature, it is generally advisable to use between 5 and 7 response categories and an uncertainty category, unless there is a compelling reason to force respondents to choose between 2 competing perspectives or alternatives.

Content

Items should not be included on questionnaires when the only justification for inclusion is that the investigator feels the information "would be really interesting to know." Rather, for each item, you should ask yourself how it addresses the study's research question and how it will be used in the data analysis stage of the study. Researchers should develop a data analysis plan in advance of administering a questionnaire to determine exactly how each question will be used in the analysis. When the relationship between a particular item and the study's research question is unclear, or it is not known how an item will be used in the analysis, the item should be removed from the questionnaire.

Wording and Placement

The wording of questions should be kept simple, regardless of the education level of the respondents. Questions should be kept as short and direct as possible since shorter surveys tend to have higher response rates. Each question should be scrutinized to ensure it is appropriate for the respondents and does not require or assume an inappropriate level of knowledge about a topic. Since first impressions are important for setting the tone of a questionnaire, never begin with sensitive or threatening questions. Questionnaires should begin with simple, introductory ("warm-up")" questions to help establish trust and an appropriate frame of mind for respondents. Other successful strategies are: (1) when addressing multiple topics, insert an introductory statement immediately preceding each topic (e.g., "In the next section we would like to ask you about ..."); (2) request demographic information at the end of the questionnaire; and (3) always provide explicit instructions to avoid any confusion on the part of respondents.

Additional, clear information on survey content and structure is available in 2 books from Sage Publications. By following simple guidelines and common sense, most family practice researchers can construct valid and reliable questionnaires. As a final safeguard, once a final draft of the questionnaire is completed, the researcher should always be the first respondent. By placing yourself in the respondent's role and taking the time to think about and respond to each question, problems with the instrument that were overlooked are sometimes identified.

Analysing Surveys

It is not within the scope of this project to address statistical analysis of survey data. Before attempting data analysis, investigators should receive appropriate training or consult with a qualified professional. There are 3 topics that can and should be understood by novice researchers related to data analysis.

Coding

Before analysing survey data it is necessary to assign numbers (codes) to the responses obtained. Since the computer program that is used for analysing data does not know what the numbers mean, the researcher assigns meaning to the codes so that the results can be interpreted correctly. Coding refers to the process of developing the codes, assigning them to responses, and documenting the decision rules used for assigning specific codes to specific response categories. For example, almost all questionnaires contain missing values when respondents elect to not answer an item. Unique codes need to be assigned to distinguish between an item's missing values, items that may not be applicable to a particular respondent, and responses that have a "none" or "no opinion" category.

Data can be entered into appropriate data files once codes have been assigned to responses and a codebook compiled that defines the codes and their corresponding response categories. It is important to ensure that the data are free of errors (are clean) prior to performing data analysis. Although many methods can be used for data cleaning (i.e., data can be entered twice and results compared consistency), at a minimum all of the codes should be checked to ensure only legitimate codes appear.

Frequency distributions are tables produced by statistical software that display the number of respondents in each response category for each item (variable) used in the analysis. By carefully examining frequency tables, the researcher can check for illegitimate codes. Frequency tables also display the relative distribution of responses and allow identification of items that do not conform to expectations given what is known about the study population.

Sample Size

Since it is usually not possible to study all of the members of the group (population) of interest in a study, a subset (sample) of the population is generally selected for study from the sampling frame. Sampling is the process by which study subjects are selected from the target population, while the sample frame is the members of a population who have a chance of being included in the survey. In probability samples, each member of the sampling frame has a known probability of being selected for the study, whereas in nonprobability samples, the probability of selection is unknown. When a high degree of precision in sampling is needed to unambiguously identify the magnitude of a problem in a population or the factors that cause the problem, then probability sampling techniques must be used.

When conducting an analytical study that examines precisely whether statistically significant differences exist between groups in a population, power analysis is used to determine what size sample is needed to detect the differences. Estimates of sample size based on power are inversely related to the expected size of the differences "(effect size)"-that is, detecting smaller differences requires a larger sample. If an analytical study is undertaken to determine the magnitude of the differences between 2 groups, it is necessary to work with a statistician or other methodology expert to perform the appropriate power analysis.

In contrast to analytical studies, exploratory and descriptive studies can frequently be conducted without the need for a power analysis. While some descriptive studies may require the use of probability techniques and precise sample estimates, this often is not the case for studies that establish the existence of a problem or estimating its dimensions. When conducting an exploratory or descriptive study using a survey design and a nonprobability sampling technique, considerations other than effect size or precision are used to determine sample size. For example, the availability of eligible respondents, limitations of time and resources, and the need for pilot study data can all contribute to selecting a nonprobability sample. When these types of sampling techniques are used, however, it is important to remember that the validity and reliability of the findings are not assured, and the findings cannot be used to demonstrate the existence of differences between groups. The findings of these types of studies are only suggestive and have limited application beyond the specific study setting.

Response Rate

The response rate is a measure indicating the percentage of the identified sample that completed and returned the questionnaire. It is calculated by dividing the number of completed questionnaires by the total sample size identified for the study. For example, if a study is mailed to 500 physicians questionnaires and 100 returned a completed questionnaire, the response rate would be 20% (100/500).

The response rate for mailed questionnaires is extremely variable. Charities are generally content with a 1% to 3% response rate, the US Census Bureau expects to achieve a 99% rate, and among the general population, a 10% response rate is not uncommon. Although an 80% response rate is possible from an extremely motivated population, a rate of 70% is generally considered excellent.

The effect of nonresponse on the results of a survey depend on the degree to which those not responding are systematically different from the population from which they are drawn. When the response rate is high (i.e., 95%), the results obtained from the sample will likely provide accurate information about the target population (sampling frame) even if the nonrespondents are distinctly different. However, if nonrespondents differ in a systematic way from the target population and the response rate is low, bias in how much the survey results accurately reflect the true characteristics of the target population is likely.

When calculating the response rate, participants who have died or retired can be removed from the denominator as appropriate. Nonrespondents, however, who refuse to participate, do not return the survey, or have moved should be included. This bias tends to be more problematic in "sensitive" areas of research than in studies of common, nonthreatening topics. Imputing values for missing data from nonrespondents is complex and generally should not be undertaken.

Given the importance of response rate, every effort must be made to obtain as many completed questionnaires as possible and strategies to maximize the response rate should be integrated into the study design. Some simple means for improving response rates include constructing a short questionnaire, sending a well-written and personalized cover letter containing your signature, and emphasizing the importance of the study and the confidentiality of responses. It is also advisable to include a self-addressed, stamped envelope for return responses, and sometimes a small incentive is worthwhile. The National Centre for Education Statistics notes that all surveys require some follow-up to achieve desirable response rates. Survey researchers, therefore, should develop procedures for monitoring responses and implement follow-up plans shortly after the survey begins.

Generally, 2 or 3 mailings are used to maximize response rates. Use of post card reminders is an inexpensive, though untested, method to increase response. Several randomized studies have reported an increase in response rate from physicians in private practice with the use of monetary incentives, although the optimum amount is debated. Everett et al compared the use of a $1 incentive vs no monetary incentive and found a significant increase with the incentive group (response rates: 63% in the $1 group; 45% in the no incentive group; P <.0001). Other studies have compared $2, $5, $10, $20, and $25 incentives and found that $2 or $5 incentives are most cost effective. Similar findings have been reported for physician surveys in other countries. In an assessment of incentive for enrollees in a health plan, a $2 incentive was more cost effective than a $5 incentive. A $1 incentive was as effective as $2 in significantly increasing response rate in a low-income population. Quality of responses have not varied by use of incentives and there does not appear to be an incentive-bias.

Use of lottery appears to also increase response rate in both physicians and the lay public, although there are no studies comparing lottery to a monetary incentive enclosed for all participants. Use of either certified or priority return mail appears to increase response rates, and may be more cost effective when used for the second mailing.

Pilot Testing

Though pilot testing is generally included in the development of a survey, it is often inadequately conducted. Frequently, investigators are eager to answer their research question and pilot testing is synonymous with letting a few colleagues take a quick look and make a few comments. One of the questions in the survey asked about how time is allotted for faculty to pursue scholarly activities and research (Format A). Unfortunately, the question mixes 2 types of time in 1 question: extended time away from the institution (sabbatical and mini-sabbatical) and time in the routine schedule. This was confusing to respondents and could have been avoided by separating the content into 2 separate questions (Format B).

Investigators should consider carefully whom to include in the pilot testing. Not only should this include the project team and survey "experts", but it should also include a sample of the target audience. Pilot testing among multiple groups provides feedback about the wording and clarity of questions, appropriateness of the questions for the target population, and the presence of redundant or unnecessary items. One of the authors (C.R.W.) recently worked on her first questionnaire project. Among the many lessons she learned was the value of a team in providing assistance, the importance of considering if the time spent on a particular activity makes it cost effective, and the need to be flexible depending on circumstances. She found that establishing good communication with the team cuts down on errors and wasted effort. Rewarding the team for all of their hard work improves morale and provides a positive model for future projects. The mailed self-administered questionnaire is an important tool in primary care research. For family practice to continue its maturation as a research discipline, family practitioners need to be conversant in survey methodology and familiar with its pitfalls. We hope this primer-designed specifically for use in the family practice setting-will provide not only basic guidelines for novices but will also inspire further investigation.

TYPES OF RESEARCH METHODOLOGY

Behavioural research is conducted by scientists who are interested in understanding the behaviour of human beings and animals. These scientists believe that knowledge gained through personal intuition or the claims of others is not a sufficient basis for drawing conclusions about behaviour. They demand that knowledge be gained through the accumulation of empirical data, as prescribed by the scientific method. Behavioural scientists understand that the scientific approach is not perfect, but it is better than any other known way of drawing conclusions about behaviour. Although science is designed to create a collection of facts, it is not entirely free of values. The values of scientists influence how they interpret their data, what and whom they study, and how they report their research. For instance, some scientists conduct basic research, whereas others conduct applied research. One of the important goals of the scientific method is to make clear to others which aspects of the research process are based on facts and which are based on values. There are three major research designs in behavioural research. There are advantages and disadvantages to each of the approaches, and each provides an essential avenue of scientific investigation. Descriptive research, such as surveys and naturalistic observation, is designed to provide a snapshot of the current state of affairs.

Descriptive research may be either qualitative or quantitative in orientation. Correlational research is designed to discover relationships among variables and to allow the prediction of future events from present knowledge. The relationships among variables are frequently described using the Pearson correlation coefficient. Because correlational research cannot provide evidence about causal relationships between variables, experimental research is often employed to do so. Experiments involve the creation of equivalence among research participants in more than one group, followed by an active manipulation of a given experience for these groups and a measurement of the influence of the manipulation. The goal is to assess the causal impact of the manipulation. Because each of the three types of research designs has both strengths and limitations, it is very important to learn to think critically about research. Such critical evaluation will allow you to select the appropriate research design and to determine what conclusions can and cannot be drawn from research.

REFERENCES

- Babbie, E.R.: *Survey Research Methods*. Belmont, CA: Wadsworth, 1973.
- Mittal, Kapila: *Research Methodology in Social Sciences*, Vista International, 2006.
- Mohamed Haneefa K:*Research on Library Computerisation*, Ess Ess Pub, 2006.

3

Hypotheses in Research

The building blocks of hypotheses are variables. A variable is anything that varies, changes, or has differences. Something that never changes is called a constant. Science does not try to explain much by constants. It relies on the study of variables. Variables that only have two extremes are called attributes. In social science, we deal mostly with two types of variables: independent and dependent. Independent variables are those things thought to be the cause or bring about change in other variables. Dependent variables are those things changed or affected by independent variables, sometimes through other variables (often called intervening variables). Independent variables always come before dependent variables in time and space.

Hypotheses are simply if-then sentences that can be categorized in certain logical forms, such as no difference (null hypothesis), associated difference, directionality of difference, and magnitude of difference. A good hypothesis implies all these in a single sentence, and the trick is to express them as briefly as possible and in simple English. Let's take a look at how this is done:

Differences in Variable A have no relationship to differences in Variable B (null hypothesis)

If Variable A changes, then Variable B changes, *or*

There is a relationship between Variable A and Variable B, *or* Variable A affects Variable B (all examples of associated difference, sometimes called nondirectional hypotheses)

If Variable A increases, then Variable B increases, *or*

If Variable A decreases, then Variable B decreases (both examples of directional hypotheses)

but you can also have inverse relationships, *such as*

If Variable A increases, then Variable B decreases, *or*

If Variable A decreases, then Variable B increases

If Variable A increases by 2 points (12% or whatever), then Variable B increases by 3 points (or whatever) (magnitude of difference)

and, you can also have directionality with magnitude in an inverse relationship, *as in*

If Variable A decreases by 5%, then Variable increases by 3%

The point is that the more specific you make your hypotheses, the better. Not only may you be able to use more powerful statistics, but you will be engaging in what is called confirmatory research, instead of what is called exploratory research. The more your topic has been previously researched by others, the more it is expected that you will use confirmatory research. Exploratory research is used only in previously uncharted areas, or by those who honestly don't know anything about their topic. You'll note that the last example above contains all the elements of previous examples, so you can always drop down to a less rigorous hypothesis, but you can't or shouldn't move up to a more specific one after you've already done your research. Also, the null hypothesis remains unstated or implied as no differences, no matter how complex your other (called alternative) hypotheses get. Technically, all statistical tests are tests of the null hypothesis first, which is rejected in favour of degrees of confidence in the alternatives.

An important part of the research process that goes along with hypothesis formulation is constructing your operational definitions. These are definitions of your variables for research purposes. They are important so others can understand and replicate your research. Researchers need to define their variables very precisely, especially the dependent variables. If "crime" is your dependent variable, you need to be very precise about exactly what kind of crime you have in mind: violent crime; property crime; vice crime; etc. Context is important for operational definitions. You want the concepts they represent to be as close as possible to the original constructs that existed in the mind of the first person who came up with the idea (you are investigating) in the first place.

Many different criteria can be found in the literature over what are the desirable qualities of a "good" hypothesis. If you are a theoretician, then a scientific hypothesis is what you are after, and this will resemble (although not be exactly the same) as your scientific theory. You must "test" your hypothesis before it has any implications for theory. A scientific hypothesis that has not been fully tested is usually called a "working hypothesis." A useful hypothesis (and utility may very well be the most desirable quality) will enable prediction, or at least reasoning. It will allow you to explore, observe, ask and answer questions. Some people like to call their hypothesis an "educated guess," but the word "conjecture" is more appropriate for something like this. In the end, the "best" hypotheses usually stick pretty close to the original interpretation of the person that first conceived of the whole idea in the first place.

HYPOTHESES

An hypothesis is a specific statement of prediction. It describes in concrete (rather than theoretical) terms what you expect will happen in your study. Not all studies have hypotheses. Sometimes a study is designed to be exploratory. There is no formal hypothesis, and perhaps the purpose of the study is to explore some area more thoroughly in order to develop some specific hypothesis or prediction that can be tested in future research. A single study may have one or many hypotheses.

Actually, whenever I talk about an hypothesis, I am really thinking simultaneously about *two* hypotheses. Let's say that you predict that there will be a relationship between two variables in your study. The way we would formally set up the hypothesis test is to formulate two hypothesis statements, one that describes your prediction and one that describes all the other possible outcomes with respect to the hypothesized relationship. Your prediction is that variable A and variable B will be related (you don't care whether it's a positive or negative relationship). Then the only other possible outcome would be that variable A and variable B are *not* related. Usually, we call the hypothesis that you support (your prediction) the *alternative* hypothesis, and we call the hypothesis that describes the remaining possible outcomes the *null* hypothesis. Sometimes we use a notation like H_A or H_1 to represent the alternative hypothesis or your prediction, and H_O or H_0 to represent the null case. You have to be careful here, though. In some studies, your prediction might very well be that there will be no difference or change. In this case, you are essentially trying to find support for the null hypothesis and you are opposed to the alternative.

If your prediction specifies a direction, and the null therefore is the no difference prediction and the prediction of the opposite direction, we call this a *one-tailed hypothesis*. For instance, let's imagine that you are investigating the effects of a new employee training program and that you believe one of the outcomes will be that there will be *less* employee absenteeism. Your two hypotheses might be stated something like this:

The null hypothesis for this study is:

H_O: As a result of the XYZ company employee training program, there will either be no significant difference in employee absenteeism or there will be a significant *increase*.

which is tested against the alternative hypothesis:

H_A: As a result of the XYZ company employee training program, there will be a significant *decrease* in employee absenteeism.

The alternative hypothesis — your prediction that the program will decrease absenteeism — is shown there. The null must account for the other two possible conditions: no difference, or an increase in absenteeism. A hypothetical distribution of absenteeism differences. We can see that the term "one-tailed" refers to the tail of the distribution on the outcome variable.

When your prediction does *not* specify a direction, we say you have a *two-tailed hypothesis*. For instance, let's assume you are studying a new drug treatment for depression. The drug has gone through some initial animal trials, but has not yet been tested on humans. You believe (based on theory and the previous research) that the drug will have an effect, but you are not confident enough to hypothesize a direction and say the drug will reduce depression (after all, you've seen more than enough promising drug treatments come along that eventually were shown to have severe side effects that actually worsened symptoms). In this case, you might state the two hypotheses like this:

The null hypothesis for this study is:

H_O: As a result of 300mg./day of the ABC drug, there will be no significant difference in depression.

which is tested against the alternative hypothesis:

H_A: As a result of 300mg./day of the ABC drug, there will be a significant difference in depression.

The important thing to remember about stating hypotheses is that you formulate your prediction (directional or not), and then you formulate a second hypothesis that is mutually exclusive of the first and incorporates all possible alternative outcomes for that case. When your study analysis is completed, the idea is that you will have to choose between the two hypotheses. If your prediction was correct, then you would (usually) reject the null hypothesis and accept the alternative. If your original prediction was not supported in the data, then you will accept the null hypothesis and reject the alternative. The logic of hypothesis testing is based on these two basic principles:

- the formulation of two mutually exclusive hypothesis statements that, together, exhaust all possible outcomes
- the testing of these so that one is necessarily accepted and the other rejected

STATISTICAL HYPOTHESIS TESTING

A statistical hypothesis test is a method of making decisions using data, whether from a controlled experiment or an observational study (not controlled). In statistics, a result is called statistically significant if it is unlikely to have occurred by chance alone. The phrase "*test of significance*" was coined by Ronald Fisher: "Critical tests of this kind may be called tests of significance, and when such tests are available we may discover whether a second sample is or is not significantly different from the first." Hypothesis testing is sometimes called confirmatory data analysis, in contrast to exploratory data analysis. In frequency probability, these decisions are almost always made using null-hypothesis tests (i.e., tests that answer the question *Assuming that the null hypothesis is true, what is the probability of observing a value for the test statistic that is at least as extreme as the value that was actually observed?*) One use of hypothesis testing is deciding whether experimental results contain enough information to cast doubt on conventional wisdom. Statistical hypothesis testing is a key technique of frequentist statistical inference, and is widely used, but also much criticized. While controversial, the Bayesian approach to hypothesis testing is to base rejection of the hypothesis on the posterior probability. Other approaches to reaching a decision based on data are available via decision theory and optimal decisions. The *critical region* of a hypothesis test is the set of all outcomes which, if they occur, will lead us to decide that there is a difference. That is, cause the null hypothesis to be rejected in favour of the alternative hypothesis. The critical region is usually denoted by C.

Examples

The following examples should solidify these ideas.

Example 1-Court Room Trial

A statistical test procedure is comparable to a trial; a defendant is considered not guilty as long as his guilt is not proven. The prosecutor tries to prove the guilt of the defendant. Only when there is enough charging evidence the defendant is condemned. In the start of the procedure, there are two hypotheses H_0: "the defendant is not guilty", and H_1: "the defendant is guilty". The first one is called *null hypothesis*, and is for the time being accepted. The second one is called *alternative (hypothesis)*. It is the hypothesis one tries to prove.

The hypothesis of innocence is only rejected when an error is very unlikely, because one doesn't want to condemn an innocent defendant. Such an error is called *error of the first kind* (i.e. the condemnation of an innocent person), and the occurrence of this error is controlled to be rare. As a consequence of this asymmetric behaviour, the *error of the second kind* (setting free a guilty person), is often rather large.

The Testing Process

In the statistical literature, statistical hypothesis testing plays a fundamental role. The usual line of reasoning is as follows:

1. We start with a research hypothesis of which the truth is unknown.
2. The first step is to state the relevant null and alternative hypotheses. This is important as mis-stating the hypotheses will muddy the rest of the process. Specifically, the null hypothesis allows to attach an attribute: it should be chosen in such a way that it allows us to conclude whether the alternative hypothesis can either be accepted or stays undecided as it was before the test.
3. The second step is to consider the statistical assumptions being made about the sample in doing the test; for example, assumptions about the statistical independence or about the form of the distributions of the observations. This is equally important as invalid assumptions will mean that the results of the test are invalid.
4. Decide which test is appropriate, and stating the relevant test statistic T.
5. Derive the distribution of the test statistic under the null hypothesis from the assumptions. In standard cases this will be a well-known result. For example the test statistics may follow a Student's t distribution or a normal distribution.
6. The distribution of the test statistic partitions the possible values of T into those for which the null-hypothesis is rejected, the so called critical region, and those for which it is not.
7. Compute from the observations the observed value t_{obs} of the test statistic T.
8. Decide to either fail to reject the null hypothesis or reject it in favour of the alternative. The decision rule is to reject the null hypothesis H_0 if the observed value t_{obs} is in the critical region, and to accept or "fail to reject" the hypothesis otherwise.

It is important to note the philosophical difference between accepting the null hypothesis and simply failing to reject it. The "fail to reject" terminology highlights the fact that the null hypothesis is assumed to be true from the start of the test; if there is a lack of evidence against it, it simply continues to be assumed true. The phrase "accept the null hypothesis" may suggest it has been proved simply because it has not been disproved, a logical fallacy known as the argument from ignorance. Unless a test with particularly high power is used, the idea of "accepting" the null hypothesis may be dangerous. Nonetheless the terminology is prevalent throughout statistics, where its meaning is well understood. Alternatively, if the testing procedure forces us to reject the null hypothesis (H-null), we can accept the alternative hypothesis (H-alt) and we conclude that the research hypothesis is supported by the data. This fact expresses that our procedure is based on probabilistic considerations in the sense we accept that using another set could lead us to a different conclusion.

Definition of Terms

The following definitions are mainly based on the exposition in the book by Lehmann and Romano:

Simple hypothesis : Any hypothesis which specifies the population distribution completely.

Composite hypothesis : Any hypothesis which does *not* specify the population distribution completely.

Statistical test : A decision function that takes its values in the set of hypotheses.

Region of acceptance : The set of values for which we fail to reject the null hypothesis.

Region of rejection/Critical region: The set of values of the test statistic for which the null hypothesis is rejected.

Power of a test $(1 - b)$: The test's probability of correctly rejecting the null hypothesis. The complement of the false negative rate, b.

Size/Significance level of a test ($\acute{a}$): For simple hypotheses, this is the test's probability of *incorrectly* rejecting the null hypothesis. The false positive rate. For composite hypotheses this is the upper bound of the probability of rejecting the null hypothesis over all cases covered by the null hypothesis.

Most powerful test: For a given *size* or *significance level*, the test with the greatest power.

Uniformly most powerful test (UMP): A test with the greatest *power* for all values of the parameter being tested.

Consistent test: When considering the properties of a test as the sample size grows, a test is said to be consistent if, for a fixed size of test, the power against any fixed alternative approaches 1 in the limit.

Unbiased test : For a specific alternative hypothesis, a test is said to be unbiased when the probability of rejecting the null hypothesis is not less than the significance level when the alternative is true *and* is less than or equal to the significance level when the null hypothesis is true.

Conservative test : A test is conservative if, when constructed for a given nominal significance level, the true probability of *incorrectly* rejecting the null hypothesis is never greater than the nominal level.

Uniformly most powerful unbiased (UMPU) : A test which is UMP in the set of all unbiased tests.

p-value: The probability, assuming the null hypothesis is true, of observing a result at least as extreme as the test statistic.

Interpretation

The direct interpretation is that if the p-value is less than the required significance level, then we say the null hypothesis is rejected at the given level of significance. Criticism on this interpretation can be found in the corresponding section.

Origins

Hypothesis testing is largely the product of Ronald Fisher, Jerzy Neyman, Karl Pearson and (son) Egon Pearson. Fisher was an agricultural statistician who emphasized rigorous experimental design and methods to extract a result from few samples assuming Gaussian distributions. Neyman (who teamed with the younger Pearson) emphasized mathematical rigor and methods to obtain more results from many samples and a wider range of distributions. Modern hypothesis testing is an (extended) hybrid of the Fisher vs Neyman/Pearson formulation, methods and terminology developed in the early 20th century.

Importance

Statistical hypothesis testing plays an important role in the whole of statistics and in statistical inference. For example, Lehmann (1992) in a review of the fundamental paper by Neyman and Pearson (1933) says: "Nevertheless, despite their shortcomings, the new paradigm formulated in the 1933 paper, and the many developments carried out within its framework continue to play a central role in both the theory and practice of statistics and can be expected to do so in the foreseeable future".

Potential Misuse

One of the more common problems in significance testing is the tendency for multiple comparisons to yield spurious significant differences even where the null hypothesis is true. For instance, in a study of twenty comparisons, using an á-level of 5%, one comparison will likely yield a significant result despite the null hypothesis being true. In these cases p-values are adjusted in order to control either the familywise error rate or the false discovery rate.

Yet another common pitfall often happens when a researcher writes the qualified statement "we found no statistically significant difference," which is then misquoted by others as "they found that there was no difference." Actually, statistics cannot be used to prove that there is exactly zero difference between two populations. Failing to find evidence that there is a difference does not constitute evidence that there is no difference. This principle is sometimes described by the maxim "Absence of evidence is not evidence of absence."

According to J. Scott Armstrong, attempts to educate researchers on how to avoid pitfalls of using statistical significance have had little success. In the papers "Significance Tests Harm Progress in Forecasting," and "Statistical Significance Tests are Unnecessary Even When Properly Done," Armstrong makes the case that even when done properly, statistical significance tests are of no value. A number of attempts failed to find empirical evidence supporting the use of significance tests. Tests of statistical significance are harmful to the development of scientific knowledge because they distract researchers from the use of proper methods. Armstrong suggests authors should avoid tests of statistical significance; instead, they should report on effect sizes, confidence intervals, replications/extensions, and meta-analyses.

SIGNIFICANCE AND PRACTICAL IMPORTANCE

A common misconception is that a statistically significant result is always of practical significance, or demonstrates a large effect in the population. Unfortunately, this problem is commonly encountered in scientific writing. Given a sufficiently large sample, extremely small and non-notable differences can be found to be statistically significant, and statistical significance says nothing about the practical significance of a difference. Use of the statistical significance test has been called seriously flawed and unscientific by authors Deirdre McCloskey and Stephen Ziliak. They point out that "insignificance" does not mean unimportant, and propose that the scientific community should abandon usage of the test altogether, as it can cause false hypotheses to be accepted and true hypotheses to be rejected.

Some statisticians have commented that pure "significance testing" has what is actually a rather strange goal of detecting the existence of a "real" difference between two populations. In practice a difference can almost always be found given a large enough sample. The typically more relevant goal of science is a determination of causal effect size. The amount and nature of the difference, in other words, is what should be studied. Many researchers also feel that hypothesis testing is something of a misnomer. In practice a single statistical test in a single study never "proves" anything. An additional problem is that frequentist analyses of p-values are considered by some to overstate "statistical significance".

Meta-criticism

The criticism here is of the application, or of the interpretation, rather than of the method. Attacks and defenses of the null-hypothesis significance test are collected in Harlow *et al.*. The original purposes of Fisher's formulation, as a tool for the experimenter, was to plan the experiment and to easily assess the information content of the small sample. There is little criticism, Bayesian in nature, of the formulation in its original context.

In other contexts, complaints focus on flawed interpretations of the results and over-dependence/emphasis on one test. Numerous attacks on the formulation have failed to supplant it as a criterion for publication in scholarly journals. The most persistent attacks originated from the field of Psychology. After review, the American Psychological Association did not explicitly deprecate the use of null-hypothesis significance testing, but adopted enhanced publication guidelines which implicitly reduced the relative importance of such testing.

The International Committee of Medical Journal Editors recognizes an obligation to publish negative (not statistically significant) studies under some circumstances. The applicability of the null-hypothesis testing to the publication of observational (as contrasted to experimental) studies is doubtful.

Philosophical Criticism

Philosophical criticism to hypothesis testing includes consideration of borderline cases. Any process that produces a crisp decision from uncertainty is subject to claims of unfairness near the decision threshold. (Consider close election results.) The premature death of a laboratory rat during testing can impact doctoral theses and academic tenure decisions.

"... surely, God loves the .06 nearly as much as the .05"

The statistical significance required for publication has no mathematical basis, but is based on long tradition.

"It is usual and convenient for experimenters to take 5% as a standard level of significance, in the sense that they are prepared to ignore all results which fail to reach this standard, and, by this means, to eliminate, the greater part of the fluctuations which chance causes have introduced into their experimental results."

Ambivalence attacks all forms of decision making. A mathematical decision-making process is attractive because it is objective and transparent. It is repulsive because it allows authority to avoid taking personal responsibility for decisions.

Pedagogic Criticism

Pedagogic criticism of the null-hypothesis testing includes the counter-intuitive formulation, the terminology and confusion about the interpretation of results.

"Despite the stranglehold that hypothesis testing has on experimental psychology, I find it difficult to imagine a less insightful means of transiting from data to conclusions." Students find it difficult to understand the formulation of statistical null-hypothesis testing. In rhetoric, examples often support an argument, but a mathematical proof "is a logical argument, not an empirical one". A single counterexample results in the rejection of a conjecture. Karl Popper defined science by its vulnerability to disproof by data. Null-hypothesis testing shares the mathematical and scientific perspective rather than the more familiar rhetorical one. Students expect hypothesis testing to be a statistical tool for illumination of the research hypothesis by the sample; it is not. The test asks indirectly whether the sample can illuminate the research hypothesis.

Students also find the terminology confusing. While Fisher disagreed with Neyman and Pearson about the theory of testing, their terminologies have been blended. The blend is not seamless or standardized. While this article teaches a pure Fisher formulation, even it mentions Neyman and Pearson terminology (Type II error and the alternative hypothesis). The typical introductory statistics text is less consistent. The Sage Dictionary of Statistics would not agree with the title of this article, which it would call null-hypothesis testing. "...there is no alternate hypothesis in Fisher's scheme: Indeed, he violently opposed its inclusion by Neyman and Pearson." In discussing test results, "significance" often has two distinct meanings in the same sentence; One is a probability, the other is a subject-matter measurement (such as currency). The significance (meaning) of (statistical) significance is significant (important).

There is widespread and fundamental disagreement on the interpretation of test results. "A little thought reveals a fact widely understood among statisticians: The null hypothesis, taken literally (and that's the only way you can take it in formal hypothesis testing), is almost always false in the real world....

If it is false, even to a tiny degree, it must be the case that a large enough sample will produce a significant result and lead to its rejection. So if the null hypothesis is always false, what's the big deal about rejecting it?" "How has the virtually barren technique of hypothesis testing come to assume such importance in the process by which we arrive at our conclusions from our data?"

Null-hypothesis testing just answers the question of "how well the findings fit the possibility that chance factors alone might be responsible." Null-hypothesis significance testing does not determine the truth or falsity of claims. It determines whether confidence in a claim based solely on a sample-based estimate exceeds a threshold. It is a research quality assurance test, widely used as one requirement for publication of experimental research with statistical results. It is uniformly agreed that statistical significance is not the only consideration in assessing the importance of research results. Rejecting the null hypothesis is not a sufficient condition for publication.

"Statistical significance does not necessarily imply practical significance!"

Practical Criticism

Practical criticism of hypothesis testing includes the sobering observation that published test results are often contradicted. Mathematical models support the conjecture that most published medical research test results are flawed. Null-hypothesis testing has not achieved the goal of a low error probability in medical journals.

Straw man

Hypothesis testing is controversial when the alternative hypothesis is suspected to be true at the outset of the experiment, making the null hypothesis the reverse of what the experimenter actually believes; it is put forward as a straw man only to allow the data to contradict it. Many statisticians have pointed out that rejecting the null hypothesis says nothing or very little about the likelihood that the null is true. Under traditional null hypothesis testing, the null is rejected when the conditional probability P (Data as or more extreme than observed | Null) is very small, say 0.05. However, some say researchers are really interested in the probability P (Null | Data as actually observed) which cannot be inferred from a p-value: some like to present these as inverses of each other but the events "Data as or more extreme than observed" and "Data as actually observed" are very different. In some cases, P (Null | Data) approaches 1 while P (Data as or more extreme than observed | Null) approaches 0, in other words, we can reject the null when it's virtually certain to be true. For this and other reasons, Gerd Gigerenzer has called null hypothesis testing "mindless statistics" while Jacob Cohen described it as a ritual conducted to convince ourselves that we have the evidence needed to confirm our theories.

DEVELOPING THE RESEARCH HYPOTHESIS

The first stage in a research project is developing an idea. These ideas can come through an interest in solving important social problems, through the use of the inductive method to organize existing facts, and through the exercise of the deductive method to derive predictions from existing theories. The last approach is perhaps the most useful because it ensures that the new research is related to existing research and thus contributes to the accumulation of scientific knowledge.

Before beginning a research project the scientist conducts a literature search, usually by using computer databases to locate abstracts of relevant articles. The literature search involves locating both secondary-and primary-source material. Being knowledgeable about previous research from other research laboratories is essential to the development of effective research. The literature search frequently leads the scientist to modify and refine his/her original research ideas. One of the goals of science is to organize relationships into explanatory principles such as laws and theories. Laws are general principles that apply to all situations. Theories are integrated set of principles that explain and predict many observed events within a given domain. Good theories are both general and parsimonious, they form the basis of future scientific research, and they make predictions that can be tested and falsified.

Theories are tested in the form of research hypotheses—specific and testable predictions regarding the relationship between or among two or more variables. Once a scientist develops a research hypothesis, she or he tests it using either a correlational or an experimental research design.

HYPOTHESIS FORMULATION

When research is conducted hypothesis formulation is one of the most preliminary step. Hypothesis formulation helps in formulating research problem. Hypothesis formulation is not a necessary but an important step of research. A valid and reasonable research can be conducted without any hypothesis. Hypothesis can be one and it can be as many as possible.

Definition of Hypothesis:

A hypothesis is a possible answer to a research question. It is a presumption or a hunch on the bases of which a study has to be conducted. This hypothesis is tested for possible rejection or approval. If hypothesis get accepted it shows that your hunch was right if it get rejected it still does not mean that your research was not valid but it means that it is the opposite way you thought and perceived. Whether it is approved or not it gives you some conclusion and adds to the available body of knowledge. A hypothesis which has been tested again and again by various researchers can still be tested for making it more valid but if the hypothesis ha been approved in such a manner that it has become a law than it is better to test something that adds to the available knowledge rather than approving something which has been approved many times before.

Example: For example if you want to conduct a study on the Effects of Parental Depression on the Academic Performance of Children, you may like to conduct it without any hypothesis but then you will have many dimensions to think upon and will be more likely get distracted. If you formulate a hypothesis, that parental depression results in depression in children too and this depression leads to low grades, your research will get a direction and you will not think about the broader effects of depression everything is well defined you have to test the impact of depression on the children's depression and as well as on the grades of children. You may not need to test the impacts on the extra curricular activities, class conduct and other such things.

Characteristics of a Well-formulated Research Hypothesis:

Testable and Verifiable: A research hypothesis has to be checked for possible approval or rejection. This analysis is done statistically and, therefore it should be such that can be tested and analysed. After analysis the results can be obtained. Some hypothesis can not be tested because they are too subjective and they are not suitable for research. Research needs objectivity and evidences without these two things any research is impossible to conduct. For example you may want to conduct a research on the existence of God but to prove the existence of God is a far different phenomenon and even you may formulate a hypothesis is but you can not test it statistically, therefore, such hypothesis and research questions should be avoided.

Simple and Clear: The wording of the hypothesis should have to be simple and clear. Any complex ideas and wordings should be avoided. A simple hypothesis will make it easier for you to carry on through out the research and will be easy for the reader to understand. In addition to the terminology and phrasing the hypothesis should have to be clear in your mind from every perspective. If there are any ambiguities or questions in your mind, resolve them at this stage; if they are not clear you will find it hard to conduct the study in later stages.

Relevant: The hypothesis should have to be relevant to the study that you are about to conduct. An irrelevant hypothesis will lead to an invalid research. Hypothesis is the possible answer to your research question if your presumption or your presumed answer is wrong and irrelevant your method to find its accuracy too will not result in any relevant conclusions. Check whether your hypothesis is related to the direction in which you have planned to take your research or not.

Importance of Research Hypothesis

For a new researcher it is important to have research hypothesis so as to be directional. Research hypothesis can be present in research and it may not be but if it is present it can have following benefits.

Clarity: Hypothesis brings clarity to research. It makes your mind clear about the way in which you have to carry on the research. Methodology of research depends greatly on research hypothesis. Clarity brings 50 % chances of success in research. At each step you need to be clear about every aspect and dimension. If you are not clear about a single thing you should not go forward, stay where ever you are and resolve the issue and then move to the next step.

Focus: You formulate your research hypothesis and you get a focal point in your research. You need not go off the track and stay intact to the main objective which you set after the hypothesis. Your research becomes organized and haphazard actions are minimized.

Direction: Hypothesis sets a direction of research. This direction shows you what should be the objectives, methodology, mode of analysis and research design. With hypothesis you have a confidence that whatever you have presumed will be tested rather than testing something that is irrelevant to the research.

Objectivity: Every research requires objectivity but without hypothesis you may collect data which is not relevant to the research and hence decreases the objectivity of the research. When you know that your hypothesis only deals with a particular aspect of the phenomenon you will not collect data that is not required and the objectivity and validity of the research increases.

Add to the Body of Knowledge: A hypothesis add to the available body of knowledge. For example you study different literature and you find out that this much work has already been done on this topic and you should concentrate on the gaps that are yet to be filled by new research you formulate a hypothesis and keep your direction towards it.

HYPOTHESIS TESTING AND INFERENTIAL STATISTICS

Hypothesis testing is accomplished through a set of procedures designed to determine whether observed data can be interpreted as providing support for the research hypothesis. These procedures, based on inferential statistics, are specified by the scientific method and are set in place before the scientist begins to collect data. Because it is not possible to directly test the research hypothesis, observed data are compared to what is expected under the null hypothesis, as specified by the sampling distribution of the statistic.

Because all data have random error, scientists can never be certain that the data they have observed actually support their hypotheses. Statistical significance is used to test whether data can be interpreted as supporting the research hypothesis. The probability of incorrectly rejecting the null hypothesis (known as a Type 1 error) is constrained by setting alpha to a known value such as .05 and only rejecting the null hypothesis if the likelihood that the observed data occurred by chance (the *p*-value) is less than alpha. The probability of incorrectly failing to reject a false null hypothesis (a Type 2 error) can only be estimated. The power of a statistical test refers to the likelihood of correctly rejecting a false null hypothesis.

The effect size statistic is often used as a measure of the magnitude of a relationship between variables because it is not influenced by the sample size in the research design. The strength of a relationship may also be considered in terms of the proportion of variance in the dependent measure that is explained by the independent variable. The effect size of many relationships in scientific research is small, which makes them difficult to discover.

HYPOTHESIS TESTING RESEARCH

Social science research, and by extension business research, uses a number of different approaches to study a variety of issues. This research may be a very informal, simple process or it may be a formal, somewhat sophisticated process. Regardless of the type of process, all research begins with a generalized idea in the form of a research question or a hypothesis. A research question usually is posed in the beginning of a research effort or in a specific area of study that has had little formal research. A research question may take the form of a basic question about some issue or phenomena or a question about the relationship between two or more variables. For example, a research question might be: "Do flexible work hours improve employee productivity?" Another question might be: "How do flexible hours influence employees' work?"

A hypothesis differs from a research question; it is more specific and makes a prediction. It is a tentative statement about the relationship between two or more variables. The major difference between a research question and a hypothesis is that a hypothesis predicts an experimental outcome. For example, a hypothesis might state: "There is a positive relationship between the availability of flexible work hours and employee productivity."

Hypotheses provide the following benefits:

1. They determine the focus and direction for a research effort.
2. Their development forces the researcher to clearly state the purpose of the research activity.
3. They determine what variables will not be considered in a study, as well as those that will be considered.
4. They require the researcher to have an operational definition of the variables of interest.

The worth of a hypothesis often depends on the researcher's skills. Since the hypothesis is the basis of a research study, it is necessary for the hypothesis be developed with a great deal of thought and contemplation. There are basic criteria to consider when developing a hypothesis, in order to ensure that it meets the needs of the study and the researcher. A good hypothesis should:

1. Have logical consistency. Based on the current research literature and knowledge base, does this hypothesis make sense?
2. Be in step with the current literature and/or provide a good basis for any differences. Though it does not have to support the current body of literature, it is necessary to provide a good rationale for stepping away from the mainstream.
3. Be testable. If one cannot design the means to conduct the research, the hypothesis means nothing.
4. Be stated in clear and simple terms in order to reduce confusion.

HYPOTHESIS TESTING PROCESS

Hypothesis testing is a systematic method used to evaluate data and aid the decision-making process. Following is a typical series of steps involved in hypothesis testing:

1. State the hypotheses of interest
2. Determine the appropriate test statistic
3. Specify the level of statistical significance
4. Determine the decision rule for rejecting or not rejecting the null hypothesis
5. Collect the data and perform the needed calculations
6. Decide to reject or not reject the null hypothesis.

Stating the Hypotheses

A research study includes at least two hypotheses—the null hypothesis and the alternative hypothesis. The hypothesis being tested is referred to as the null hypothesis and it is designated as H It also is referred to as the hypothesis of no difference and should include a statement of equality (=, e", or £). The alternative hypothesis presents the alternative to the null and includes a statement of inequality ("). The null hypothesis and the alternative hypothesis are complementary.

The null hypothesis is the statement that is believed to be correct throughout the analysis, and it is the null hypothesis upon which the analysis is based. For example, the null hypothesis might state that the average age of entering college freshmen is 21 years.

H_0 The average age of entering college freshman = 21 years

If the data one collects and analyses indicates that the average age of entering college freshmen is greater than or less than 21 years, the null hypothesis is rejected. In this case the alternative hypothesis could be stated in the following three ways: (1) the average age of entering college freshman is not 21 years (the average age of entering college freshmen " 21); (2) the average age of entering college freshman is less than 21 years (the average age of entering college freshmen < 21); or (3) the average age of entering college freshman is greater than 21 years (the average age of entering college freshmen > 21 years).

The choice of which alternative hypothesis to use is generally determined by the study's objective. The preceding second and third examples of alternative hypotheses involve the use of a "one-tailed" statistical test. This is referred to as "one-tailed" because a direction (greater than [>] or less than [<]) is implied in the statement. The first example represents a "two-tailed" test. There is inequality expressed (age 21 years), but the inequality does not imply direction. One-tailed tests are used more often in management and marketing research because there usually is a need to imply a specific direction in the outcome. For example, it is more likely that a researcher would want to know if Product A performed better than Product B (Product A performance > Product B performance), or vice versa (Product A performance < Product B performance), rather than whether Product A performed differently than Product B (Product A performance Product B performance). Additionally, more useful information is gained by knowing that employees who work from 7:00 a.m. to 4:00 p.m. are more productive than those who work from 3:00 p.m. to 12:00 a.m. (early shift employee production > late shift employee production), rather than simply knowing that these employees have different levels of productivity (early shift employee production late shift employee production).

Both the alternative and the null hypotheses must be determined and stated prior to the collection of data. Before the alternative and null hypotheses can be formulated it is necessary to decide on the desired or expected conclusion of the research. Generally, the desired conclusion of the study is stated in the alternative hypothesis. This is true as long as the null hypothesis can include a statement of equality. For example, suppose that a researcher is interested in exploring the effects of amount of study time on tests scores. The researcher believes that students who study longer perform better on tests. Specifically, the research suggests that students who spend four hours studying for an exam will get a better score than those who study two hours. In this case the hypotheses might be:

H_0 The average test scores of students who study 4 hours for the test = the average test scores of those who study 2 hours.

H_1 The average test score of students who study 4 hours for the test < the average test scores of those who study 2 hours.

As a result of the statistical analysis, the null hypothesis can be *rejected* or *not rejected*. As a principle of rigorous scientific method, this subtle but important point means that the null hypothesis cannot be *accepted.* If the null is rejected, the alternative hypothesis can be accepted; however, if the null is not rejected, we can't conclude that the null hypothesis is true. The rationale is that evidence that supports a hypothesis is not conclusive, but evidence that negates a hypothesis is ample to discredit a hypothesis. The analysis of study time and test scores provides an example. If the results of one study indicate that the test scores of students who study 4 hours are significantly better than the test scores of students who study two hours, the null hypothesis can be rejected because the researcher has found one case when the null is not true. However, if the results of the study indicate that the test scores of those who study 4 hours are not significantly better than those who study 2 hours, the null hypothesis cannot be rejected. One also cannot conclude that the null hypothesis is accepted because these results are only one set of score comparisons. Just because the null hypothesis is true in one situation does not mean it is always true.

Determining the Appropriate Test Statistic

The appropriate test statistic (the statistic to be used in statistical hypothesis testing) is based on various characteristics of the sample population of interest, including sample size and distribution. The test statistic can assume many numerical values. Since the value of the test statistic has a significant effect on the decision, one must use the appropriate statistic in order to obtain meaningful results.

Specifying the Statistical Significance Level

As previously noted, one can reject a null hypothesis or fail to reject a null hypothesis. A null hypothesis that is rejected may, in reality, be true or false. Additionally, a null hypothesis that fails to be rejected may, in reality, be true or false. The outcome that a researcher desires is to reject a false null hypothesis or to fail to reject a true null hypothesis. However, there always is the possibility of rejecting a true hypothesis or failing to reject a false hypothesis.

Rejecting a null hypothesis that is true is called a Type I error and failing to reject a false null hypothesis is called a Type II error. The probability of committing a Type I error is termed á and the probability of committing a Type II error is termed â. As the value of á increases, the probability of committing a Type I error increases. As the value of â increases, the probability of committing a Type II error increases. While one would like to decrease the probability of committing of both types of errors, the reduction of á results in the increase of â and vice versa. The best way to reduce the probability of decreasing both types of error is to increase sample size.

The probability of committing a Type I error, á, is called the level of significance. Before data is collected one must specify a level of significance, or the probability of committing a Type I error (rejecting a true null hypothesis). There is an inverse relationship between a researcher's desire to avoid making a Type I error and the selected value of á; if not making the error is particularly important, a low probability of making the error is sought. The greater the desire is to not reject a true null hypothesis, the lower the selected value of á. In theory, the value of á can be any value between 0 and 1. However, the most common values used in social science research are .05, .01, and .001, which respectively correspond to the levels of 95 percent, 99 percent, and 99.9 percent likelihood that a Type I error is not being made. The tradeoff for choosing a higher level of certainty (significance) is that it will take much stronger statistical evidence to ever reject the null hypothesis.

Determining the Decision Rule

Before data are collected and analysed it is necessary to determine under what circumstances the null hypothesis will be rejected or fail to be rejected. The decision rule can be stated in terms of the computed test statistic, or in probabilistic terms. The same decision will be reached regardless of which method is chosen.

Collecting the Data and Performing the Calculations

The method of data collection is determined early in the research process. Once a research question is determined, one must make decisions regarding what type of data is needed and how the data will be collected. This decision establishes the bases for how the data will be analysed. One should use only approved research methods for collecting and analysing data.

Deciding Whether to Reject the Null Hypothesis

This step involves the application of the decision rule. The decision rule allows one to reject or fail to reject the null hypothesis. If one rejects the null hypothesis, the alternative hypothesis can be accepted.

REFERENCES

- Bhanwar Lal Garg: *An Introduction to Research Methodology*, RBSA Pub, 2002.
- Fowler, Floyd J., : *Survey Research Methods,* Newbury Park, CA: Sage, 1993.
- Garg, Ajit Lal : *An Introduction to Research Methodology*, RBSA Pub, 2002.
- Jack Murrin, *Valuation: Measuring and Managing the Value of Companies,* New York, Wiley, 1994.
- Kapila Mittal: *Research Methodology in Social Sciences*, Vista International, 2006.

4

Research Design

Research designs are concerned with turning the research question into a testing project. The best design depends on your research questions. Every design has its positive and negative sides. The research design has been considered as a "blueprint" for research, dealing with at least four problems: what questions to study, what data are relevant, what data to collect, and how to analyse the results. Research design can be divided into fixed and flexible research designs (Robson, 1993). Others have referred to this distinction with 'quantitative research designs' and 'qualitative research designs'. However, fixed designs need not be quantitative, and flexible design need not be qualitative. In fixed designs the design of the study is fixed before the main stage of data collection takes place. Fixed designs are normally theory-driven; otherwise it's impossible to know in advance which variables need to be controlled and measured. Often these variables are quantitative. Flexible designs allow for more freedom during the data collection. One reason for using a flexible research design can be that the variable of interest is not quantitatively measurable, such as culture. In other cases, theory might not be available before one starts the research.

EXPERIMENTAL DESIGN

In an experimental design, the researcher actively tries to change the situation, circumstances or experience of participants (manipulation), which leads to a change in behaviour of the participants of the study. The participants are assigned to different conditions, and variables of interest are measured. All other variables are controlled Experiments are normally highly fixed before the data collection starts. Read more about experiental research designs here Experiment.

Non-experimental Research Designs

Non-experimental research is almost the same as experimental research, the only difference is that non-experimental research does not involve a manipulation of the situation, circumstances or experience of the participants. Non-experimental research designs can be split up in three designs. First, relational designs, in which a range of variables is measured. These designs are also called correlational studies, since the correlation is most often used analysis. The second type is comparative designs. These designs compare two natural groups. The third type of non-experimental research is a longitudinal design.

Quasi Experiment

Quasi research designs are research design that follow the experimental procedure, but do not randomly assign people to (treatment and comparison) groups.

Examples of Flexible (Qualitative) Research Designs

Case Study

In a case study, one single unit is extensively studied. That can be a case of a person, organization, group or situation. Famous case studies are for example the descriptions about the patients of Freud, who were thoroughly analysed and described. Read more on case study. Bell (1999) states "a case study approach is particularly appropriate for individual researchers because it gives an opportunity for one aspect of a problem to be studied in some depth within a limited time scale".

Ethnographic Study

This type of research is involved with a group, organization, culture, or community. Normally the researcher shares a lot of time with the group. Read more on Ethnography.

TYPES OF DESIGNS

What are the different major types of research designs? We can classify designs into a simple threefold classification by asking some key questions. First, does the design use random assignment to groups? If random assignment is used, we call the design a randomized experiment or true experiment. If random assignment is not used, then we have to ask a second question: Does the design use *either* multiple groups or multiple waves of measurement? If the answer is yes, we would label it a quasi-experimental design. If no, we would call it a non-experimental design. This threefold classification is especially useful for describing the design with respect to internal validity. A randomized experiment generally is the strongest of the three designs when your interest is in establishing a cause-effect relationship. A non-experiment is generally the weakest in this respect. I have to hasten to add here, that I don't mean that a non-experiment is the weakest of the three designs *overall*, but only with respect to internal validity or causal assessment. In fact, the simplest form of non-experiment is a one-shot survey design that consists of nothing but a single observation O. This is probably one of the most common forms of research and, for some research questions — especially descriptive ones — is clearly a strong design. When I say that the non-experiment is the weakest with respect to internal validity, all I mean is that it isn't a particularly good method for assessing the cause-effect relationship that you think might exist between a program and its outcomes.

To illustrate the different types of designs, consider one of each in design notation. The first design is a posttest-only randomized experiment. You can tell it's a randomized experiment because it has an R at the beginning of each line, indicating random assignment. The second design is a pre-post nonequivalent groups quasi-experiment. We know it's not a randomized experiment because random assignment wasn't used. And we know it's not a non-experiment because there are both multiple groups and multiple waves of measurement. That means it must be a quasi-experiment. We add the label "nonequivalent" because in this design we do not explicitly control the assignment and the groups may be nonequivalent or not similar to each other. Finally, we show a posttest-only nonexperimental design. You might use this design if you want to study the effects of a natural disaster like a flood or tornado and you want to do so by interviewing survivors. Notice that in this design, you don't have a comparison group (e.g., interview in a town down the road the road that didn't have the tornado to see what differences the tornado caused) and you don't have multiple waves of measurement (e.g., a pre-tornado level of how people in the ravaged town were doing before the disaster). Does it make sense to do the non-experimental study? Of course! You could gain lots of valuable information by well-conducted post-disaster interviews. But you may have a hard time establishing which of the things you observed are due to the disaster rather than to other factors like the peculiarities of the town or pre-disaster characteristics.

EXPLORATORY RESEARCH

Exploratory research is a type of research conducted for a problem that has not been clearly defined. Exploratory research helps determine the best research design, data collection method and selection of subjects. It should draw definitive conclusions only with extreme caution. Given its fundamental nature, exploratory research often concludes that a perceived problem does not actually exist.

Exploratory research often relies on secondary research such as reviewing available literature and/or data, or qualitative approaches such as informal discussions with consumers, employees, management or competitors, and more formal approaches through in-depth interviews, focus groups, projective methods, case studies or pilot studies. The Internet allows for research methods that are more interactive in nature. For example, RSS feeds efficiently supply researchers with up-to-date information; major search engine search results may be sent by email to researchers by services such as Google Alerts; comprehensive search results are tracked over lengthy periods of time by services such as Google Trends; and websites may be created to attract worldwide feedback on any subject.

The results of exploratory research are not usually useful for decision-making by themselves, but they can provide significant insight into a given situation. Although the results of qualitative research can give some indication as to the "why", "how" and "when" something occurs, it cannot tell us "how often" or "how many". Exploratory research is not typically generalizable to the population at large. Social exploratory research "seeks to find out how people get along in the setting under question, what meanings they give to their actions, and what issues concern them. The goal is to learn 'what is going on here?' and to investigate social phenomena without explicit expectations." This methodology is also at times referred to as a grounded theory approach to qualitative research or interpretive research, and is an attempt to unearth a theory from the data itself rather than from a predisposed hypothesis.

Earl Babbie identifies three purposes of social science research. The purposes are exploratory, descriptive and explanatory. Exploratory research is used when problems are in a preliminary stage. Exploratory research is used when the topic or issue is new and when data is difficult to collect. Exploratory research is flexible and can address research questions of all types (what, why, how). Exploratory research is often used to generate formal hypotheses. Shields and Tajalli link exploratory research with the conceptual framework working hypothesis.

Applied Research

Applied research in administration is often exploratory because there is need for flexibility in approaching the problem. In addition there are often data limitations and a need to make a decision within a short time period. Qualitative research methods such as case study or field research are often used in exploratory research.

There are three types of objectives in a marketing research project.

- Exploratory research or formulative research
- Descriptive research
- Causal research.

Exploratory research or formulative research: The objective of exploratory research is to gather preliminary information that will help define problems and suggest hypotheses.'

Descriptive Research: The objective of descriptive research is to describe things, such as the market potential for a product or the demographics and attitudes of consumers who buy the product.'

DESCRIPTIVE RESEARCH

Descriptive research, also known as statistical research, describes data and characteristics about the population or phenomenon being studied. Descriptive research answers the questions *who*, *what*, *where*, *when* and *how*...

Although the data description is factual, accurate and systematic, the research cannot describe what caused a situation. Thus, Descriptive research cannot be used to create a *causal relationship*, where one variable affects another. In other words, descriptive research can be said to have a low requirement for internal validity.

The description is used for frequencies, averages and other statistical calculations. Often the best approach, prior to writing descriptive research, is to conduct a survey investigation. Qualitative research often has the aim of *description* and researchers may follow-up with examinations of why the observations exist and what the implications of the findings are.

In short descriptive research deals with everything that can be counted and studied. But there are always restrictions to that. Your research must have an impact to the lives of the people around you. For example, finding the most frequent disease that affects the children of a town. The reader of the research will know what to do to prevent that disease thus, more people will live a healthy life.

Social Science Research

Earl Babbie identifies exploration, description and explanation as the three purposes of social science research. Descriptive research classifies phenomena. Descriptive research generally precedes explanatory research. For example, over time chemists have described the elements through the periodic table. The periodic table's description of the elements allows people and families to think about the elements in helpful ways. It allows for explanation and prediction when elements are combined.

WHAT IS DESCRIPTIVE RESEARCH?

Descriptive research does not fit neatly into the definition of either quantitative or qualitative research methodologies, but instead it can utilize elements of both, often within the same study. The term descriptive research refers to the type of research question, design, and data analysis that will be applied to a given topic. Descriptive statistics tell what is, while inferential statistics try to determine cause and effect.

The type of question asked by the researcher will ultimately determine the type of approach necessary to complete an accurate assessment of the topic at hand. Descriptive studies, primarily concerned with finding out "what is," might be applied to investigate the following questions: Do teachers hold favourable attitudes toward using computers in schools? What kinds of activities that involve technology occur in sixth-grade classrooms and how frequently do they occur? What have been the reactions of school administrators to technological innovations in teaching the social sciences? How have high school computing courses changed over the last 10 years? How do the new multimediated textbooks compare to the print-based textbooks? How are decisions being made about using Channel One in schools, and for those schools that choose to use it, how is Channel One being implemented? What is the best way to provide access to computer equipment in schools? How should instructional designers improve software design to make the software more appealing to students? To what degree are special-education teachers well versed concerning assistive technology? Is there a relationship between experience with multimedia computers and problem-solving skills? How successful is a certain satellite-delivered Spanish course in terms of motivational value and academic achievement? Do teachers actually implement technology in the way they perceive? How many people use the AECT gopher server, and what do they use if for?

Descriptive research can be either quantitative or qualitative. It can involve collections of quantitative information that can be tabulated along a continuum in numerical form, such as scores on a test or the number of times a person chooses to use a-certain feature of a multimedia program, or it can describe categories of information such as gender or patterns of interaction when using technology in a group situation. Descriptive research involves gathering data that describe events and then organizes, tabulates, depicts, and describes the data collection. It often uses visual aids such as graphs and charts to aid the reader in understanding the data distribution. Because the human mind cannot extract the full import of a large mass of raw data, descriptive statistics are very important in reducing the data to manageable form. When in-depth, narrative descriptions of small numbers of cases are involved, the research uses description as a tool to organize data into patterns that emerge during analysis. Those patterns aid the mind in comprehending a qualitative study and its implications.

Most quantitative research falls into two areas: studies that describe events and studies aimed at discovering inferences or causal relationships. Descriptive studies are aimed at finding out "what is," so observational and survey methods are frequently used to collect descriptive data. Studies of this type might describe the current state of multimedia usage in schools or patterns of activity resulting from group work at the computer. An example of this is Cochenour, Hakes, and Neal's (1994) study of trends in compressed video applications with education and the private sector.

Descriptive studies report summary data such as measures of central tendency including the mean, median, mode, deviance from the mean, variation, percentage, and correlation between variables. Survey research commonly includes that type of measurement, but often goes beyond the descriptive statistics in order to draw inferences. Signer's (1991) survey of computer-assisted instruction and at-risk students, or Nolan, McKinnon, and Soler's (1992) research on achieving equitable access to school computers. Thick, rich descriptions of phenomena can also emerge from qualitative studies, case studies, observational studies, interviews, and portfolio assessments. Robinson's (1994) case study of a televised news program in classrooms and Lee's (1994) case study about identifying values concerning school restructuring are excellent examples of case studies.

Descriptive research is unique in the number of variables employed. Like other types of research, descriptive research can include multiple variables for analysis, yet unlike other methods, it requires only one variable (Borg & Gall, 1989). For example, a descriptive study might employ methods of analysing correlations between multiple variables by using tests such as Pearson's Product Moment correlation, regression, or multiple regression analysis. Good examples of this are the Knupfer and Hayes (1994) study about the effects of the Channel One broadcast on knowledge of current events, Manaev's (1991) study about mass media effectiveness, McKenna's (1993) study of the relationship between attributes of a radio program and it's appeal to listeners, Orey and Nelson's (1994) examination of learner interactions with hypermedia environments, and Shapiro's (1991) study of memory and decision processes.

On the other hand, descriptive research might simply report the percentage summary on a single variable. Examples of this are the tally of reference citations in selected instructional design and technology journals by Anglin and Towers (1992); Barry's (1994) investigation of the controversy surrounding advertising and Channel One; Lu, Morlan, Lerchlorlarn, Lee, and Dike's (1993) investigation of the international utilization of media in education (1993); and Pettersson, Metallinos, Muffoletto, Shaw, and Takakuwa's (1993) analysis of the use of verbo-visual information in teaching geography in various countries.

Descriptive statistics utilize data collection and analysis techniques that yield reports concerning the measures of central tendency, variation, and correlation. The combination of its characteristic summary and correlational statistics, along with its focus on specific types of research questions, methods, and outcomes is what distinguishes descriptive research from other research types.

Three main purposes of research are to describe, explain, and validate findings. Description emerges following creative exploration, and serves to organize the findings in order to fit them with explanations, and then test or validate those explanations (Krathwohl, 1993). Many research studies call for the description of natural or man-made phenomena such as their form, structure, activity, change over time, relation to other phenomena, and so on. The description often illuminates knowledge that we might not otherwise notice or even encounter. Several important scientific discoveries as well as anthropological information about events outside of our common experiences have resulted from making such descriptions. For example, astronomers use their telescopes to develop descriptions of different parts of the universe, anthropologists describe life events of socially atypical situations or cultures uniquely different from our own, and educational researchers describe activities within classrooms concerning the implementation of technology. This process sometimes results in the discovery of stars and stellar events, new knowledge about value systems or practices of other cultures, or even the reality of classroom life as new technologies are implemented within schools.

Educational researchers might use observational, survey, and interview techniques to collect data about group dynamics during computer-based activities. These data could then be used to recommend specific strategies for implementing computers or improving teaching strategies. Two excellent studies concerning the role of collaborative groups were conducted by Webb (1982), and Rysavy and Sales (1991). Noreen Webb's landmark study used descriptive research techniques to investigate collaborative groups as they worked within classrooms. Rysavy and Sales also apply a descriptive approach to study the role of group collaboration for working at computers. The Rysavy and Sales approach did not observe students in classrooms, but reported certain common findings that emerged through a literature search.

Descriptive studies have an important role in educational research. They have greatly increased our knowledge about what happens in schools. Some of the important books in education have reported studies of this type: Life in Classrooms, by Philip Jackson; The Good High School, by Sara Lawrence Lightfoot; Teachers and Machines: The Classroom Use of Technology Since 1920, by Larry Cuban; A Place Called School, by John Goodlad; Visual Literacy: A Spectrum of Learning, by D. M. Moore and Dwyer; Computers in Education: Social, Political, and Historical Perspectives, by Muffoletto and Knupfer; and Contemporary Issues in American Distance Education, by M. G. Moore.

Henry J. Becker's (1986) series of survey reports concerning the implementation of computers into schools across the United States as well as Nancy Nelson Knupfer's (1988) reports about teacher's opinions and patterns of computer usage also fit partially within the realm of descriptive research. Both studies describe categories of data and use statistical analysis to examine correlations between specific variables. Both also go beyond the bounds of descriptive research and conduct further statistical procedures appropriate to their research questions, thus enabling them to make further recommendations about implementing computing technology in ways to support grassroots change and equitable practices within the schools. Finally, Knupfer's study extended the analysis and conclusions in order to yield suggestions for instructional designers involved with educational computing.

The Nature of Descriptive Research

The descriptive function of research is heavily dependent on instrumentation for measurement and observation. Researchers may work for many years to perfect such instrumentation so that the resulting measurement will be accurate, reliable, and generalizable. Instruments such as the electron microscope, standardized tests for various purposes, the United States census, Michael Simonson's questionnaires about computer usage, and scores of thoroughly validated questionnaires are examples of some instruments that yield valuable descriptive data. Once the instruments are developed, they can be used to describe phenomena of interest to the researchers.

The intent of some descriptive research is to produce statistical information about aspects of education that interests policy makers and educators. The National Centre for Education Statistics specializes in this kind of research. Many of its findings are published in an annual volume called Digest of Educational Statistics. The centre also administers the National Assessment of Educational Progress (NAEP), which collects descriptive information about how well the nation's youth are doing in various subject areas. A typical NAEP publication is The Reading Report Card, which provides descriptive information about the reading achievement of junior high and high school students during the past 2 decades.

On a larger scale, the International Association for the Evaluation of Education Achievement (IEA) has done major descriptive studies comparing the academic achievement levels of students in many different nations, including the United States. Within the United States, huge amounts of information are being gathered continuously by the Office of Technology Assessment, which influences policy concerning technology in education. As a way of offering guidance about the potential of technologies for distance education, that office has published a book called Linking for Learning: A New Course for Education, which offers descriptions of distance education and its potential.

There has been an ongoing debate among researchers about the value of quantitative versus qualitative research, and certain remarks have targeted descriptive research as being less pure than traditional experimental, quantitative designs. Rumours abound that young researchers must conduct quantitative research in order to get published in Educational Technology Research and Development and other prestigious journals in the field. One camp argues the benefits of a scientific approach to educational research, thus preferring the experimental, quantitative approach, while the other camp posits the need to recognize the unique human side of educational research questions and thus prefers to use qualitative research methodology.

Because descriptive research spans both quantitative and qualitative methodologies, it brings the ability to describe events in greater or less depth as needed, to focus on various elements of different research techniques, and to engage quantitative statistics to organize information in meaningful ways. The citations within this chapter provide ample evidence that descriptive research can indeed be published in prestigious journals.

Descriptive studies can yield rich data that lead to important recommendations. For example, Galloway (1992) bases recommendations for teaching with computer analogies on descriptive data, and Wehrs (1992) draws reasonable conclusions about using expert systems to support academic advising. On the other hand, descriptive research can be misused by those who do not understand its purpose and limitations. For example, one cannot try to draw conclusions that show cause and effect, because that is beyond the bounds of the statistics employed.

Borg and Gall (1989) classify the outcomes of educational research into the four categories of description, prediction, improvement, and explanation. They say that descriptive research describes natural or man-made educational phenomena that is of interest to policy makers and educators. Predictions of educational phenomenon seek to determine whether certain students are at risk and if teachers should use different techniques to instruct them. Research about improvement asks whether a certain technique does something to help students learn better and whether certain interventions can improve student learning by applying causal-comparative, correlational, and experimental methods. The final category of explanation posits that research is able to explain a set of phenomena that leads to our ability to describe, predict, and control the phenomena with a high level of certainty and accuracy. This usually takes the form of theories.

The methods of collecting data for descriptive research can be employed singly or in various combinations, depending on the research questions at hand. Descriptive research often calls upon quasi-experimental research design (Campbell & Stanley, 1963). Some of the common data collection methods applied to questions within the realm of descriptive research include surveys, interviews, observations, and portfolios.

EXPERIMENTAL DESIGN

Experimental designs are often touted as the most "rigorous" of all research designs or, as the "gold standard" against which all other designs are judged. In one sense, they probably are. If you can implement an experimental design well (and that is a big "if" indeed), then the experiment is probably the strongest design with respect to internal validity. Why? Recall that internal validity is at the centre of all causal or cause-effect inferences. When you want to determine whether some program or treatment *causes* some outcome or outcomes to occur, then you are interested in having strong internal validity. Essentially, you want to assess the proposition:

If X, then Y

or, in more colloquial terms:

If the program is given, then the outcome occurs

Unfortunately, it's not enough just to show that when the program or treatment occurs the expected outcome also happens. That's because there may be lots of reasons, other than the program, for why you observed the outcome. To really show that there is a causal relationship, you have to simultaneously address the two propositions:

If X, then Y

and

If not *X, then* not *Y*

Or, once again more colloquially:

If the program is given, then the outcome occurs

and

If the program is not *given, then the outcome does* not *occur*

If you are able to provide evidence for both of these propositions, then you've in effect isolated the program from all of the other potential causes of the outcome. You've shown that when the program is present the outcome occurs and when it's not present, the outcome doesn't occur. That points to the causal effectiveness of the program.

Think of all this like a fork in the road. Down one path, you implement the program and observe the outcome. Down the other path, you don't implement the program and the outcome doesn't occur.

But, how do we take *both* paths in the road in the same study? How can we be in two places at once? Ideally, what we want is to have the same conditions — the same people, context, time, and so on — and see whether when the program is given we get the outcome and when the program is not given we don't. Obviously, we can never achieve this hypothetical situation. If we give the program to a group of people, we can't simultaneously not give it! So, how do we get out of this apparent dilemma?

Perhaps we just need to think about the problem a little differently. What if we could create two groups or contexts that are as similar as we can possibly make them? If we could be confident that the two situations are comparable, then we could administer our program in one and not give the program in the other. And, if the two contexts are comparable, then this is like taking both forks in the road simultaneously! We can have our cake and eat it too, so to speak.

That's exactly what an experimental design tries to achieve. In the simplest type of experiment, we create two groups that are "equivalent" to each other. One group (the program or treatment group) gets the program and the other group (the comparison or control group) does not. In all other respects, the groups are treated the same. They have similar people, live in similar contexts, have similar backgrounds, and so on. Now, if we observe differences in outcomes between these two groups, then the differences must be due to the only thing that differs between them — that one got the program and the other didn't.

OK, so how do we create two groups that are "equivalent"? The approach used in experimental design is to assign people randomly from a common pool of people into the two groups. The experiment relies on this idea of random assignment to groups as the basis for obtaining two groups that are similar. Then, we give one the program or treatment and we don't give it to the other. We observe the same outcomes in both groups.

The key to the success of the experiment is in the random assignment. In fact, even with random assignment we never expect that the groups we create will be exactly the same. How could they be, when they are made up of different people? We rely on the idea of probability and assume that the two groups are "probabilistically equivalent" or equivalent within known probabilistic ranges.

So, if we randomly assign people to two groups, and we have enough people in our study to achieve the desired probabilistic equivalence, then we may consider the experiment to be strong in internal validity and we probably have a good shot at assessing whether the program causes the outcome(s).

But there are lots of things that can go wrong. We may not have a large enough sample. Or, we may have people who refuse to participate in our study or who drop out part way through. Or, we may be challenged successfully on ethical grounds (after all, in order to use this approach we have to deny the program to some people who might be equally deserving of it as others). Or, we may get resistance from the staff in our study who would like some of their "favourite" people to get the program. Or, they mayor might insist that her daughter be put into the new program in an educational study because it may mean she'll get better grades. The bottom line here is that experimental design is intrusive and difficult to carry out in most real world contexts. And, because an experiment is often an intrusion, you are to some extent setting up an artificial situation so that you can assess your causal relationship with high internal validity. If so, then you are limiting the degree to which you can generalize your results to real contexts where you haven't set up an experiment. That is, you have reduced your external validity in order to achieve greater internal validity.

In the end, there is just no simple answer (no matter what anyone tells you!). If the situation is right, an experiment can be a very strong design to use. But it isn't automatically so. My own personal guess is that randomized experiments are probably appropriate in no more than 10% of the social research studies that attempt to assess causal relationships.

Experimental design is a fairly complex subject in its own right. I've been discussing the simplest of experimental designs — a two-group program versus comparison group design. But there are lots of experimental design variations that attempt to accomplish different things or solve different problems. In this section you'll explore the basic design and then learn some of the principles behind the major variations.

QUASI-EXPERIMENTAL DESIGNS

Quasi-experimental designs are designs in which there is a comparison group but it is either not possible or not feasible to use random assignment to assign participants to groups. Random assignment, increases internal validity and reduces the likelihood of bias because each subject has non-zero probability of being placed in each group. For example, it would not be ethical to recruit a group of volunteers for a study about homelessness and then randomly assign one group to a condition of homelessness for a period of time. You might, however, be able to find a group of individuals who are currently homeless and compare them to a group of people who are living in permanent housing. Thus without a comparison group of students who did not have the alcohol education class in our example, we would be unsure if the class itself led to the results on the quiz. To deal with this, you might also give the quiz to several other students who did not participate in the class. In other words, you would use a comparison group that had no access to the material to control for these issues. This would be an example of a slightly more sophisticated design known as the *posttest-only with non-equivalent group design.* In research notation it would be:

X O

O (different group)

Again, X would represent the class lecture and O would represent the posttest. Now, if the students in the class who received the lecture scored much higher on the quiz, you could assert that *maybe* it was due to the lecture. We cannot be certain, however, that there are not inherent differences between the two groups. Confounding variables such as family experience with alcohol abuse, religious beliefs, and sex may have an impact on the level of knowledge each group has concerning the effects of alcohol on the body.

Let us imagine for a moment that you are a case manager working in a community mental health agency with adults. You have been offering a support group for your consumers in which you discuss issues such as daily living skills, money management, and other skills necessary for independent living. The group begins every eight weeks and meets once a week for the two-month period.

You have noticed that several of your consumers seem to feel better about themselves after participating in the group. Perhaps you review the literature and find several studies that suggest that support groups are an effective way to increase the self-esteem of your consumers. After completing your literature review, you develop the following hypothesis: "Participants will report an increase in self-esteem following an eight-week support group."

To test this hypothesis, you ask the participants who begin the next eight-week period to complete a self-esteem measurement instrument before the beginning of the first class. As a comparison, you ask an equal number of participants (who are not attending the group, but who are consumers at your agency) to complete the same instrument. Then at the end of the eight weeks, you ask both your support group and the comparison group to complete the self-esteem questionnaire again. In research notation this would be:

O X O

O O

The Os represent the pretest and posttest, and the X represents the support group (the intervention). We could argue that if the experimental group (the group that participated in the support group) had remarkably higher scores on their self-esteem scale after completing the support group (compared to the scores on the pretest), then the difference may be attributed to the support group itself. The scores of the comparison group would strengthen this argument if the comparison group's scores remained similar from the pretest to the posttest (i.e., their scores did not increase or decrease over time).

All research designs have inherent limitations, and the pretest-posttest non-equivalent comparison group design is no exception. Logic would dictate that we could not rule out any alternative explanations for the perceived changes in the experimental group. How do we know, for example, that something else outside the group did not happen to cause the group to feel better about themselves? Perhaps all the members of the group suddenly found new jobs, received promotions, or felt that the climate at their places of work became friendlier toward them. Any number of variables could account for a change in the group outside the influence of the support group itself. Time series designs are slightly more rigorous than simple quasi-experimental designs such as the pretest-posttest non-equivalent group design outlined above. Imagine again that you are working as a case manager at a community mental health agency.

You are working with adults who participate in your support group. This time, instead of recruiting other consumers to serve as a comparison group, let us imagine that all the consumers in your agency are participating in your support group—effectively eliminating the chance to have a comparison group.

One solution is the *time series design.* To use this design, you as the researcher would simply give the same self-esteem questionnaire at several points in time before the support group begins. Perhaps you would ask respondents to complete the questionnaire every other day for a week. Then the support group would begin, and after its completion, you would ask them to complete the same questionnaire again every other day for a week. The three pretests could be compared to the posttests. In research notation, this research design would look like this:

O O O X O O O

Again, the Os represent the self-esteem questionnaire and the X represents the support group. Because there is no comparison group, the researcher uses the self-esteem questionnaires at various points in time as a comparison group by comparing the groups' overall scores over time.

If, over the course of a week, the pretests seem to reflect a low level of self-esteem and then the group's level of self-esteem dramatically improves after they complete the support group, you could argue that the intervention may be correlated with the increase in self-esteem. Notice, however, that we are not saying that the intervention *caused* a change in self-esteem; we are simply stating that there is a correlation. The next design we will examine is the *time series design with non-equivalent comparison group*. This is simply a variation of the time series design. Perhaps you are able to find a group of consumers who are not willing to participate in your support group but are willing to serve as a comparison group. You may ask both groups to fill out the self-esteem questionnaire a total of three times over the course of seven days before the support group begins and then again three times over seven days after the end of the support group. In research notation, this would look like this:

O O O X O O O

O O O O O O

The Os represent the self-esteem questionnaire and the X represents the intervention. We said that the strength of the time series design was that the questionnaire repeated over time served as its own comparison group. When you include the additional component of the comparison group, your design is strengthened. You can now compare the pretest scores with the posttest scores, and these can be evaluated against those of the comparison group. Let us assume for a moment that the comparison group's scores stayed fairly similar over time. Logic would tell us that there is a strong possibility that the support group was effective (assuming that the scores of the experimental group increased after the intervention, of course). Like all research designs, quasi-experimental designs have both strengths and weaknesses.

On one hand, they are methodologically stronger than pre-experimental designs because they use a comparison group with pre-and posttests and/or test the findings at several points in time. However, they cannot rule out alternative explanations for any observed changes in groups. For instance, the members of one group may have much higher IQs than the other group or might be more motivated to participate in the study. These could be alternative explanations for observed changes in groups.

CAUSAL RESEARCH

If the objective is to determine which variable might be causing a certain behaviour, i.e. whether there is a cause and effect relationship between *variables*, causal research must be undertaken. In order to determine causality, it is important to hold the variable that is assumed to cause the change in the other variable(s) constant and then measure the changes in the other variable(s). This type of research is very complex and the researcher can never be completely certain that there are not other factors influencing the causal relationship, especially when dealing with people's attitudes and motivations. There are often much deeper psychological considerations, that even the respondent may not be aware of.

CLASSIFYING EXPERIMENTAL DESIGNS

Although there are a great variety of experimental design variations, we can classify and organize them using a simple signal-to-noise ratio metaphor. In this metaphor, we assume that what we observe or see can be divided into two components, the signal and the noise (by the way, this is directly analogous to the true score theory of measurement). But because there is so much variability or noise in the series, it is difficult even to detect the downward slope. When we divide the series into its two components, we can clearly see the slope. In most research, the signal is related to the key variable of interest

— the construct you're trying to measure, the program or treatment that's being implemented. The noise consists of all of the random factors in the situation that make it harder to see the signal — the lighting in the room, local distractions, how people felt that day, etc. We can construct a ratio of these two by dividing the signal by the noise. In research, we want the signal to be high relative to the noise. For instance, if you have a very powerful treatment or program (i.e., strong signal) and very good measurement (i.e., low noise) you will have a better chance of seeing the effect of the program than if you have either a strong program and weak measurement or a weak program and strong measurement.

With this in mind, we can now classify the experimental designs into two categories: signal enhancers or noise reducers. Notice that doing either of these things — enhancing signal or reducing noise — improves the quality of the research. The *signal-enhancing experimental designs* are called the factorial designs. In these designs, the focus is almost entirely on the setup of the program or treatment, its components and its major dimensions. In a typical factorial design we would examine a number of different variations of a treatment. There are two major types of *noise-reducing experimental designs*: covariance designs and blocking designs. In these designs we typically use information about the makeup of the sample or about pre-program variables to remove some of the noise in our study.

COVARIANCE DESIGNS

Design Notation: The basic Analysis of Covariance Design (ANCOVA or ANACOVA) is a just pretest-posttest randomized experimental design. The notation shown here suggests that the pre-program measure is the same one as the post-program measure (otherwise we would use subscripts to distinguish the two), and so we would call this a pretest. But you should note that the pre-program measure doesn't have to be a pretest — it can be any variable measured prior to the program intervention. It is also possible for a study to have more than one covariate.

The pre-program measure or pretest is sometimes also called a "covariate" because of the way it's used in the data analysis — we "covary" it with the outcome variable or posttest in order to remove variability or noise. Thus, the ANCOVA design falls in the class of a "noise reduction" experimental design.

In social research we frequently hear about statistical "adjustments" that attempt to control for important factors in our study. For instance, we might read that an analysis "examined posttest performance after adjusting for the income and educational level of the participants." In this case, "income" and "education level" are covariates. Covariates are the variables you "adjust for" in your study. Sometimes the language that will be used is that of "removing the effects" of one variable from another. For instance, we might read that an analysis "examined posttest performance after removing the effect of income and educational level of the participants."

How Does A Covariate Reduce Noise? One of the most important ideas in social research is how we make a statistical adjustment — adjust one variable based on its covariance with another variable. If you understand this idea, you'll be well on your way to mastering social research. What I want to do here is to show you a series of graphs that illustrate pictorially what we mean by adjusting for a covariate.

Let's begin with data from a simple ANCOVA design. The pre-post bivariate distribution. Each "dot" on the graph represents the pretest and posttest score for an individual. We use an 'X' to signify a program or treated case and an 'O' to describe a control or comparison case. You should be able to see a few things immediately. First, you should be able to see a whopping treatment effect! It's so obvious that you don't even need statistical analysis to tell you whether there's an effect (although you may want to use statistics to estimate its size and probability). How do I know there's an effect? Look at any pretest value (value on the horizontal axis). Now, look up from that value — you are looking up the posttest scale from lower to higher posttest scores. Do you see any pattern with respect to the groups? It should be obvious to you that the program cases (the 'X's) tend to score higher on the posttest at any given pretest value. Second, you should see that the posttest variability has a range of about 70 points.Now, let's fit some straight lines to the data. The lines on the graph are regression lines that describe the pre-post relationship for each of the groups. The regression line shows the expected posttest score for any pretest score. The treatment effect is even clearer with the regression lines. You should see that the line for the treated group is about 10 points higher than the line for the comparison group at any pretest value.

What we want to do is remove some of the variability in the posttest while preserving the difference between the groups. Or, in other terms, we want to "adjust" the posttest scores for pretest variability. In effect, we want to "subtract out" the pretest. You might think of this as subtracting the line from each group from the data for each group. How do we do that? Well, why don't we actually subtract?!? Find the posttest difference between the line for a group and each actual value. We call each of these differences a residual — it's what's left over when you subtract a line from the data.

Now, here comes the tricky part. What does the data look like when we subtract out a line? You might think of it almost like turning the above graph clockwise until the regression lines are horizontal. Now, look at how big the posttest variability or range is in the figure (as indicated by the red double arrow). You should see that the range is considerably smaller that the 70 points we started out with above. You should also see that the difference between the lines is the same as it was before. So, we have in effect reduced posttest variability while maintaining the group difference. We've lowered the noise while keeping the signal at its original strength. The statistical adjustment procedure will result in a more efficient and more powerful estimate of the treatment effect.

You should also note the shape of the pre-post relationship. Essentially, the plot now looks like a zero correlation between the pretest and, in fact, it is. How do I know it's a zero correlation? Because any line that can be fitted through the data well would be horizontal. There's no slope or relationship. And, there shouldn't be. This graph shows the pre-post relationship *after we've removed the pretest*! If we've removed the pretest from the posttest there will be no pre-post correlation left.

Finally, let's redraw the axes to indicate that the pretest has been removed. Here, the posttest values are the original posttest values minus the line (the predicted posttest values). That's why we see that the new posttest axis has 0 at it's centre. Negative values on the posttest indicate that the original point fell below the regression line on the original axis. Here, we can better estimate that the posttest range is about 50 points instead of the original 70, even though the difference between the regression lines is the same. We've lowered the noise while retaining the signal.

The adjustment for a covariate in the ANCOVA design is accomplished with the statistical analysis, not through rotation of graphs. Some thoughts to conclude this topic. The ANCOVA design is a noise-reducing experimental design. It *"adjusts"* posttest scores for variability on the covariate (pretest). This is what we mean by *"adjusting"* for the effects of one variable on another in social research. You can use *any* continuous variable as a covariate, but the pretest is usually best. Why? Because the pretest is usually the variable that would be most highly correlated with the posttest (a variable should correlate highly with itself, shouldn't it?). Because it's so highly correlated, when you "subtract it out" or "remove' it, you're removing more extraneous variability from the posttest. The rule in selecting covariates is to select the measure(s) that correlate most highly with the outcome and, for multiple covariates, have little intercorrelation (otherwise, you're just adding in redundant covariates and you will actually lose precision by doing that). For example, you probably wouldn't want to use both gross and net income as two covariates in the same analysis because they are highly related and therefore redundant as adjustment variables.

REFERENCES

- Maxwell, J. A.: *Qualitative Research Design: An Interactive Approach*. Thousand Oaks, CA: Sage Publishing, 1996.
- Mittal, Kapila: *Research Methodology in Social Sciences*, Vista International, 2006.
- Gupta, Sudhir: *Workshop on Research Methodology*, Centrum Press, 2011.
- Kanak Kanti Bagchi: *Research Methodology in Social Sciences: A Practical Guide*, Abhijeet Pub, 2007.

5

Sample Survey Design and Analysis

Researchers often use sample survey methodology to obtain information about a large aggregate or population by selecting and measuring a sample from that population. Due to the variability of characteristics among items in the population, researchers apply scientific sample designs in the sample selection process to reduce the risk of a distorted view of the population, and they make inferences about the population based on the information from the sample survey data. In order to make statistically valid inferences for the population, they must incorporate the sample design in the data analysis. Traditional SAS® procedures, such as the MEANS procedure and the GLM procedure, compute statistics under the assumption that the sample is drawn from an infinite population by simple random sampling. These procedures generally do not correctly estimate the variance of an estimator if they are applied to a sample drawn by a complex sample design. SAS users have requested procedures that analyse data from complex sample surveys.

The SURVEYFREQ Procedure

The SURVEYFREQ procedure produces one-way to n-way frequency and crosstabulation tables from sample survey data. These tables include estimates of population totals, population proportions (overall proportions, and also row and column proportions), and corresponding standard errors. Confidence limits, coefficients of variation, and design effects are also available. The procedure provides a variety of options to customize your table display.

For one-way frequency tables, PROC SURVEYFREQ provides Rao-Scott chi-square goodness-of-fit tests, which are adjusted for the sample design. You can test a null hypothesis of equal proportions for a one-way frequency table, or you can input other null hypothesis proportions for the test. For two-way frequency tables, PROC SURVEYFREQ provides design-based tests of no association between the row and column variables. These tests include the Rao-Scott chi-square test, the Rao-Scott likelihood-ratio test, the Wald chi-square test, and the Wald log-linear chi-square test.

The following statements illustrate the syntax of PROC SURVEYFREQ:

```
proc surveyfreq data=SIS_Survey;
  tables Response;
  strata  State  NewUser;
  cluster School;
   weight SamplingWeight;
run;
```

The SURVEYLOGISTIC Procedure.

The SURVEYLOGISTIC procedure fits linear logistic regression models for discrete response survey data by the method of pseudo-maximum likelihood, incorporating the sample design into the analysis. The SURVEYLOGISTIC procedure enables you to use categorical classification variables as explanatory variables, using the familiar syntax for main effects and interactions employed in the GLM and LOGISTIC procedures. The following link functions are available in PROC SURVEYLOGISTIC: the cumulative logit function (CLOGIT), the generalized logit function (GLOGIT), the probit function (PROBIT), and the complementary log-log function (CLOGLOG). Design-based variances of the estimated regression parameters and the odds ratios are estimated using a Taylor series expansion approximation.

The following statements illustrate the syntax of PROC SURVEYLOGISTIC:

```
proc surveylogistic data=SampleStrata;
   strata state type/list;
   model Rating (order=internal) = Usage;
   weight SamplingWeight;
run;
```

The SURVEYMEANS Procedure.

The SURVEYMEANS procedure provides estimates of population means and population totals from sample survey data. The sample design can be a complex sample design with stratification, clustering, and unequal weighting. PROC SURVEYMEANS also provides domain analysis (subgroup or subpopulation analysis). The procedure uses the Taylor series expansion method to provide estimates of design-based variances for the quantities of interest.

You can use the SURVEYMEANS procedure to compute the following statistics:

- estimates of population means, with corresponding standard errors and *t* tests
- estimates of population totals, with corresponding estimated standard deviations and *t* tests
- estimates of proportions for categorical variables and corresponding *t* tests
- ratio estimates population means and proportions, and their standard errors
- confidence limits for estimated population total, population mean, and proportions
- data summary information
- estimates of domain means, domain totals, and domain proportions and their standard errors

The following statements illustrate the syntax of PROC SURVEYMEANS:

```
proc surveymeans data=Company mean sum;
   var Asset Sale Value Profit;
   weight Weight;
run;
```

The SURVEYPHREG Procedure

PROC SURVEYPHREG performs regression analysis based on the Cox proportional hazards model for sample survey data. The procedure provides design-based variance estimates, confidence intervals, and hypothesis tests concerning the parameters and model effects.

The following statements illustrate the syntax of PROC SURVEYPHREG:

```
proc surveyphreg data = LibrarySurvey;
    weight SamplingWeight;
    strata Branch;
    model lenBorrow*Returned(0) = Age;
run;
```

The SURVEYREG Procedure

PROC SURVEYREG fits linear regression models for survey data and computes regression coefficients and their variance-covariance matrix. The procedure enables you to specify classification effects with the same syntax as in the GLM procedure. The procedure also provides hypothesis tests for the model effects, for any specified estimable linear functions of model parameters, and for custom hypothesis tests of linear combinations of the regression parameters. The procedure computes design-based confidence limits of the parameter estimates and their linear estimable functions.

The following statements illustrate the syntax of PROC SURVEYREG:

```
proc surveyreg data=Farms total=TotalInStrata;
   strata State Region/list;
   model CornYield = FarmArea/covb;
   weight Weight;
run;
```

The SURVEYSELECT Procedure

The SURVEYSELECT procedure provides a variety of methods for selecting probability-based random samples. The procedure can select a simple random sample or can sample according to a complex multistage sample design that includes stratification, clustering, and unequal probabilities of selection.

With probability sampling, each unit in the survey population has a known, positive probability of selection. This property of probability sampling avoids selection bias and enables you to use statistical theory to make valid inferences from the sample to survey population.

In addition to methods for equal probability selection, PROC SURVEYSELECT also provides probability proportional to size (PPS) selection methods. In PPS sampling, a unit's selection probability is proportional to its size measure. PPS sampling is often used in cluster sampling, where you select clusters (groups of sampling units) of varying sizes in the first stage of selection. Available PPS methods include without replacement, with replacement, systematic, and sequential with minimum replacement. The procedure can apply these methods for stratified and replicated sample designs.

To select a sample with PROC SURVEYSELECT, you input a SAS data set that contains the sampling frame or list the units from which the sample will be selected. You also specify the selection methods, the desired sample size or sampling rate, and other parameters. The SURVEYSELECT procedure selects the sample, producing an output data set that contains the selected units, their selection probabilities, and sampling weights.

The SURVEYSELECT procedure uses fast, efficient algorithms for these sample selection methods. Thus, it performs well even for very large input data sets or sampling frames, which can occur in practice for large scale sample surveys.

The following statements illustrate the syntax of PROC SURVEYSELECT:

```
proc surveyselect data=Customers
   method=srs n=15
   seed=1953 out=SampleStrata;
   strata State Type;
run;
```

A Note on Variance Estimation.

The survey analysis procedures provide a choice of variance estimation methods for complex survey designs. In addition to the Taylor series linearization method, the procedures offer two replication-based (resampling) methods—balanced repeated replication (BRR) and the delete-1 jackknife. These variance estimation methods usually give similar, satisfactory results. The choice of a variance estimation method can depend on the sample design used, the sample design information available, the parameters to be estimated, and computational issues.

The Taylor series linearization method is appropriate for all designs in which the first-stage sample is selected with replacement, or in which the first-stage sampling fraction is small, as it often is in practice. The Taylor series method obtains a linear approximation for the estimator and then uses the variance estimate for this approximation to estimate the variance of the estimate itself. When there are clusters (PSUs) in the sample design, the procedures estimate the variance from the variation among the PSUs. When the design is stratified, the procedures pool stratum variance estimates to compute the overall variance estimate.

For a multistage sample design, the Taylor series method uses only the first stage of the sample design. Therefore, the required input includes only first-stage cluster (PSU) and first-stage stratum identification. You do not need to input design information about any additional stages of sampling.

Replication methods for variance estimation draw multiple replicates (or subsamples) from the full sample by following a specific resampling scheme. Commonly used resampling schemes include balanced repeated replication (BRR) and the jackknife. The parameter of interest is estimated from each replicate, and the variability among the replicate estimates is used to estimate the overall variance of the parameter estimate.

The BRR variance estimation method requires a stratified sample design with two PSUs in each stratum. Each replicate is obtained by deleting one PSU per stratum according to the corresponding Hadamard matrix and adjusting the original weights for the remaining PSUs. The adjusted weights are called replicate weights. The survey procedures also provide Fay's method, which is a modification of the BRR method.

The jackknife method deletes one PSU at a time from the full sample to create replicates, and modifies the original weights to obtain replicate weights. The total number of replicates equals the number of PSUs. If the sample design is stratified, each stratum must contain at least two PSUs, and the jackknife is applied separately within each stratum.

Instead of having the survey procedures generate replicate weights for the analysis, you can directly input your own replicate weights. This can be useful if you need to do multiple analyses with the same set of replicate weights or if you have access to replicate weights without complete design information.

SAMPLING (STATISTICS)

In statistics and survey methodology, sampling is concerned with the selection of a subset of individuals from within a population to estimate characteristics of the whole population.

Researchers rarely survey the entire population because the cost of a census is too high. The three main advantages of sampling are that the cost is lower, data collection is faster, and since the data set is smaller it is possible to ensure homogeneity and to improve the accuracy and quality of the data.

Each observation measures one or more properties (such as weight, location, colour) of observable bodies distinguished as independent objects or individuals. In survey sampling, weights can be applied to the data to adjust for the sample design, particularly stratified sampling (blocking). Results from probability theory and statistical theory are employed to guide practice. In business and medical research, sampling is widely used for gathering information about a population.

Process

The sampling process comprises several stages:

- Defining the population of concern
- Specifying a sampling frame, a set of items or events possible to measure
- Specifying a sampling method for selecting items or events from the frame
- Determining the sample size
- Implementing the sampling plan
- Sampling and data collecting.

Population Definition

Successful statistical practice is based on focused problem definition. In sampling, this includes defining the population from which our sample is drawn. A population can be defined as including all people or items with the characteristic one wishes to understand. Because there is very rarely enough time or money to gather information from everyone or everything in a population, the goal becomes finding a representative sample (or subset) of that population.

Sometimes that which defines a population is obvious. For example, a manufacturer needs to decide whether a batch of material from production is of high enough quality to be released to the customer, or should be sentenced for scrap or rework due to poor quality. In this case, the batch is the population.

Although the population of interest often consists of physical objects, sometimes we need to sample over time, space, or some combination of these dimensions. For instance, an investigation of supermarket staffing could examine checkout line length at various times, or a study on endangered penguins might aim to understand their usage of various hunting grounds over time. For the time dimension, the focus may be on periods or discrete occasions.

In other cases, our 'population' may be even less tangible. For example, Joseph Jagger studied the behaviour of roulette wheels at a casino in Monte Carlo, and used this to identify a biased wheel. In this case, the 'population' Jagger wanted to investigate was the overall behaviour of the wheel (i.e. the probability distribution of its results over infinitely many trials), while his 'sample' was formed from observed results from that wheel. Similar considerations arise when taking repeated measurements of some physical characteristic such as the electrical conductivity of copper.

This situation often arises when we seek knowledge about the cause system of which the *observed* population is an outcome. In such cases, sampling theory may treat the observed population as a sample from a larger 'superpopulation'. For example, a researcher might study the success rate of a new 'quit smoking' program on a test group of 100 patients, in order to predict the effects of the program if it were made available nationwide. Here the superpopulation is "everybody in the country, given access to this treatment"-a group which does not yet exist, since the program isn't yet available to all.

Note also that the population from which the sample is drawn may not be the same as the population about which we actually want information. Often there is large but not complete overlap between these two groups due to frame issues etc.. Sometimes they may be entirely separate-for instance, we might study rats in order to get a better understanding of human health, or we might study records from people born in 2008 in order to make predictions about people born in 2009.

Time spent in making the sampled population and population of concern precise is often well spent, because it raises many issues, ambiguities and questions that would otherwise have been overlooked at this stage.

Sampling Frame

In the most straightforward case, such as the sentencing of a batch of material from production (acceptance sampling by lots), it is possible to identify and measure every single item in the population and to include any one of them in our sample. However, in the more general case this is not possible. There is no way to identify all rats in the set of all rats. Where voting is not compulsory, there is no way to identify which people will actually vote at a forthcoming election (in advance of the election). These imprecise populations are not amenable to sampling in any of the ways below and to which we could apply statistical theory.

As a remedy, we seek a sampling frame which has the property that we can identify every single element and include any in our sample. The most straightforward type of frame is a list of elements of the population (preferably the entire population) with appropriate contact information. For example, in an opinion poll, possible sampling frames include an electoral register and a telephone directory.

Probability and Nonprobability Sampling

A probability sampling scheme is one in which every unit in the population has a chance (greater than zero) of being selected in the sample, and this probability can be accurately determined. The combination of these traits makes it possible to produce unbiased estimates of population totals, by weighting sampled units according to their probability of selection.

Example: We want to estimate the total income of adults living in a given street. We visit each household in that street, identify all adults living there, and randomly select one adult from each household. (For example, we can allocate each person a random number, generated from a uniform distribution between 0 and 1, and select the person with the highest number in each household). We then interview the selected person and find their income. People living on their own are certain to be selected, so we simply add their income to our estimate of the total. But a person living in a household of two adults has only a one-in-two chance of selection. To reflect this, when we come to such a household, we would count the selected person's income twice towards the total. (In effect, the person who is *selected from that household is taken as representing the person who* isn't *selected.)*

In the above example, not everybody has the same probability of selection; what makes it a probability sample is the fact that each person's probability is known. When every element in the population *does* have the same probability of selection, this is known as an 'equal probability of selection' (EPS) design. Such designs are also referred to as 'self-weighting' because all sampled units are given the same weight.

Probability sampling includes: Simple Random Sampling, Systematic Sampling, Stratified Sampling, Probability Proportional to Size Sampling, and Cluster or Multistage Sampling. These various ways of probability sampling have two things in common:

1. Every element has a known nonzero probability of being sampled and
2. involves random selection at some point.

Nonprobability sampling is any sampling method where some elements of the population have *no* chance of selection (these are sometimes referred to as 'out of coverage'/ 'undercovered'), or where the probability of selection can't be accurately determined. It involves the selection of elements based on assumptions regarding the population of interest, which forms the criteria for selection. Hence, because the selection of elements is nonrandom, nonprobability sampling does not allow the estimation of sampling errors. These conditions give rise to exclusion bias, placing limits on how much information a sample can provide about the population. Information about the relationship between sample and population is limited, making it difficult to extrapolate from the sample to the population.

Example: We visit every household in a given street, and interview the first person to answer the door. In any household with more than one occupant, this is a nonprobability sample, because some people are more likely to answer the door (e.g. an unemployed person who spends most of their time at home is more likely to answer than an employed housemate who might be at work when the interviewer calls) and it's not practical to calculate these probabilities.

Nonprobability Sampling includes: Accidental Sampling, Quota Sampling and Purposive Sampling. In addition, nonresponse effects may turn *any* probability design into a nonprobability design if the characteristics of nonresponse are not well understood, since nonresponse effectively modifies each element's probability of being sampled.

Sampling Methods

Within any of the types of frame identified above, a variety of sampling methods can be employed, individually or in combination. Factors commonly influencing the choice between these designs include:

- Nature and quality of the frame
- Availability of auxiliary information about units on the frame
- Accuracy requirements, and the need to measure accuracy
- Whether detailed analysis of the sample is expected
- Cost/operational concerns.

Simple Random Sampling

In a simple random sample ('SRS') of a given size, all such subsets of the frame are given an equal probability. Each element of the frame thus has an equal probability of selection: the frame is not subdivided or partitioned. Furthermore, any given *pair* of elements has the same chance of selection as any other such pair (and similarly for triples, and so on). This minimises bias and simplifies analysis of results. In particular, the variance between individual results within the sample is a good indicator of variance in the overall population, which makes it relatively easy to estimate the accuracy of results.

However, SRS can be vulnerable to sampling error because the randomness of the selection may result in a sample that doesn't reflect the makeup of the population. For instance, a simple random sample of ten people from a given country will *on average* produce five men and five women, but any given trial is likely to overrepresent one sex and underrepresent the other. Systematic and stratified techniques, attempt to overcome this problem by using information about the population to choose a more representative sample.

SRS may also be cumbersome and tedious when sampling from an unusually large target population. In some cases, investigators are interested in research questions specific to subgroups of the population. For example, researchers might be interested in examining whether cognitive ability as a predictor of job performance is equally applicable across racial groups. SRS cannot accommodate the needs of researchers in this situation because it does not provide subsamples of the population. Stratified sampling, addresses this weakness of SRS.

Simple random sampling is always an EPS design, but not all EPS designs are simple random sampling.

Systematic Sampling

Systematic sampling relies on arranging the target population according to some ordering scheme and then selecting elements at regular intervals through that ordered list. Systematic sampling involves a random start and then proceeds with the selection of every kth element from then onwards. In this case, k=(population size/sample size). It is important that the starting point is not automatically the first in the list, but is instead randomly chosen from within the first to the kth element in the list. A simple example would be to select every

10th name from the telephone directory (an 'every 10th' sample, also referred to as 'sampling with a skip of 10').

As long as the starting point is randomized, systematic sampling is a type of probability sampling. It is easy to implement and the stratification induced can make it efficient, *if* the variable by which the list is ordered is correlated with the variable of interest. 'Every 10th' sampling is especially useful for efficient sampling from databases.

Example: Suppose we wish to sample people from a long street that starts in a poor district (house #1) and ends in an expensive district (house #1000). A simple random selection of addresses from this street could easily end up with too many from the high end and too few from the low end (or vice versa), leading to an unrepresentative sample. Selecting (e.g.) every 10th street number along the street ensures that the sample is spread evenly along the length of the street, representing all of these districts. (Note that if we always start at house #1 and end at #991, the sample is slightly biased towards the low end; by randomly selecting the start between #1 and #10, this bias is eliminated.)

However, systematic sampling is especially vulnerable to periodicities in the list. If periodicity is present and the period is a multiple or factor of the interval used, the sample is especially likely to be *un*representative of the overall population, making the scheme less accurate than simple random sampling.

Example: Consider a street where the odd-numbered houses are all on the north (expensive) side of the road, and the even-numbered houses are all on the south (cheap) side. Under the sampling scheme given above, it is impossible' to get a representative sample; either the houses sampled will all *be from the odd-numbered, expensive side, or they will* all *be from the even-numbered, cheap side.*

Another drawback of systematic sampling is that even in scenarios where it is more accurate than SRS, its theoretical properties make it difficult to *quantify* that accuracy. (In the two examples of systematic sampling that are given above, much of the potential sampling error is due to variation between neighbouring houses-but because this method never selects two neighbouring houses, the sample will not give us any information on that variation.) The systematic sampling is an EPS method, because all elements have the same probability of selection (in the example given, one in ten). It is *not* 'simple random sampling' because different subsets of the same size have different selection probabilities-e.g. the set {4,14,24,...,994} has a one-in-ten probability of selection, but the set {4,13,24,34,...} has zero probability of selection.

Stratified Sampling

Where the population embraces a number of distinct categories, the frame can be organized by these categories into separate "strata." Each stratum is then sampled as an independent sub-population, out of which individual elements can be randomly selected. There are several potential benefits to stratified sampling.

First, dividing the population into distinct, independent strata can enable researchers to draw inferences about specific subgroups that may be lost in a more generalized random sample.

Second, utilizing a stratified sampling method can lead to more efficient statistical estimates (provided that strata are selected based upon relevance to the criterion in question, instead of availability of the samples). Even if a stratified sampling approach does not lead to increased statistical efficiency, such a tactic will not result in less efficiency than would simple random sampling, provided that each stratum is proportional to the group's size in the population.

Third, it is sometimes the case that data are more readily available for individual, pre-existing strata within a population than for the overall population; in such cases, using a stratified sampling approach may be more convenient than aggregating data across groups (though this may potentially be at odds with the previously noted importance of utilizing criterion-relevant strata).

Finally, since each stratum is treated as an independent population, different sampling approaches can be applied to different strata, potentially enabling researchers to use the approach best suited (or most cost-effective) for each identified subgroup within the population.

There are, however, some potential drawbacks to using stratified sampling. First, identifying strata and implementing such an approach can increase the cost and complexity of sample selection, as well as leading to increased complexity of population estimates. Second, when examining multiple criteria, stratifying variables may be related to some, but not to others, further complicating the design, and potentially reducing the utility of the strata. Finally, in some cases (such as designs with a large number of strata, or those with a specified minimum sample size per group), stratified sampling can potentially require a larger sample than would other methods (although in most cases, the required sample size would be no larger than would be required for simple random sampling.

A stratified sampling approach is most effective when three conditions are met

1. Variability within strata are minimized
2. Variability between strata are maximized
3. The variables upon which the population is stratified are strongly correlated with the desired dependent variable.

Advantages over other sampling methods:

1. Focuses on important subpopulations and ignores irrelevant ones.
2. Allows use of different sampling techniques for different subpopulations.
3. Improves the accuracy/efficiency of estimation.
4. Permits greater balancing of statistical power of tests of differences between strata by sampling equal numbers from strata varying widely in size.

Disadvantages:

1. Requires selection of relevant stratification variables which can be difficult.
2. Is not useful when there are no homogeneous subgroups.
3. Can be expensive to implement.

Poststratification

Stratification is sometimes introduced after the sampling phase in a process called "poststratification". This approach is typically implemented due to a lack of prior knowledge of an appropriate stratifying variable or when the experimenter lacks the necessary information to create a stratifying variable during the sampling phase. Although the method is susceptible to the pitfalls of post hoc approaches, it can provide several benefits in the right situation. Implementation usually follows a simple random sample. In addition to allowing for stratification on an ancillary variable, poststratification can be used to implement weighting, which can improve the precision of a sample's estimates.

Oversampling

Choice-based sampling is one of the stratified sampling strategies. In choice-based sampling, the data are stratified on the target and a sample is taken from each stratum so that the rare target class will be more represented in the sample. The model is then built on this biased sample. The effects of the input variables on the target are often estimated with more precision with the choice-based sample even when a smaller overall sample size is taken, compared to a random sample. The results usually must be adjusted to correct for the oversampling.

Probability Proportional to Size Sampling

In some cases the sample designer has access to an "auxiliary variable" or "size measure", believed to be correlated to the variable of interest, for each element in the population. These data can be used to improve accuracy in sample design. One option is to use the auxiliary variable as a basis for stratification.

Another option is probability-proportional-to-size ('PPS') sampling, in which the selection probability for each element is set to be proportional to its size measure, up to a maximum of 1. In a simple PPS design, these selection probabilities can then be used as the basis for Poisson sampling. However, this has the drawback of variable sample size, and different portions of the population may still be over-or under-represented due to chance variation in selections. To address this problem, PPS may be combined with a systematic approach.

Example: Suppose we have six schools with populations of 150, 180, 200, 220, 260, and 490 students respectively (total

1500 students), and we want to use student population as the basis for a PPS sample of size three. To do this, we could allocate the first school numbers 1 to 150, the second school 151 to 330 (= 150 + 180), the third school 331 to 530, and so on to the last school (1011 to 1500). We then generate a random start between 1 and 500 (equal to 1500/3) and count through the school populations by multiples of 500. If our random start was 137, we would select the schools which have been allocated numbers 137, 637, and 1137, i.e. the first, fourth, and sixth schools.

The PPS approach can improve accuracy for a given sample size by concentrating sample on large elements that have the greatest impact on population estimates. PPS sampling is commonly used for surveys of businesses, where element size varies greatly and auxiliary information is often available-for instance, a survey attempting to measure the number of guest-nights spent in hotels might use each hotel's number of rooms as an auxiliary variable. In some cases, an older measurement of the variable of interest can be used as an auxiliary variable when attempting to produce more current estimates.

Cluster Sampling

Sometimes it is more cost-effective to select respondents in groups ('clusters'). Sampling is often clustered by geography, or by time periods. (Nearly all samples are in some sense 'clustered' in time-although this is rarely taken into account in the analysis.) For instance, if surveying households within a city, we might choose to select 100 city blocks and then interview every household within the selected blocks. Clustering can reduce travel and administrative costs. An interviewer can make a single trip to visit several households in one block, rather than having to drive to a different block for each household.

It also means that one does not need a sampling frame listing all elements in the target population. Instead, clusters can be chosen from a cluster-level frame, with an element-level frame created only for the selected clusters. The sample only requires a block-level city map for initial selections, and then a household-level map of the 100 selected blocks, rather than a household-level map of the whole city.

Cluster sampling generally increases the variability of sample estimates above that of simple random sampling, depending on how the clusters differ between themselves, as compared with the within-cluster variation. For this reason, cluster sampling requires a larger sample than SRS to achieve the same level of accuracy-but cost savings from clustering might still make this a cheaper option.

Cluster sampling is commonly implemented as multistage sampling. This is a complex form of cluster sampling in which two or more levels of units are embedded one in the other. The first stage consists of constructing the clusters that will be used to sample from. In the second stage, a sample of primary units is randomly selected from each cluster (rather than using all units contained in all selected clusters). In following stages, in each of those selected clusters, additional samples of units are selected, and so on. All ultimate units (individuals, for instance) selected at the last step of this procedure are then surveyed. This technique, thus, is essentially the process of taking random subsamples of preceding random samples.

Multistage sampling can substantially reduce sampling costs, where the complete population list would need to be constructed (before other sampling methods could be applied). By eliminating the work involved in describing clusters that are not selected, multistage sampling can reduce the large costs associated with traditional cluster sampling.

Quota Sampling

In quota sampling, the population is first segmented into mutually exclusive sub-groups, just as in stratified sampling. Then judgment is used to select the subjects or units from each segment based on a specified proportion. For example, an interviewer may be told to sample 200 females and 300 males between the age of 45 and 60. It is this second step which makes the technique one of non-probability sampling. In quota sampling the selection of the sample is non-random. For example interviewers might be tempted to interview those who look most helpful. The problem is that these samples may be biased because not everyone gets a chance of selection. This random element is its greatest weakness and quota versus probability has been a matter of controversy for many years.

Convenience Sampling or Accidental Sampling

Convenience sampling (sometimes known as grab or opportunity sampling) is a type of nonprobability sampling which involves the sample being drawn from that part of the population which is close to hand. That is, a population is selected because it is readily available and convenient. It may be through meeting the person or including a person in the sample when one meets them or chosen by finding them through technological means such as the internet or through phone. The researcher using such a sample cannot scientifically make generalizations about the total population from this sample because it would not be representative enough. For example, if the interviewer were to conduct such a survey at a shopping centre early in the morning on a given day, the people that he/she could interview would be limited to those given there at that given time, which would not represent the views of other members of society in such an area, if the survey were to be conducted at different times of day and several times per week. This type of sampling is most useful for pilot testing. Several important considerations for researchers using convenience samples include:

1. Are there controls within the research design or experiment which can serve to lessen the impact of a non-random convenience sample, thereby ensuring the results will be more representative of the population?
2. Is there good reason to believe that a particular convenience sample would or should respond or behave differently than a random sample from the same population?
3. Is the question being asked by the research one that can adequately be answered using a convenience sample?

In social science research, snowball sampling is a similar technique, where existing study subjects are used to recruit more subjects into the sample.

Line-intercept Sampling

Line-intercept sampling is a method of sampling elements in a region whereby an element is sampled if a chosen line segment, called a "transect", intersects the element.

Panel Sampling

Panel sampling is the method of first selecting a group of participants through a random sampling method and then asking that group for the same information again several times over a period of time. Therefore, each participant is given the same survey or interview at two or more time points; each period of data collection is called a "wave". This longitudinal sampling-method allows estimates of changes in the population, for example with regard to chronic illness to job stress to weekly food expenditures. Panel sampling can also be used to inform researchers about within-person health changes due to age or to help explain changes in continuous dependent variables such as spousal interaction. There have been several proposed methods of analysing panel data, including MANOVA, growth curves, and structural equation modelling with lagged effects.

Replacement of Selected Units

Sampling schemes may be *without replacement* ('WOR'-no element can be selected more than once in the same sample) or *with replacement* ('WR'-an element may appear multiple times in the one sample). For example, if we catch fish, measure them, and immediately return them to the water before continuing with the sample, this is a WR design, because we might end up catching and measuring the same fish more than once. However, if we do not return the fish to the water (e.g. if we eat the fish), this becomes a WOR design.

Sample Size

Formulas, tables, and power function charts are well known approaches to determine sample size.

Steps for Using Sample Size Tables

1. Postulate the effect size of interest, á, and â.
2. Check sample size table

1. Select the table corresponding to the selected á
2. Locate the row corresponding to the desired power
3. Locate the column corresponding to the estimated effect size.
4. The intersection of the column and row is the minimum sample size required.

Sampling and Data Collection

Good data collection involves:

- Following the defined sampling process
- Keeping the data in time order
- Noting comments and other contextual events
- Recording non-responses

Most sampling books and papers written by non-statisticians focus only in the data collection aspect, which is just a small though important part of the sampling process.

Errors in Sample Surveys

Survey results are typically subject to some error. Total errors can be classified into sampling errors and non-sampling errors. The term "error" here includes systematic biases as well as random errors.

Sampling Errors and Biases

Sampling errors and biases are induced by the sample design. They include:

1. Selection bias: When the true selection probabilities differ from those assumed in calculating the results.
2. Random sampling error: Random variation in the results due to the elements in the sample being selected at random.

Non-sampling Error

Non-sampling errors are caused by other problems in data collection and processing. They include:

1. Overcoverage: Inclusion of data from outside of the population.
2. Undercoverage: Sampling frame does not include elements in the population.
3. Measurement error: E.g. when respondents misunderstand a question, or find it difficult to answer.
4. Processing error: Mistakes in data coding.
5. Non-response: Failure to obtain complete data from all selected individuals.

After sampling, a review should be held of the exact process followed in sampling, rather than that intended, in order to study any effects that any divergences might have on subsequent analysis. A particular problem is that of *non-response.*

Two major types of nonresponse exist: unit nonresponse (referring to lack of completion of any part of the survey) and item nonresponse (submission or participation in survey but failing to complete one or more components/questions of the survey). In survey sampling, many of the individuals identified as part of the sample may be unwilling to participate, not have the time to participate (opportunity cost), or survey administrators may not have been able to contact them. In this case, there is a risk of differences, between respondents and nonrespondents, leading to biased estimates of population parameters. This is often addressed by improving survey design, offering incentives, and conducting follow-up studies which make a repeated attempt to contact the unresponsive and to characterize their similarities and differences with the rest of the frame. The effects can also be mitigated by weighting the data when population benchmarks are available or by imputing data based on answers to other questions.

Nonresponse is particularly a problem in internet sampling. Reasons for this problem include improperly designed surveys, over-surveying (or survey fatigue), and the fact that potential participants hold multiple e-mail addresses, which they don't use anymore or don't check regularly.

Survey Weights

In many situations the sample fraction may be varied by stratum and data will have to be weighted to correctly represent the population. Thus for example, a simple random sample of individuals in the United Kingdom might include some in remote Scottish islands who would be inordinately expensive to sample. A cheaper method would be to use a stratified sample with urban and rural strata. The rural sample could be under-represented in the sample, but weighted up appropriately in the analysis to compensate.

More generally, data should usually be weighted if the sample design does not give each individual an equal chance of being selected. For instance, when households have equal selection probabilities but one person is interviewed from within each household, this gives people from large households a smaller chance of being interviewed. This can be accounted for using survey weights. Similarly, households with more than one telephone line have a greater chance of being selected in a random digit dialing sample, and weights can adjust for this.

Weights can also serve other purposes, such as helping to correct for non-response.

History

Random sampling by using lots is an old idea, mentioned several times in the Bible. In 1786 Pierre Simon Laplace estimated the population of France by using a sample, along with ratio estimator. He also computed probabilistic estimates of the error. These were not expressed as modern confidence intervals but as the sample size that would be needed to achieve a particular upper bound on the sampling error with probability 1000/1001. His estimates used Bayes' theorem with a uniform prior probability and assumed that his sample was random.

In the USA the 1936 *Literary Digest* prediction of a Republican win in the presidential election went badly awry, due to severe bias. More than two million people responded to the study with their names obtained through magazine subscription lists and telephone directories. It was not appreciated that these lists were heavily biased towards Republicans and the resulting sample, though very large, was deeply flawed.

STATISTICAL SAMPLING TECHNIQUES

Statistical sampling techniques are the strategies applied by researchers during the statistical sampling process.

This process is done when the researchers aims to draw conclusions for the entire population after conducting a study on a sample taken from the same population.

CONCERNS IN STATISTICAL SAMPLING

This is the primary concern in statistical sampling. The sample obtained from the population must be representative of the same population. This can be accomplished by using randomized statistical sampling techniques or probability sampling like cluster sampling and stratified sampling. The reason behind representativeness being the primary concern in statistical sampling is that it allows the researcher to draw conclusions for the entire population. If the sample is not representative of the population, conclusions cannot be drawn since the results that the researcher obtained from the sample will be different from the results if the entire population is to be tested.

Practicability of statistical sampling techniques allows the researchers to estimate the possible number of subjects that can be included in the sample, the type of sampling technique, the duration of the study, the number of materials, ethical concerns, availability of the subjects/samples, the need for the study and the amount of workforce that the study demands. All these factors contribute to the decisions of the researcher regarding to the study design.

There are two types of sampling risks, first is the risk of incorrect acceptance of the research hypothesis and the second is the risk for incorrect rejection. These risks pertain to the possibility that when a test is conducted to a sample, the results and conclusions may be different from the results and conclusions when the test is conducted to the entire population. The risk of incorrect acceptance pertains to the risk that the sample can yield a conclusion that supports a theory about the population when it is actually not existent in the population. On the other hand, the risk of incorrect rejection pertains to the risk that the sample can yield a conclusion that rejects a theory about the population when in fact, the theory holds true in the population. Comparing the two types of risks, researchers fear the risk of incorrect rejection more than the risk of incorrect acceptance. Consider this example; an experimental drug was tested for its debilitating side effects. With the risk of incorrect acceptance, the researcher will conclude that the drug indeed has negative side effects but the truth is that it doesn't. The entire population will then abstain from taking the drug. But with the risk of incorrect rejection, the researcher will conclude that the drug has no negative side effects. The entire population will then take the drug knowing that it has no side effects but all of them will then suffer the consequences of the mistake of the researcher.

SAMPLING TECHNIQUES

Wastewater sampling is generally performed by one of two methods, grab sampling or composite sampling. Grab sampling is just what it sounds like; all of the test material is collected at one time. As such, a grab sample reflects performance only at the point in time that the sample was collected, and then only if the sample was properly collected. Composite sampling consists of a collection of numerous individual discrete samples taken at regular intervals over a period of time, usually 24 hours. The material being sampled is collected in a common container over the sampling period. The analysis of this material, collected over a period of time, will therefore represent the average performance of a wastewater treatment plant during the collection period.

Numerous industry references list various parameters for wastewater testing and whether samples should be collected using grab sampling or composite sampling methods. For example, grab sampling allows the analysis of specific types of unstable parameters such as pH, dissolved oxygen, chlorine residual, nitrites and temperature. However, the most widely used indicators of treatment plant performance, including CBOD5 (five day carbonaceous biochemical oxygen demand), TSS (total suspended solids) and TN (total nitrogen) require the use of composite sampling techniques. STANDARD METHODS (20th Edition, Section 1060 § B, "Collection and Sampling") states "A sample can represent only the composition of its source at the time and place of collection." Grab samples may be used to represent "some well-mixed surface waters, but rarely, wastewater streams" for water quality evaluation. The widely varying flow patterns of residential treatment plants make it impossible to evaluate performance by analysing a single grab sample of effluent. Residential treatment plants receive a frequent number of short hydraulic surges throughout the day followed by intermittent periods of no flow whatsoever.

Routine variations in the volume and strength characteristics of incoming wastewater create fluctuations in the quality of treatment plant effluent. Therefore, an effluent grab sample taken at one specific time throughout the daily flow pattern will not be representative of system performance over the entire day. The CODE OF FEDERAL REGULATIONS stipulates that treatment plant performance must be evaluated by tabulating 30-day averages of plant effluent. By definition, a single grab sample can never be used to evaluate the long-term performance of any wastewater treatment plant.

While the limitations of determining system performance by grab sampling are apparent, the use of grab samples for the evaluation of a residential treatment unit is further compromised if the sample is collected from a location where the effluent does not have sufficient velocity to keep the effluent solids in suspension. directs that samples be collected "at points where the sample stream or tank is well mixed." The manual goes on to say "avoid taking samples at points where solids settling occurs or floating debris is present. These situations occur normally in quiescent areas, where the velocity of the flow has decreased."

For this reason, plant performance can never be evaluated by a sample of effluent taken from a pump chamber, distribution box, sump, roadside ditch or any device that contains effluent below the flow line. The intermittent flow pattern of an individual residence intensifies this problem by allowing effluent solids to settle out within a sump during low flow periods. Even the few solids present in a high quality effluent will settle out when retained within a sump. If only a very few solids settle within a sump during a low flow period today, they remain and accumulate with additional solids settling out over successive days. Any sample drawn from a sump will contain effluent suspended solids combined with days, weeks, months or years worth of accumulated solids. A sample of liquid from such a sump cannot be analysed for overall system performance, as it is scientifically impossible to determine what portion of the solids were suspended in the effluent and what portion of the solids had accumulated in the sump over a period of time. Using any sample drawn from a sump to evaluate the performance of a residential wastewater treatment plant is simply inappropriate. Samples must be taken from a location where the effluent is free-flowing and has sufficient velocity to keep the effluent solids in suspension.

Composite samples of effluent collected, stored, analysed, tabulated and averaged over an extended period of time provide the only verifiable indication of treatment plant performance.

Collecting and analysing these composite samples is often an expensive and time-consuming process. For these reasons, most regulatory organizations recognize independent third-party certifiers, who use composite sampling methods to conduct performance evaluation and accurately measure system performance in a standardized, reproducible setting. Attempting to evaluate a residential treatment system in the field by analysing a grab sample taken from a sump or any other containment vessel provides a compound degree of error and will yield erroneous conclusions about system performance.

SURVEY SAMPLING METHODS

It is incumbent on the researcher to clearly define the target population. There are no strict rules to follow, and the researcher must rely on logic and judgment. The population is defined in keeping with the objectives of the study. Sometimes, the entire population will be sufficiently small, and the researcher can include the entire population in the study. This type of research is called a census study because data is gathered on every member of the population.

Usually, the population is too large for the researcher to attempt to survey all of its members. A small, but carefully chosen sample can be used to represent the population. The sample reflects the characteristics of the population from which it is drawn. Sampling methods are classified as either *probability* or *nonprobability*. In probability samples, each member of the population has a known non-zero probability of being selected. Probability methods include random sampling, systematic sampling, and stratified sampling. In nonprobability sampling, members are selected from the population in some nonrandom manner. These include convenience sampling, judgment sampling, quota sampling, and snowball sampling. The advantage of probability sampling is that sampling error can be calculated. Sampling error is the degree to which a sample might differ from the population. When inferring to the population, results are reported plus or minus the sampling error. In nonprobability sampling, the degree to which the sample differs from the population remains unknown.

Random sampling is the purest form of probability sampling. Each member of the population has an equal and known chance of being selected. When there are very large populations, it is often difficult or impossible to identify every member of the population, so the pool of available subjects becomes biased.

Systematic sampling is often used instead of random sampling. It is also called an Nth name selection technique. After the required sample size has been calculated, every Nth record is selected from a list of population members. As long as the list does not contain any hidden order, this sampling method is as good as the random sampling method. Its only advantage over the random sampling technique is simplicity. Systematic sampling is frequently used to select a specified number of records from a computer file.

Stratified sampling is commonly used probability method that is superior to random sampling because it reduces sampling error. A stratum is a subset of the population that share at least one common characteristic. Examples of stratums might be males and females, or managers and non-managers. The researcher first identifies the relevant stratums and their actual representation in the population. Random sampling is then used to select a *sufficient* number of subjects from each stratum. "*Sufficient*" refers to a sample size large enough for us to be reasonably confident that the stratum represents the population. Stratified sampling is often used when one or more of the stratums in the population have a low incidence relative to the other stratums.

Convenience sampling is used in exploratory research where the researcher is interested in getting an inexpensive approximation of the truth. As the name implies, the sample is selected because they are convenient. This nonprobability method is often used during preliminary research efforts to get a gross estimate of the results, without incurring the cost or time required to select a random sample.

Judgment sampling is a common nonprobability method. The researcher selects the sample based on judgment. This is usually and extension of convenience sampling. For example, a researcher may decide to draw the entire sample from one "representative" city, even though the population includes all cities. When using this method, the researcher must be confident that the chosen sample is truly representative of the entire population. Quota sampling is the nonprobability equivalent of stratified sampling. Like stratified sampling, the researcher first identifies the stratums and their proportions as they are represented in the population. Then convenience or judgment sampling is used to select the required number of subjects from each stratum. This differs from stratified sampling, where the stratums are filled by random sampling.

Snowball sampling is a special nonprobability method used when the desired sample characteristic is rare. It may be extremely difficult or cost prohibitive to locate respondents in these situations. Snowball sampling relies on referrals from initial subjects to generate additional subjects. While this technique can dramatically lower search costs, it comes at the expense of introducing bias because the technique itself reduces the likelihood that the sample will represent a good cross section from the population.

SIMPLE RANDOM SAMPLE

In statistics, a simple random sample is a subset of individuals (a sample) chosen from a larger set (a population). Each individual is chosen randomly and entirely by chance, such that each individual has the same probability of being chosen at any stage during the sampling process, and each subset of k individuals has the same probability of being chosen for the sample as any other subset of k individuals. This process and technique is known as simple random sampling, and should not be confused with Random Sampling. In small populations and often in large ones, such sampling is typically done "without replacement" ('SRSWOR'), i.e., one deliberately avoids choosing any member of the population more than once. Although simple random sampling can be conducted with replacement instead, this is less common and would normally be described more fully as simple random sampling with replacement ('SRSWR'). Sampling done without replacement is no longer independent, but still satisfies exchangeability, hence many results still hold. Further, for a small sample from a large population, sampling without replacement is approximately the same as sampling with replacement, since the odds of choosing the same individual twice is low. An unbiased random selection of individuals is important so that in the long run, the sample represents the population. However, this does not guarantee that a particular sample is a perfect representation of the population. Simple random sampling merely allows one to draw externally valid conclusions about the entire population based on the sample. Conceptually, simple random sampling is the simplest of the probability sampling techniques. It requires a complete sampling frame, which may not be available or feasible to construct for large populations. Even if a complete frame is available, more efficient approaches may be possible if other useful information is available about the units in the population.

Advantages are that it is free of classification error, and it requires minimum advance knowledge of the population other than the frame. Its simplicity also makes it relatively easy to interpret data collected via SRS. For these reasons, simple random sampling best suits situations where not much information is available about the population and data collection can be efficiently conducted on randomly distributed items, or where the cost of sampling is small enough to make efficiency less important than simplicity. If these conditions are not true, stratified sampling or cluster sampling may be a better choice.

Systematic Random Sample

In a simple random sample, one person must take a random sample from a population, and not have any order in which one chooses the specific individual. Let us assume you had a school with 1000 students, divided equally into boys and girls, and you wanted to select 100 of them for further study. You might put all their names in a bucket and then pull 100 names out. Not only does each person have an equal chance of being selected, we can also easily calculate the probability of a given person being chosen, since we know the sample size (n) and the population (N) and it becomes a simple matter of division:

n/N or $100/1000 = 0.10$ (10%)

This means that every student in the school has a 10% or 1 in 10 chance of being selected using this method. Further, all combinations of 100 students have the same probability of selection. If a systematic pattern is introduced into random sampling, it is referred to as "systematic (random) sampling". For instance, if the students in our school had numbers attached to their names ranging from 0001 to 1000, and we chose a random starting point, e.g. 0533, and then pick every 10th name thereafter to give us our sample of 100 (starting over with 0003 after reaching 0993). In this sense, this technique is similar to cluster sampling, since the choice of the first unit will determine the remainder. Thing is no longer simple random sampling, because some combinations of 100 students have a larger selection probability than others-for instance, {3, 13, 23,..., 993} has a 1/10 chance of selection, while {1, 2, 3,..., 100} cannot be selected under this method.

Sampling a Dichotomous Population

If the members of the population come in two kinds, say "red" and "black", one can consider the distribution of the number of red elements in a sample of a given size. That distribution depends on the numbers of red and black elements in the full population. For a simple random sample *with* replacement, the distribution is a *binomial distribution*. For a simple random sample *without* replacement, one obtains a *hypergeometric distribution*.

Simple random sampling is one of the most popular types of random or probability sampling.

There are many methods to proceed with simple random sampling. The most primitive and mechanical would be the lottery method. Each member of the population is assigned a unique number. Each number is placed in a bowl or a hat and mixed thoroughly. The blind-folded researcher then picks numbered tags from the hat. All the individuals bearing the numbers picked by the researcher are the subjects for the study. Another way would be to let a computer do a random selection from your population. For populations with a small number of members, it is advisable to use the first method but if the population has many members, a computer-aided random selection is preferred.

One of the best things about simple random sampling is the ease of assembling the sample. It is also considered as a fair way of selecting a sample from a given population since every member is given equal opportunities of being selected. Another key feature of simple random sampling is its representativeness of the population. Theoretically, the only thing that can compromise its representativeness is luck. If the sample is not representative of the population, the random variation is called sampling error. An unbiased random selection and a representative sample is important in drawing conclusions from the results of a study. Remember that one of the goals of research is to be able to make conclusions pertaining to the population from the results obtained from a sample. Due to the representativeness of a sample obtained by simple random sampling, it is reasonable to make generalizations from the results of the sample back to the population.

One of the most obvious limitations of simple random sampling method is its need of a complete list of all the members of the population. Please keep in mind that the list of the population must be complete and up-to-date. This list is usually not available for large populations. In cases as such, it is wiser to use other sampling techniques.

STRATIFIED SAMPLING

In statistics, stratified sampling is a method of sampling from a population. In statistical surveys, when subpopulations within an overall population vary, it is advantageous to sample each subpopulation (stratum) independently. Stratification is the process of dividing members of the population into homogeneous subgroups before sampling. The strata should be mutually exclusive: every element in the population must be assigned to only one stratum. The strata should also be collectively exhaustive: no population element can be excluded. Then random or systematic sampling is applied within each stratum. This often improves the representativeness of the sample by reducing sampling error. It can produce a weighted mean that has less variability than the arithmetic mean of a simple random sample of the population.

In computational statistics, stratified sampling is a method of variance reduction when Monte Carlo methods are used to estimate population statistics from a known population.

Stratified sampling strategies:

1. Proportionate allocation uses a sampling fraction in each of the strata that is proportional to that of the total population. For instance, if the population consists of 60% in the male stratum and 40% in the female stratum,

then the relative size of the two samples (three males, two females) should reflect this proportion.

2. Optimum allocation (or Disproportionate allocation)- Each stratum is proportionate to the standard deviation of the distribution of the variable. Larger samples are taken in the strata with the greatest variability to generate the least possible sampling variance.

A real-world example of using stratified sampling would be for a political survey. If the respondents needed to reflect the diversity of the population, the researcher would specifically seek to include participants of various minority groups such as race or religion, based on their proportionality to the total population. A stratified survey could thus claim to be more representative of the population than a survey of simple random sampling or systematic sampling.

Similarly, if population density varies greatly within a region, stratified sampling will ensure that estimates can be made with equal accuracy in different parts of the region, and that comparisons of sub-regions can be made with equal statistical power. For example, in Ontario a survey taken throughout the province might use a larger sampling fraction in the less populated north, since the disparity in population between north and south is so great that a sampling fraction based on the provincial sample as a whole might result in the collection of only a handful of data from the north.

Randomized stratification can also be used to improve population representativeness in a study.

Disadvantages

It is not useful when there are no similar subgroups. It cannot be used when amount of data in subgroups is not equal but total data in a subgroup are of equal importance as it gives more importance to subgroups with more data.

Practical Example

In general the size of the sample in each stratum is taken in proportion to the size of the stratum. This is called proportional allocation. Suppose that in a company there are the following staff.

- male, full time: 90
- male, part time: 18
- female, full time: 9
- female, part time: 63
- Total: 180

and we are asked to take a sample of 40 staff, stratified according to the above categories.

The first step is to find the total number of staff (180) and calculate the percentage in each group.

- % male, full time = 90/180 = 50%
- % male, part time = 18/180 = 10%
- % female, full time = 9/180 = 5%
- % female, part time = 63/180 = 35%

This tells us that of our sample of 40,

- 50% should be male, full time.
- 10% should be male, part time.
- 5% should be female, full time.
- 35% should be female, part time.
- 50% of 40 is 20.
- 10% of 40 is 4.
- 5% of 40 is 2.
- 35% of 40 is 14.

Another easy way without having to calculate the percentage is to multiply each group size by the sample size and divide by the total population size (size of entire staff):

- male, full time = 90 x (40/180) = 20
- male, part time = 18 x (40/180) = 4
- female, full time = 9 x (40/180) = 2
- female, part time = 63 x (40/180) = 14

SYSTEMATIC SAMPLING

Using this procedure each element in the population has a known and equal probability of selection. This makes systematic sampling functionally similar to simple random sampling. It is however, much more efficient (if variance within systematic sample is more than variance of population). The researcher must ensure that the chosen sampling interval does not hide a pattern. Any pattern would threaten randomness. A random starting point must also be selected.

Systematic sampling is to be applied only if the given population is logically homogeneous, because systematic sample units are uniformly distributed over the population.

Example: Suppose a supermarket wants to study buying habits of their customers, then using systematic sampling they can choose every 10 or 15th customer entering the supermarket and conduct the study on this sample.

This is random sampling with a system. From the sampling frame, a starting point is chosen at random, and choices thereafter are at regular intervals. For example, suppose you want to sample 8 houses from a street of 120 houses. 120/8=15, so every 15th house is chosen after a random starting point between 1 and 15. If the random starting point is 11, then the houses selected are 11, 26, 41, 56, 71, 86, 101, and 116.

If, as more frequently, the population is not evenly divisible (suppose you want to sample 8 houses out of 125, where 125/8=15.625), should you take every 15th house or every 16th house? If you take every 16th house, 8*16=128, so there is a risk that the last house chosen does not exist. On the other hand, if you take every 15th house, 8*15=120, so the last five houses will never be selected. The random starting point should instead be selected as a noninteger between 0 and 15.625 (inclusive on one endpoint only) to ensure that every house has equal chance of being selected; the interval should now be nonintegral (15.625); and each noninteger selected should be rounded up to the next integer. If the random starting point is 3.6, then the houses selected are 4, 19, 35, 51, 66, 82, 98, and 113, where there are 3 cyclic intervals of 15 and 5 intervals of 16.

To illustrate the danger of systematic skip concealing a pattern, suppose we were to sample a planned neighbourhood where each street has ten houses on each block. This places houses #1, 10, 11, 20, 21, 30... on block corners; corner blocks may be less valuable, since more of their area is taken up by streetfront etc. that is unavailable for building purposes. If we then sample every 10th household, our sample will either be made up *only* of corner houses (if we start at 1 or 10) or have *no* corner houses (any other start); either way, it will not be representative.

Systematic sampling may also be used with non-equal selection probabilities. In this case, rather than simply counting through elements of the population and selecting every k^{th} unit, we allocate each element a space along a number line according to its selection probability. We then generate a random start from a uniform distribution between 0 and 1, and move along the number line in steps of 1.

CLUSTER SAMPLING

Cluster Sampling is a sampling technique used when "natural" groupings are evident in a statistical population. It is often used in marketing research. In this technique, the total population is divided into these groups (or clusters) and a sample of the groups is selected. Then the required information is collected from the elements within each selected group. This may be done for every element in these groups or a subsample of elements may be selected within each of these groups. A common motivation for cluster sampling is to reduce the average cost per interview. Given a fixed budget, this can allow an increased sample size. Assuming a fixed sample size, the technique gives more accurate results when most of the variation in the population is within the groups, not between them.

Cluster Elements

Elements within a cluster should ideally be as heterogeneous as possible, but there should be homogeneity between cluster means. Each cluster should be a small scale representation of the total population. The clusters should be mutually exclusive and collectively exhaustive. A random sampling technique is then used on any relevant clusters to choose which clusters to include in the study. In single-stage cluster sampling, all the elements from each of the selected clusters are used. In two-stage cluster sampling, a random sampling technique is applied to the elements from each of the selected clusters.

The main difference between cluster sampling and stratified sampling is that in cluster sampling the cluster is treated as the sampling unit so analysis is done on a population of clusters (at least in the first stage). In stratified sampling, the analysis is done on elements within strata. In stratified sampling, a random sample is drawn from each of the strata, whereas in cluster sampling only the selected clusters are studied. The main objective of cluster sampling is to reduce costs by increasing sampling efficiency. This contrasts with stratified sampling where the main objective is to increase precision.

There also exists multistage sampling, where more than two steps are taken in selecting clusters from clusters.

Aspects of Cluster Sampling

One version of cluster sampling is area sampling or geographical cluster sampling. Clusters consist of geographical areas. Because a geographically dispersed population can be expensive to survey, greater economy than simple random sampling can be achieved by treating several respondents within a local area as a cluster. It is usually necessary to increase the total sample size to achieve equivalent precision in the estimators, but cost savings may make that feasible.

In some situations, cluster analysis is only appropriate when the clusters are approximately the same size. This can be achieved by combining clusters. If this is not possible, probability proportionate to size sampling is used. In this method, the probability of selecting any cluster varies with the size of the cluster, giving larger clusters a greater probability of selection and smaller clusters a lower probability. However, if clusters are selected with probability proportionate to size, the same number of interviews should be carried out in each sampled cluster so that each unit sampled has the same probability of selection.

Cluster sampling is used to estimate high mortalities in cases such as wars, famines and natural disasters.

Advantages

- Can be cheaper than other methods-e.g. fewer travel expenses, administration costs

Disadvantages

- Higher sampling error, which can be expressed in the so-called "design effect", the ratio between the number of subjects in the cluster study and the number of subjects in an equally reliable, randomly sampled unclustered study.

STATISTICS TUTORIAL: CLUSTER SAMPLING

Cluster sampling refers to a sampling method that has the following properties.

- The population is divided into N groups, called clusters.
- The researcher randomly selects n clusters to include in the sample.
- The number of observations within each cluster M_i is known, and $M = M_1 + M_2 + M_3 + ... + M_{N-1} + M_N$.
- Each element of the population can be assigned to one, and only one, cluster.

This tutorial covers two types of cluster sampling methods.

- One-stage sampling. All of the elements within selected clusters are included in the sample.
- Two-stage sampling. A subset of elements within selected clusters are randomly selected for inclusion in the sample.

Cluster Sampling: Advantages and Disadvantages

Assuming the sample size is constant across sampling methods, cluster sampling generally provides less precision than either simple random sampling or stratified sampling. This is the main disadvantage of cluster sampling.

Given this disadvantage, it is natural to ask: Why use cluster sampling?

Sometimes, the cost per sample point is less for cluster sampling than for other sampling methods. Given a fixed budget, the researcher may be able to use a bigger sample with cluster sampling than with the other methods. When the increased sample size is sufficient to offset the loss in precision, cluster sampling may be the best choice.

When to Use Cluster Sampling

Cluster sampling should be used only when it is economically justified-when reduced costs can be used to overcome losses in precision. This is most likely to occur in the following situations.

- Constructing a complete list of population elements is difficult, costly, or impossible. For example, it may not be possible to list all of the customers of a chain of hardware stores. However, it would be possible to randomly select a subset of stores (stage 1 of cluster sampling) and then interview a random sample of customers who visit those stores (stage 2 of cluster sampling).
- The population is concentrated in "natural" clusters (city blocks, schools, hospitals, etc.). For example, to conduct personal interviews of operating rocm nurses, it might make sense to randomly select a sample of hospitals (stage 1 of cluster sampling) and then interview all of the operating room nurses at that hospital. Using cluster sampling, the interviewer could conduct many interviews in a single day at a single hospital. Simple random sampling, in contrast, might require the interviewer to spend all day traveling to conduct a single interview at a single hospital.

Even when the above situations exist, it is often unclear which sampling method should be used. Test different options, using hypothetical data if necessary. Choose the most cost-effective approach; that is, choose the sampling method that delivers the greatest precision for the least cost.

MULTISTAGE SAMPLING

Multistage sampling is a complex form of cluster sampling.

Advantages

- cost and speed that the survey can be done in
- convenience of finding the survey sample
- normally more accurate than cluster sampling for the same size sample

Disadvantages

- Is not as accurate as SRS if the sample is the same size
- More testing is difficult to do

Using all the sample elements in all the selected clusters may be prohibitively expensive or not necessary. Under these circumstances, multistage cluster sampling becomes useful.

Instead of using all the elements contained in the selected clusters, the researcher randomly selects elements from each cluster. Constructing the clusters is the first stage. Deciding what elements within the cluster to use is the second stage. The technique is used frequently when a complete list of all members of the population does not exist and is inappropriate. In some cases, several levels of cluster selection may be applied before the final sample elements are reached. For example, household surveys conducted by the Australian Bureau of Statistics begin by dividing metropolitan regions into 'collection districts', and selecting some of these collection districts (first stage). The selected collection districts are then divided into blocks, and blocks are chosen from within each selected collection district (second stage). Next, dwellings are listed within each selected block, and some of these dwellings are selected (third stage). This method means that it is not necessary to create a list of every dwelling in the region, only for selected blocks. In remote areas, an additional stage of clustering is used, in order to reduce travel requirements.

Although cluster sampling and stratified sampling bear some superficial similarities, they are substantially different. In stratified sampling, a random sample is drawn from all the strata, where in cluster sampling only the selected clusters are studied, either in single stage or multi stage. Multi-stage sampling is a kind of complex sample design in which two or more levels of units are imbedded one in the other. For example: geographic areas (primary units), factories (secondary units), employees (tertiary units). At each stage, a sample of the corresponding units is selected. At first, a sample of primary units is selected, then, in each of those selected, a sample of secondary units is selected, and so on. All ultimate units (individuals, for instance) selected at the last step of this procedure are then surveyed.

The reasons for adopting such a design may be reducing costs, for example, when interviewers are assigned to persons located in a restricted area, or reducing the sample error. Multi-stage sampling is sometimes used when no general sample frame exists. In this case, a first step is to select, at random, a sample of areas, collective units, or villages from a list where they are all registered (primary units). Then, for each selected primary unit, a comprehensive enumeration of all units of lower rank is made, thus obtaining a local sample frame among which a sample of secondary units will be selected.

For example, for each village of the primary sample, a list of all housing units is established, allowing for a selection of a sample of households. Different probabilities can be used at each stage, as well as within one particular stage, for the different units to be selected. Probabilities at the successive stages multiply, so that the resulting probability for selecting one final unit is the product of the probabilities used at each step. The corresponding answers need to be weighted by the inverse of that final probability in order to obtain unbiased estimates.

A cluster sample can be seen as a two-stage sample where the secondary probability is 100 percent.

REFERENCES

- Babbie, E.R.: *Survey Research Methods*. Belmont, CA: Wadsworth, 1973.
- Christopher Scott: *The World Fertility Survey: An Assessment*. Oxford: Oxford University Press, 1987.
- Fox, J. & Tracy, P.: *Randomized Response: A Method for Sensitive Surveys*. Beverly Hills, CA: Sage, 1986.
- Heise, David R.: *Surveying Cultures: Discovering Shared Conceptions and Sentiments*. Hoboken NJ: Wiley, 2010.
- Kalton, Graham: *Introduction to Survey Sampling*. Beverly Hills, CA: Sage, 1983.

6

Non-probability Sampling

Sampling is the use of a subset of the population to represent the whole population. Probability sampling, or random sampling, is a sampling technique in which the probability of getting any particular sample may be calculated. Nonprobability sampling does not meet this criterion and should be used with caution. Nonprobability sampling techniques *cannot* be used to infer from the sample to the general population. Any generalizations obtained from a nonprobability sample must be filtered through one's knowledge of the topic being studied. Performing nonprobability sampling is considerably less expensive than doing probability sampling, but the results are of limited value.

Examples of nonprobability sampling include:

- Convenience, Haphazard or Accidental sampling-members of the population are chosen based on their relative ease of access. To sample friends, co-workers, or shoppers at a single mall, are all examples of convenience sampling.
- Snowball sampling-The first respondent refers a friend. The friend also refers a friend, etc.
- Judgmental sampling or Purposive sampling-The researcher chooses the sample based on who they think would be appropriate for the study. This is used primarily when there is a limited number of people that have expertise in the area being researched.
- Deviant Case-Get cases that substantially differ from the dominant pattern (a special type of purposive sample).

- Case study-The research is limited to one group, often with a similar characteristic or of small size.
- ad hoc quotas-A quota is established (say 65% women) and researchers are free to choose any respondent they wish as long as the quota is met.

Even studies intended to be probability studies sometimes end up being non-probability studies due to unintentional or unavoidable characteristics of the sampling method. In public opinion polling by private companies (or other organizations unable to require response), the sample can be self-selected rather than random. This often introduces an important type of error: self-selection bias. This error sometimes makes it unlikely that the sample will accurately represent the broader population. Volunteering for the sample may be determined by characteristics such as submissiveness or availability. The samples in such surveys should be treated as non-probability samples of the population, and the validity of the estimates of parameters based on them unknown.

NON-PROBABILITY SAMPLING TECHNIQUE

Non-probability sampling is a sampling technique where the samples are gathered in a process that does not give all the individuals in the population equal chances of being selected. Most researchers are bounded by time, money and workforce and because of these limitations, it is almost impossible to randomly sample the entire population and it is often necessary to employ another sampling technique, the non-probability sampling technique. In contrast with probability sampling, non-probability sample is not a product of a randomized selection processes. Subjects in a non-probability sample are usually selected on the basis of their accessibility or by the purposive personal judgment of the researcher. The downside of this is that an unknown proportion of the entire population was not sampled. This entails that the sample may or may not represent the entire population accurately. Therefore, the results of the research cannot be used in generalizations pertaining to the entire population.

TYPES OF NON-PROBABILITY SAMPLING

Convenience sampling is probably the most common of all

sampling techniques. With convenience sampling, the samples are selected because they are accessible to the researcher. Subjects are chosen simply because they are easy to recruit. This technique is considered easiest, cheapest and least time consuming. Consecutive sampling is very similar to convenience sampling except that it seeks to include ALL accessible subjects as part of the sample. This non-probability sampling technique can be considered as the best of all non-probability samples because it includes all subjects that are available that makes the sample a better representation of the entire population.

Quota sampling is a non-probability sampling technique wherein the researcher ensures equal or proportionate representation of subjects depending on which trait is considered as basis of the quota.

For example, if basis of the quota is college year level and the researcher needs equal representation, with a sample size of 100, he must select 25 1st year students, another 25 2nd year students, 25 3rd year and 25 4th year students. The bases of the quota are usually age, gender, education, race, religion and socioeconomic status.

Judgmental sampling is more commonly known as purposive sampling. In this type of sampling, subjects are chosen to be part of the sample with a specific purpose in mind. With judgmental sampling, the researcher believes that some subjects are more fit for the research compared to other individuals. This is the reason why they are purposively chosen as subjects.

Snowball sampling is usually done when there is a very small population size. In this type of sampling, the researcher asks the initial subject to identify another potential subject who also meets the criteria of the research. The downside of using a snowball sample is that it is hardly representative of the population.

- This type of sampling can be used when demonstrating that a particular trait exists in the population.
- It can also be used when the researcher aims to do a qualitative, pilot or exploratory study.
- It can be used when randomization is impossible like when the population is almost limitless.

- It can be used when the research does not aim to generate results that will be used to create generalizations pertaining to the entire population.
- It is also useful when the researcher has limited budget, time and workforce.
- This technique can also be used in an initial study which will be carried out again using a randomized, probability sampling.

CONVENIENCE SAMPLING

Convenience sampling is a non-probability sampling technique where subjects are selected because of their convenient accessibility and proximity to the researcher. The subjects are selected just because they are easiest to recruit for the study and the researcher did not consider selecting subjects that are representative of the entire population.

In all forms of research, it would be ideal to test the entire population, but in most cases, the population is just too large that it is impossible to include every individual. This is the reason why most researchers rely on sampling techniques like convenience sampling, the most common of all sampling techniques. Many researchers prefer this sampling technique because it is fast, inexpensive, easy and the subjects are readily available.

Examples

One of the most common examples of convenience sampling is using student volunteers as subjects for the research. Another example is using subjects that are selected from a clinic, a class or an institution that is easily accessible to the researcher. A more concrete example is choosing five people from a class or choosing the first five names from the list of patients. In these examples, the researcher inadvertently excludes a great proportion of the population. A convenience sample is either a collection of subjects that are accessible or a self selection of individuals willing to participate which is exemplified by your volunteers.

Uses

Researchers use convenience sampling not just because it

is easy to use, but because it also has other research advantages. In pilot studies, convenience sample is usually used because it allows the researcher to obtain basic data and trends regarding his study without the complications of using a randomized sample. This sampling technique is also useful in documenting that a particular quality of a substance or phenomenon occurs within a given sample. Such studies are also very useful for detecting relationships among different phenomena.

Criticisms

The most obvious criticism about convenience sampling is sampling bias and that the sample is not representative of the entire population. This may be the biggest disadvantage when using a convenience sample because it leads to more problems and criticisms. Systematic bias stems from sampling bias. This refers to a constant difference between the results from the sample and the theoretical results from the entire population. It is not rare that the results from a study that uses a convenience sample differ significantly with the results from the entire population. A consequence of having systematic bias is obtaining skewed results. Another significant criticism about using a convenience sample is the limitation in generalization and inference making about the entire population. Since the sample is not representative of the population, the results of the study cannot speak for the entire population. This results to a low external validity of the study.

WHAT IS A CONVENIENCE SAMPLE?

A convenience sample is a sample where the patients are selected, in part or in whole, at the convenience of the researcher. The researcher makes no attempt, or only a limited attempt, to insure that this sample is an accurate representation of some larger group or population. The classic example of a convenience sample is standing at a shopping mall and selecting shoppers as they walk by to fill out a survey. In contrast, a random sample is one where the researcher insures (usually through the use of random numbers applied to a list of the entire population) that each member of that population has an equal probability of being selected. Random samples are an important foundation of Statistics. Almost all of the mathematical theory upon which Statistics are based rely on assumptions which are consistent with a random sample. This theory is inconsistent with data collected from a convenience sample.

In general, the Statistics community frowns on convenience samples. You will often have great difficulty in generalizing the results of a convenience sample to any population that has practical relevance. Still, convenience samples can provide you with useful information, especially in a pilot study. To interpret the findings from a convenience sample properly, you have to characterize (usually in a qualitative sense) how your sample would differ from an ideal sample that was randomly selected. In particular, pay attention to who might be left out of your convenience sample or who might be underrepresented in your sample.

Also note whether the people who were left out might behave differently than the people in your convenience sample. An interview on the street corner, for example, would exclude non-ambulatory patients. If your outcome measures are not strongly related to this factor, you might be okay. An assessment of eye colour is probably safe in this setting. But a street corner interview would be a disaster if you were measuring something like the degree of disability.

You also have to be careful to qualify your findings appropriately. Findings from a convenience sample would be considered less definitive and would usually require replication in a more controlled setting. You can also qualify your results by extrapolating them only to a much more targeted and narrowly defined population.

CONVENIENCE SAMPLING EXPLAINED

Imagine that a researcher wants to understand more about the career goals of students at a single university. Let's say that the university has roughly 10,000 students. These 10,000 students are our *population* (N). Each of the 10,000 students is known as a *unit*. In order to select a *sample* (*n*) of students from this *population* of 10,000 students, we could choose to use a convenience random sample. Let's imagine that because we have a *small budget* and *limited time*, we choose a *sample size* of 100 students.

A convenience sample is simply one where the *units* that are selected for inclusion in the *sample* are the *easiest to access*. This is in stark contrast to probability sampling techniques, where the selection of *units* is made *randomly*. In our example of the 10,000 university students, we were only interested in achieving a *sample size* of 100 students who would take part in our research. As such, we would continue to invite students to take part in the research until our *sample size* was reached. Since the aim of convenience sampling is *easy access*, we may simply choose to stand at one of the main entrances to campus at the university we are interested in, where it would be easy to invite the many students that pass by to take part in the research.

Advantages of convenience sample:

- Convenience sampling is *very easy* to carry out with few rules governing how the *sample* should be collected.
- The *relative cost* and *time* required to carry out a convenience sample are *small* in comparison to probability sampling techniques. This enables you to achieve the *sample size* you want in a *relatively fast* and *inexpensive* way.
- The convenience sample may help you gather useful data and information that would not have been possible using *probability sampling techniques*, which require more formal access to *lists of populations*.

For example, imagine you were interested in understanding more about employee satisfaction in a single, large organisation in the United States. You intended to collect your data using a questionnaire. The manager who has kindly given you access to conduct your research is unable to get permission to get a *list* of all employees in the organisation, which you would need to use a *probability sampling technique* such as simple random sampling or systematic random sampling. However, the manager has managed to secure permission for you to spend two days in the organisation to collect as many questionnaire responses as possible. You decide to spend the two days at the entrance of the organisation where all employees have to pass through to get to their desks. Whilst a *probability sampling technique* would have been preferred, the convenience sample was the only sampling technique that you could use to collect data. Irrespective of the disadvantages of convenience sampling, without the use of this sampling technique, you may not have been able to get access to any data on employee satisfaction in the organisation.

Disdvantages of convenience sampling:

- The convenience sample often suffers from a number of *biases*. This can be seen in both of our examples, whether the 10,000 students we were studying, or the employees at the large organisation. In both cases, a convenience sample can lead to the *under-representation* or *over-representation* of particular *groups* within the *sample*. If we take the large organisation:

It may be that the organisation has multiple sites, with employee satisfaction varying considerably between these sites. By conducting the survey at the headquarters of the organisation, we may have missed the differences in employee satisfaction amongst those at different sites, including non-office workers. We also do not know why some employees agreed to take part in the survey, whilst others did not. Was it because some employees were simply too busy? Did they not trust the intentions of the survey? Did others take part out of kindness or because they had a particular grievance with the organisation? These types of *biases* are quite typical in convenience sampling.

- Since the *sampling frame* is *not know*, and the *sample* is *not chosen at random*, the *inherent bias* in convenience sampling means that the sample is *unlikely* to be *representative* of the *population* being studied. This undermines your ability to make *generalisations* from your *sample* to the *population* you are studying.

JUDGEMENT SAMPLING

In judgement sampling, the researcher or some other "expert" uses his/her judgement in selecting the units from the population for study based on the population's parameters.

This type of sampling technique might be the most appropriate if the population to be studied is difficult to locate or if some members are thought to be better (more knowledgeable, more willing, etc.) than others to interview. This determination is often made on the advice and with the assistance of the client. For instance, if you wanted to interview incentive travel organizers within a specific industry to determine their needs or destination preferences, you might find that not only are there relatively few, they are also extremely busy and may well be reluctant to take time to talk to you. Relying on the judgement of some knowledgeable experts may be far more productive in identifying potential interviewees than trying to develop a list of the population in order to randomly select a small number.

QUOTA SAMPLING

Quota sampling is a method for selecting survey participants. In quota sampling, a population is first segmented into mutually exclusive sub-groups, just as in stratified sampling. Then judgment is used to select the subjects or units from each segment based on a specified proportion. For example, an interviewer may be told to sample 200 females and 300 males between the age of 45 and 60. This means that individuals can put a demand on who they want to sample (targeting)

This second step makes the technique non-probability sampling. In quota sampling, the selection of the sample is non-random sample and can be unreliable. For example, interviewers might be tempted to interview those people in the street who look most helpful, or may choose to use accidental sampling to question those closest to them, for time-keeping sake. The problem is that these samples may be biased because not everyone gets a chance of selection. This non-random element is a source of uncertainty about the nature of the actual sample and quota versus probability has been a matter of controversy for many years. Quota sampling is useful when time is limited, a sampling frame is not available, the research budget is very tight or when detailed accuracy is not important. Subsets are chosen and then either convenience or judgment sampling is used to choose people from each subset. The researcher decides how many of each category is selected.

Quota sampling is the non probability version of stratified sampling. In stratified sampling, subsets of the population are created so that each subset has a common characteristic, such as gender. Random sampling chooses a number of subjects from each subset with, unlike a quota sample, each potential subject having a known probability of being selected.

DATA COLLECTION

Data collection is a term used to describe a process of preparing and collecting data-for example as part of a process improvement or similar project. The purpose of data collection is to obtain information to keep on record, to make decisions about important issues, to pass information on to others. Primarily, data is collected to provide information regarding a specific topic. Data collection usually takes place early on in an improvement project, and is often formalised through a data collection plan which often contains the following activity.

1. Pre collection activity – Agree goals, target data, definitions, methods
2. Collection – data collection
3. Present Findings – usually involves some form of sorting analysis and/or presentation.

Prior to any data collection, pre-collection activity is one of the most crucial steps in the process. It is often discovered too late that the value of their interview information is discounted as a consequence of poor sampling of both questions and informants and poor elicitation techniques. After pre-collection activity is fully completed, data collection in the field, whether by interviewing or other methods, can be carried out in a structured, systematic and scientific way. A formal data collection process is necessary as it ensures that data gathered is both defined and accurate and that subsequent decisions based on arguments embodied in the findings are valid. The process provides both a baseline from which to measure from and in certain cases a target on what to improve.

Other main types of collection include census, sample survey, and administrative by-product and each with their respective advantages and disadvantages. A census refers to data collection about everyone or everything in a group or population and has advantages, such as accuracy and detail and disadvantages, such as cost and time. A sample survey is a data collection method that includes only part of the total population and has advantages, such as cost and time and disadvantages, such as accuracy and detail. Administrative by-product data is collected as a byproduct of an organization's day-to-day operations and has advantages, such as accuracy, time simplicity and disadvantages, such as no flexibility and lack of control.

PRIMARY & SECONDARY DATA - WHAT'S THE DIFFERENCE?

Primary research entails the use of immediate data in determining the survival of the market. The popular ways to collect primary data consist of surveys, interviews and focus groups, which shows that direct relationship between potential customers and the companies. Whereas secondary research is a means to reprocess and reuse collected information as an indication for betterments of the service or product. Both primary and secondary data are useful for businesses but both may differ from each other in various aspects. In secondary data, information relates to a past period. Hence, it lacks aptness and therefore, it has unsatisfactory value. Primary data is more accommodating as it shows latest information.

Secondary data is obtained from some other organization than the one instantaneously interested with current research project. Secondary data was collected and analysed by the organization to convene the requirements of various research objectives. Primary data is accumulated by the researcher particularly to meet up the research objective of the subsisting project. Secondary data though old may be the only possible source of the desired data on the subjects, which cannot have primary data at all. For example, survey reports or secret records already collected by a business group can offer information that cannot be obtained from original sources.

Firm in which secondary data are accumulated and delivered may not accommodate the exact needs and particular requirements of the current research study. Many a time, alteration or modifications to the exact needs of the investigator may not be sufficient. To that amount usefulness of secondary data will be lost. Primary data is completely tailor-made and there is no problem of adjustments. Secondary data is available effortlessly, rapidly and inexpensively. Primary data takes a lot of time and the unit cost of such data is relatively high.

SECONDARY DATA

Secondary data is data collected by someone other than the user. Common sources of secondary data for social science include censuses, surveys, organizational records and data collected through qualitative methodologies or qualitative research. Primary data, by contrast, are collected by the investigator conducting the research.

Secondary data analysis saves time that would otherwise be spent collecting data and, particularly in the case of quantitative data, provides larger and higher-quality databases than would be unfeasible for any individual researcher to collect on their own.

In addition to that, analysts of social and economic change consider secondary data essential, since it is impossible to conduct a new survey that can adequately capture past change and/or developments.

Sources of Secondary Data

As is the case in primary research, secondary data can be obtained from two different research strands:

- Quantitative: Census, housing, social security as well as electoral statistics and other related databases.
- Qualitative: Semi-structured and structured interviews, focus groups transcripts, field notes, observation records and other personal, research-related documents.

A clear benefit of using secondary data is that much of the background work needed has been already been carried out, for example: literature reviews, case studies might have been carried out, published texts and statistic could have been already used elsewhere, media promotion and personal contacts have also been utilized. This wealth of background work means that secondary data generally have a pre-established degree of validity and reliability which need not be re-examined by the researcher who is re-using such data.

Furthermore, secondary data can also be helpful in the research design of subsequent primary research and can provide a baseline with which the collected primary data results can be compared to. Therefore, it is always wise to begin any research activity with a review of the secondar

Secondary Analysis or Re-use of Qualitative Data

Qualitative data re-use provides a unique opportunity to study the raw materials of the recent or more distant past to gain insights for both methodological and theoretical purposes. In the secondary analysis of qualitative data, good documentation can not be underestimated as it provides necessary background and much needed context both of which make re-use a more worthwhile and systematic endeavour. Actually one could go as far as claim that qualitative secondary data analysis "can be understood, not so much as the analysis of pre-existing data; rather as involving a process of re-contextualising, and re-constructing, data".

PRIMARY AND SECONDARY DATA

Data, or facts, may be derived from several sources. Data can be classified as primary data and secondary data. Primary data is data gathered for the first time by the researcher; secondary data is data taken by the researcher from secondary sources, internal or external. The researcher must thoroughly search secondary data sources before commissioning any efforts for collecting primary data. There are many advantages in searching for and analysing data before attempting the collection of primary data. In some cases, the secondary data itself may be sufficient to solve the problem. Usually the cost of gathering secondary data is much lower than the cost of organizing primary data. Moreover, secondary data has several supplementary uses. It also helps to plan the collection of primary data, in case, it becomes necessary. We shall therefore discuss secondary data first and then take up primary data.

Secondary data is of two kinds, internal and external. Secondary data – whether internal or external – is data already collected by others, for purposes other than the solution of the problem on hand.

Business firms always have as great deal of internal secondary data with them. Sales statistics constitute the most important component of secondary data in marketing and the researcher uses it extensively. All the output of the MIS of the firm generally constitutes internal secondary data. This data is readily available; the market researcher gets it without much effort, time and money.

Sources of External Secondary Data – Examples

The Internet is a great source of external secondary data. Many published, statistics and figures are available on the internet either free or for a fee. The yellow pages of telephone directories/stand alone yellow pages have become an established source of elementary business information. Tata Press, which first launched a stand alone yellow pages directory for Mumbai City, and 'GETIT' yellow pages have been leading in this field. Today, yellow pages publications are available for all cities and major town a in the country. New Horizons, a joint venture between the Living Media group of publications and Singapore Telecom has been publishing stand alone directories for specific businesses. Business India data base of the Business India publications had been publishing the Delhi Pages directory.

The Thomas Register is the world's most powerful industrial buying guide. It ensures a fast, frictionless flow of information between buyers and sellers of industrial goods and services. This purchasing tool is now available in India. The Thomas Register of Indian manufacturers or TRIM – is India's first dedicated manufacture-to-manufacture register. It features 120,000 listing of 40,000 industrial manufacturers and industrial service categories. It is available in print, CD forms and on the internet. The source Directory brought out by Mumbai based Source Publishers is another example. It covers contact information on advertising agencies and related services and products, music companies, market research agencies, marketing and sales promotion consultants, publication, radio stations and cable and satellite station telemarketing services, among others. It currently has editions for Metro cites.

The Industrial Product Finder (IPF): IPF details the many application of the new products and tells what is available and from whom. Most manufacturers of industrial products ensure that a description of their product is published in IPF before they hit the market. Phone data service: Agencies providing phone data services have also come up in major cities in recent times Melior Communication for example, offers a tele-data service. Basic data on a number of subjects/products can be had through call to the agency. The service is termed Tell me Business through phone service. Its main aim, like that of yellow pages, is to bring buyers and sellers of products together. It also provides some elementary databank support to researchers.

PRIMARY RESEARCH

Primary research consists in research to collect original data. It is often undertaken after the researcher has gained some insight into the issue by collecting secondary data. This can be through numerous forms, including questionnaires, direct observation and telephone interviews amongst others.

The term primary research is widely used in academic research, market research and competitive intelligence. There are advantages and disadvantages to primary research.

Advantages:

- Addresses specific research issues as the researcher controls the search design to fit their needs
- Great control; not only does primary research enable the marketer to focus on specific subjects, it also enables the researcher to have a higher control over how the information is collected. Taking this into account, the researcher can decide on such requirements as size of project, timeframe and goal.

Disadvantages:

- Compared to secondary research, primary data may be very expensive in preparing and carrying out the research. Costs can be incurred in producing the paper for questionnaires or the equipment for an experiment of some sort.
- In order to be done properly, primary data collection requires the development and execution of a research plan. It takes longer to undertake primary research than to acquire secondary data.
- Some research projects, while potentially offering information that could prove quite valuable, may not be within the reach of a researcher.
- By the time the research is complete it may be out of date.
- Low response rate has to be expected.

An example of primary research: the government wants to know if people are pleased with how the government is being run, so they hand out questionnaires to the public asking if they are happy and, if not, how to improve.

QUESTIONNAIRE CONSTRUCTION

A questionnaire is a series of questions asked to individuals to obtain statistically useful information about a given topic. When properly constructed and responsibly administered, questionnaires become a vital instrument by which statements can be made about specific groups or people or entire populations. Questionnaires are frequently used in quantitative marketing research and social research.

They are a valuable method of collecting a wide range of information from a large number of individuals, often referred to as respondents. Adequate questionnaire construction is critical to the success of a survey.

Inappropriate questions, incorrect ordering of questions, incorrect scaling, or bad questionnaire format can make the survey valueless, as it may not accurately reflect the views and opinions of the participants. A useful method for checking a questionnaire and making sure it is accurately capturing the intended information is to pretest among a smaller subset of target respondents.

Questionnaire Construction Issues

- Know how (and whether) you will use the results of your research before you start. If, for example, the results won't influence your decision or you can't afford to implement the findings or the cost of the research outweighs its usefulness, then save your time and money; don't bother doing the research.
- The research objectives and frame of reference should be defined beforehand, including the questionnaire's context of time, budget, manpower, intrusion and privacy.
- How (randomly or not) and from where (your sampling frame) you select the respondents will determine whether you will be able to generalize your findings to the larger population.

- The nature of the expected responses should be defined and retained for interpretation of the responses, be it preferences (of products or services), facts, beliefs, feelings, descriptions of past behaviour, or standards of action.
- Unneeded questions are an expense to the researcher and an unwelcome imposition on the respondents. All questions should contribute to the objective(s) of the research.
- If you "research backwards" and determine what you want to say in the report.(i.e., Package A is more/less preferred by X% of the sample vs. Package B, and y% compared to Package C) then even though you don't know the exact answers yet, you will be certain to ask all the questions you need-and only the ones you need-in such a way (metrics) to write your report.
- The topics should fit the respondents' frame of reference. Their background may affect their interpretation of the questions. Respondents should have enough information or expertise to answer the questions truthfully.
- The type of scale, index, or typology to be used shall be determined.
- The level of measurement you use will determine what you can do with and conclude from the data. If the response option is yes/no then you will only know how many or what percent of your sample answered yes/no. You cannot, however, conclude what the average respondent answered.
- The types of questions (closed, multiple-choice, open) should fit the statistical data analysis techniques available and your goals.
- Questions and prepared responses to choose from should be neutral as to intended outcome. A biased question or questionnaire encourages respondents to answer one way rather than another. Even questions without bias may leave respondents with expectations.
- The order or "natural" grouping of questions is often relevant. Prior previous questions may bias later questions.

- The wording should be kept simple: no technical or specialized words.
- The meaning should be clear. Ambiguous words, equivocal sentence structures and negatives may cause misunderstanding, possibly invalidating questionnaire results. Double negatives should be reworded as positives.
- If a survey question actually contains more than one issue, the researcher will not know which one the respondent is answering. Care should be taken to ask one question at a time.
- The list of possible responses should be collectively exhaustive. Respondents should not find themselves with no category that fits their situation. One solution is to use a final category for "other ________".
- The possible responses should also be mutually exclusive. Categories should not overlap. Respondents should not find themselves in more than one category, for example in both the "married" category and the "single" category-there may be need for separate questions on marital status and living situation.
- Writing style should be conversational, yet concise and accurate and appropriate to the target audience.
- Many people will not answer personal or intimate questions. For this reason, questions about age, income, marital status, etc. are generally placed at the end of the survey. This way, even if the respondent refuses to answer these "personal" questions, he/she will have already answered the research questions.
- "Loaded" questions evoke emotional responses and may skew results.
- Presentation of the questions on the page (or computer screen) and use of white space, colors, pictures, charts, or other graphics may affect respondent's interest or distract from the questions.
- Numbering of questions may be helpful.
- Questionnaires can be administered by research staff, by volunteers or self-administered by the respondents. Clear, detailed instructions are needed in either case, matching the needs of each audience.

Types of Questions

1. Contingency questions-A question that is answered only if the respondent gives a particular response to a previous question. This avoids asking questions of people that do not apply to them (for example, asking men if they have ever been pregnant).
2. Matrix questions-Identical response categories are assigned to multiple questions. The questions are placed one under the other, forming a matrix with response categories along the top and a list of questions down the side. This is an efficient use of page space and respondents' time.
3. Closed ended questions-Respondents' answers are limited to a fixed set of responses. Most scales are closed ended. Other types of closed ended questions include:
   - o Yes/no questions-The respondent answers with a "yes" or a "no".
   - o Multiple choice-The respondent has several option from which to choose.
   - o Scaled questions-Responses are graded on a continuum (example : rate the appearance of the product on a scale from 1 to 10, with 10 being the most preferred appearance). Examples of types of scales include the Likert scale, semantic differential scale, and rank-order scale..
4. Open ended questions-No options or predefined categories are suggested. The respondent supplies their own answer without being constrained by a fixed set of possible responses. Examples of types of open ended questions include:
   - o Completely unstructured-For example, "What is your opinion of questionnaires?"
   - o Word association-Words are presented and the respondent mentions the first word that comes to mind.
   - o Sentence completion-Respondents complete an incomplete sentence. For example, "The most

important consideration in my decision to buy a new house is..."

- o Story completion-Respondents complete an incomplete story.
- o Picture completion-Respondents fill in an empty conversation balloon.
- o Thematic apperception test-Respondents explain a picture or make up a story about what they think is happening in the picture

Question Sequence

- Questions should flow logically from one to the next.
- The researcher must ensure that the answer to a question is not influenced by previous questions.
- Questions should flow from the more general to the more specific.
- Questions should flow from the least sensitive to the most sensitive.
- Questions should flow from factual and behavioural questions to attitudinal and opinion questions.
- Questions should flow from unaided to aided questions.
- According to the three stage theory (also called the sandwich theory), initial questions should be screening and rapport questions. Then in the second stage you ask all the product specific questions. In the last stage you ask demographic questions.

DATA EDITING

This chapter addresses an issue that is somewhat different than the topics covered by the rest of this thesis. This issue is data editing, or the removal of bad data by muting, one of the simplest methods of removing noise. The emphasis in this chapter is eliminating isolated high-amplitude unpredictable events. These events are unpredictable in the sense that they leave high-amplitude residuals when predictable events are removed. This is in contrast to the low-amplitude residuals normally expected as prediction errors. Data editing was one of the original methods of controlling noise in seismic data. When a seismic trace was dominated by noise, it was simply removed. For prestack data that would only be stacked, removing an offending trace would not significantly affect the stack as long as the stack fold was significant. Even then, only traces completely overwhelmed by high-amplitude noise needed attention, since moderately bad traces generally would not affect the stacked result.

In modern data processing, manual editing of traces is no longer practical since the volume of data is so large that a processor cannot examine all the data in a reasonable time. Automatic editing is especially important for three-dimensional surveys because of the huge data volumes involved. These large data volumes have led to other efforts to edit data automatically Pokhriyal et al. (1991); Pokhriyal (1993).

With modern acquisition systems, the dynamic range of the recorded data is much larger than that available with older systems. While this large dynamic range allows more accurate recording of the desired signals, higher amplitude noise is also allowed into the data. This noise may be caused either by recording unwanted signals, such as ground roll, or it may be caused by imperfections in the recording instruments. Modern data processing techniques preserve these high amplitudes, where some older data processing methods would have limited the highest amplitudes to some "reasonable" limit.

Another problem is that data is no longer simply stacked; clean prestack data is needed for processes such as velocity determination, prestack migration, and AVO measurements. The processes discussed later in this thesis will also be impacted by high-amplitude noise in the data. High-amplitude noise is a special problem when least-squares methods are being used, since the square of a high-amplitude error is likely to overwhelm the smaller errors that are of more interest.

The goal of this chapter is to locate, eliminate, and mark the position of high-amplitude noise so that it will not contaminate the least-squares techniques presented in the following chapters. Marking the locations of bad data is done for two reasons. The first is to avoid mistaking the data that was zeroed for good data. The second reason is to allow restoration of the data that has been removed with an estimate derived from an inversion processes.

The unpredictable noise will be detected when the residual of a prediction-error filter exceeds a limit that is defined from the data. This technique will be demonstrated on real data with a variety of noises.

Data should be edited before being presented as information. This action ensures that the information provided is accurate, complete and consistent. No matter what type of data you are working with, certain edits are performed on all surveys. Data editing can be performed manually, with the assistance of computer programming, or a combination of both techniques. It depends on the medium (electronic, paper) by which the data are submitted.

Micro-editing corrects the data at the record level. This process detects errors in data through checks of the individual data records. The intent at this point is to determine the consistency of the data and correct the individual data records.

Macro-editing also detects errors in data, but does this through the analysis of aggregate data (totals). The data are compared with data from other surveys, administrative files, or earlier versions of the same data. This process determines the compatibility of data.

We might ask the question "Why are there errors in our files?" There are several situations where errors can be introduced into the data, and the following list gives some of them:

- A respondent could have misunderstood a question.
- A respondent or an interviewer could have checked the wrong response.
- An interviewer could have miscoded or misunderstood a written response.
- An interviewer could have forgotten to ask a question or record the answer.
- A respondent could have provided inaccurate responses.

Always keep in mind the objectives of data editing:

- to ensure the accuracy of data;
- to establish the consistency of data;
- to determine whether or not the data are complete;

- to ensure the coherence of aggregated data; and
- to obtain the best possible data available.

Applying Editing Rules

So, how do we edit? The first step is to apply 'rules' (or factors to be taken into consideration) to the data. These rules are determined by the expert knowledge of a subject-matter specialist, the structure of the questionnaire, the history of the data, and any other related surveys or data.

Expert knowledge can come from a variety of sources. The specialist could be an analyst who has extensive experience with the type of data being edited. An expert could also be one of the survey sponsors who is familiar with the relationships between the data.

The layout and structure of the questionnaire will also impact the rules for editing data.

For example, sometimes respondents are instructed to skip certain questions if the questions do not apply to them or their situation. This specification must be respected and incorporated into the editing rules.

Lastly, other surveys relating to the same sort of variables or characteristics are used in order to establish some of the rules for editing data.

Data Editing Types

There are several types of data edits available: They include:

- Validity edits look at one question field or cell at a time. They check to ensure the record identifiers, invalid characters, and values have been accounted for; essential fields have been completed (e.g., no quantity field is left blank where a number is required); specified units of measure have been properly used; and the reporting time is within the specified limits.
- Range edits are similar to validity edits in that they look at one field at a time. The purpose of this type of edit is to ensure that the values, ratios and calculations fall within the pre-established limits.
- Duplication edits examine one full record at a time. These types of edits check for duplicated records, making

certain that a respondent or a survey item has only been recorded once. A duplication edit also checks to ensure that the respondent does not appear in the survey universe more than once, especially if there has been a name change. Finally, it ensures that the data have been entered into the system only once.

- Consistency edits compare different answers from the same record to ensure that they are coherent with one another. For example, if a person is declared to be in the 0 to 14 age group, but also claims that he or she is retired, there is a consistency problem between the two answers. Inter-field edits are another form of a consistency edit. These edits verify that if a figure is reported in one section, a corresponding figure is reported in another.
- Historical edits are used to compare survey answers in current and previous surveys. For example, any dramatic changes since the last survey will be flagged. The ratios and calculations are also compared, and any percentage variance that falls outside the established limits will be noted and questioned.
- Statistical edits look at the entire set of data. This type of edit is performed only after all other edits have been applied and the data have been corrected. The data are compiled and all extreme values, suspicious data and outliers are rejected.
- Miscellaneous edits fall in the range of special-reporting arrangements; dynamic edits particular to the survey; correct classification checks; changes to physical addresses, locations and/or contacts; and legibility edits (i.e., making sure the figures or symbols are recognizable and easy to read).

Data editing is influenced by the complexity of the questionnaire. Complexity refers to the length, as well as the number of questions asked. It also includes the detail of questions and the range of subject matter that the questionnaire may cover. In some cases, the terminology of a question can be very technical. For these types of surveys, special reporting arrangements and industry-specific edits may occur.

MULTIDIMENSIONAL TABLES AND THEIR GRAPHICAL PRESENTATION

The interactive "Multidimensional Tables" component of WinIDAMS allows you to visualize and customize multidimensional tables with frequencies, row, column and total percentages, univariate statistics (sum, count, mean, maximum, minimum, variance, standard deviation) of additional variables, and bivariate statistics. Variables in rows and/or columns can either be nested (maximum 7 variables) or they can be put at the same level. Construction of a table can be repeated for each value of up to three "page" variables. Each page of the table can also be printed, or exported in free format (comma or tabulation character delimited) or in HTML format.

IDAMS datasets used as input must have the same name for the Dictionary and Data files with extensions.dic and.dat respectively. Only one dataset can be used at a time, i.e. opening another dataset automatically closes the one being used.

Preparation of Analysis

Selection of data. A dataset selected for constructing multidimensional tables is available until it is changed when activating again the "Multidimensional Tables" component. The dialogue box lets you choose a Data file either from a list of recently used Data files (Recent) or from any folder (Existing). The Data folder of the current application is the default. Setting "Files of type:" to "IDAMS Data Files (*.dat)" displays only IDAMS Data files.

Selection of variables. Selection of a dataset for analysis calls the dialogue box for table definition. You are presented with a list of available variables and with four windows to specify variables for different purposes. Use Drag and Drop technique to move variables between and/or within required windows.

Page variables are used to construct separate pages of the table for each distinct value of each variable in turn, and for all cases taken together (Total page). Cases included on a particular page have all the same value on the page variable. Page variables are never nested. The order in which variables are specified determines the order in which pages are placed in the Table window.

Row variables are the variables whose values are used to define table rows. Their order determines the sequence of nesting use.

Column variables are the variables whose values are used to define table columns. Their order determines the sequence of nesting use.

Cell variables are variables whose values are used to calculate univariate statistics (e.g. mean) in the table cells. The order in which they are specified determines the order of their appearance in the table. There may be up to 10 cell variables.

Nesting. If more than one row and/or column variable is specified, by default they are nested. To use them sequentially, at the same level, double-click on the variable in the row or column variable list and mark the option for treating at the same level. Note: This option is not available for the first variable in a list.

Percentages. Percentages in each cell (row, column or total) can be obtained by double-clicking on the last nested row variable in the table definition window and selecting the type of percentages required.

Univariate statistics. Different statistics (sum, count, mean, maximum, minimum, variance, standard deviation) for each of the cell variables can be obtained by double-clicking on the variable in the table definition window and marking the required statistic(s). Formulas for calculating mean, variance and standard deviation can be found in section "Univariate Statistics" of "Univariate and Bivariate Tables" chapter. However, they need to be adjusted since cases are not weighted.

Missing data treatment. The default missing data treatment is applied to the first construction of the table. Then, it can be changed using the menu Change.

Missing Data Values option is used to indicate which missing data values, if any, are to be used to check for missing data in row and column variables.

Both : Variable values will be checked against the MD1 codes and against the ranges of codes defined by MD2.

MD1 : Variable values will be checked only against the MD1 codes.

MD2 : Variable values will be checked only against the ranges of codes defined by MD2.

None : MD codes will not be used. All data values will be considered valid.

By default, both MD codes are used.

Missing Data Handling option is used to indicate which missing data values should be excluded from computation of percentages and bivariate statistics.

All : Delete all missing data values.

Row : Delete missing data values of row variables.

Column : Delete missing data values of column variables.

None : Do not delete missing data values.

By default, all missing data values are deleted.

Note: Cases with missing data on cell variables are always excluded from calculation of univariate statistics. The exclusion is done cell by cell, separately for each cell variable. Thus, the number of valid cases may not be equal to the cell frequency. The statistic "Count" shows the number of valid cases.

Changing table definition. The menu command Change/ Specification calls the dialogue box with the active table definition. You can change variables for analysis, their nesting as well as requests for percentages and univariate statistics. Clicking on OK replaces the active table by a new one.

Multidimensional Tables Window

After selection of variables and a click on OK, the Multidimensional Tables window appears in the WinIDAMS document window. By default, frequencies and mean values for all cell variables are displayed. If page variables are specified, code labels (or codes) of these variables are displayed on tabs at the bottom of the table. A particular page can be accessed by a click on the required label (code). Changing the page appearance. The appearance of each page can be changed separately, the changes applying exclusively to the active page.

The following modifications are possible:

- *Increasing the font size*-use the menu command View/ Zoom In or the toolbar button Zoom In.

- *Decreasing the font size*-use the menu command View/ Zoom Out or the toolbar button Zoom Out.
- *Resetting default font size*-use the menu command View/ 100% or the toolbar button 100%.
- *Increasing / Decreasing the width of a column*-place the mouse cursor on the line which separates two columns in the column heading until it becomes a vertical bar with two arrows and move it to the right/left holding the left mouse button.
- *Minimizing the width of columns*-mark the required column(s) and use the menu command Format/Resize Columns.
- *Increasing / Decreasing the height of rows*-place the mouse cursor on the line which separates two rows in the row heading until it becomes a horizontal bar with two arrows and move it down/up holding the left mouse button.
- *Minimizing the height of rows*-mark the required row(s) and use the menu command Format/Resize Rows.
- *Hiding columns / rows*-decrease the width/height of a column/row to zero. To display back a hidden column/ row, place the mouse cursor on the line where it is hidden in the column/row heading until it becomes a vertical/horizontal bar with two arrows and double-click the left mouse button.

In addition, the command Format/Style gives access to a number of table formatting possibilities such as: selection of fonts, size of fonts, colours, etc. for the active cell or for all cells in the active line.

Bivariate statistics. Bivariate statistics (Chi-square, Phi coefficient, contingency coefficient, Cramer's V, Taus, Gamma, Lambdas and Sormer's D) are computed for each table (each page). Use the menu command Show/Statistics to display them at the end of table. If needed, this operation should be repeated for each page separately. Formulas for calculating bivariate statistics can be found in section "Bivariate Statistics" of "Univariate and Bivariate Tables" chapter.

Note that statistics are calculated only when there is one row and one column variable.

Printing a table page. The whole contents of the active page or desired parts only can be printed using the File/Print command. If you want to print only some columns and/or rows, hide the other columns/rows first. The displayed columns/rows will be printed. Exporting a table page. The whole contents of the active page or desired parts only can be exported in free format (comma or tabulation character delimited) or in HTML format. Use the File/Export command and select the required format. If you want to export only some columns and/or rows, hide the other columns/rows first. The displayed columns/rows will be exported.

Graphical Presentation of Univariate/Bivariate Tables

Frequencies displayed in a page of univariate/bivariate tables can be presented graphically using one of 24 graph styles at your disposal. Graph construction is initiated by the menu command Graph/Make. This command calls the dialogue box to select the graph style for the active page. In addition, you may ask to use logarithmic transformation of frequencies, and to provide a legend for colours and symbols used in the graph.

Projected graphics cannot be manipulated. However, they can be saved in one of the two formats, namely: JPEG file interchange format (.jpg) or Windows Bitmap format (.bmp), using the relevant commands in the File menu. They can also be copied to the Clipboard (the command Edit/Copy, toolbar button Copy or shortcut keys Ctrl/C) and passed to any text editor. It should be noted here again that only frequencies from displayed rows and columns, i.e. not from rows and/or columns which have been hidden, are used for this presentation.

USING GRAPHS AND TABLES ON PRESENTATION SLIDES

When presenting ideas that include references to data, it can be helpful to make the point using a graph or table. These visual methods can make the point much stronger than simply describing the data. While they can be powerful methods, they also have the potential to ruin a presentation if they convey the wrong message or they confuse the audience. Appropriate use of graphs and tables is one way to enhance the message you are delivering.

Graph Types

There are five basic types of graphs that are used most frequently. There are more complex types that are used for specific purposes, usually technical in nature, which will not be discussed here because they would rarely be used by most of us. A graph is really a graphical representation of one or more sets of data. A set of related data is referred to as a data series. For example, the sales of product X each year for the past five years would be one data series. Here are the five basic graph types:

Area-This graph shows the relationship of different parts to a whole over time. One example would be to show the breakdown of the total organization profit by product line over the last five years. This graph can show many (4-6) data series at a time.

Column-This graph shows the differences in individual values vertically. It can be used to show the differences between values in different time periods or other data groupings. Examples include showing the total number of phone calls each month for the past year or the number of orders received by each order method (fax, phone, e-mail, web, walk-in) over the last month. This graph works best with fewer (1-3) data series.

Bar-This graph shows the differences in individual values horizontally. It is not a good choice for showing values in different time periods. It works better for showing the results of one or two data series. One example would be to show the popularity of the top eight answers to a survey question.

Line-This graph shows values at different points in time. It is usually best to have equal time intervals along the horizontal axis of the graph. One example would be to show the trend in the number of customer service calls handled by the five offices each month over the last year. A line graph can display many (4-6) data series quite well.

Pie-This graph shows the proportions of each segment of a whole. This graph only handles one data series. An example would be to show the proportion of funding provided to the organization by each level of government in the past year. When you are deciding which type of graph to use for your situation, the decision tree below can help you. The key questions to consider are whether the data is time-sequenced and how many data series you want to show. By selecting the appropriate graph type, you can help make the message clearer to the audience.

Key Graph Elements

Colors – Make sure that you set the background colour and the colour of each data series so that there is enough contrast to be seen clearly by the audience. These colors should also be consistent with the overall colour scheme of the slides so that the graph does not look out of place.

Depth – The depth of the graph refers to whether the graph is 2-D or 3-D. There is almost no value to the third dimension, and I suggest graphs be 2-D.

Axes – All of the above graph types except the pie graph have two axes. One is for the data values and the other is for the time scale or how the data is separated. It is important to set the scale of the axes to be appropriate to the data being shown. Also, make sure that axis labels that indicate the values along each axis are big enough to be clearly read when the graph is displayed. If the axes are not clear, the graph may be misinterpreted because it is not clear to the audience what the difference between the data is.

Data Labels – When you need to more clearly indicate the data value in a graph, you can use a data label. This is a text box that contains the actual data value and it should be placed close to the graphical representation of the data point, whether it is at the end of a bar or column, above a data point on a line graph or inside the pie section in a pie graph. Make sure that the text is big enough to be read clearly and that the text colour has enough contrast with the colour underneath it.

Title – The title of the graph should focus on the interpretation of the data, not the data itself. Remember that we are using a graph to help make a point, and the title will be a key factor in the audience interpreting the graph properly. For example, instead of a title like "Sales 1996-2001", you could say "Sales Up 42% '96-'01". There is usually no need for a separate tile on a graph since the slide headline will communicate the meaning of the graph.

Legend – If you have more than one data series on a graph, you should add text labels to indicate each series instead of using a legend on the graph. Research shows that a legend distracts the audience by forcing them to split their attention between the data in the graph and the explanatory text in the legend, reducing their understanding of the graph. Instead, put any explanatory text in the graph using text boxes.

Creating the Graph

Most presentation software packages have a built-in graph creation tool. For earlier versions of Microsoft PowerPoint, it is the Microsoft Graph application, and later versions use Microsoft Excel. Most of these tools are quite robust and will meet the needs of most presenters. If you want to use a graph, understand within your presentation software how to create and edit a graph. There are specialized graphing software tools available, but these are required only when you need to use certain complex graph types or require features that are not included in the built-in tools. One way to extend the capabilities of the built-in graphing tool is to use the graphing tool to create the basic graph, and then use the drawing tools of the presentation software to add specific elements that are required for your purposes, such as lines, text boxes or arrows. Importing a graph from another software package, such as a spreadsheet is not always a good idea because it is harder to get the colors right on the import translation and it is harder to edit since the other software package must be started to do the editing.

Tables

The basic structure of a table is a set of columns and rows that contain the data and usually contain either a row or column (or both) of headings that organize the data. When deciding on the size of the table, it is a good idea to keep the six by six guideline in mind. Used in the context of tables, this guideline suggests that a table should try to have no more than six columns and no more than six rows in order to keep the amount of information to a reasonable level. In selecting the size of the table, make sure that the font size of the text in each cell of the table is big enough to be read clearly when displayed. A table is generally less effective than a graph because it only shows the data, whereas the graph shows an interpretation of the data, which is easier for the audience to understand. When you are presenting a table, you will need to provide the interpretation of the data for the audience. One way to make certain cells stand out is to change the background colour of the cell or enhance the text by changing the colour or making it bolder. Column and/or row headings should be bolded to distinguish them from the data. Most presentation software packages have a built-in table creation tool that will serve most purposes quite well. Importing a table from another software package, such as a word processor is not always a good idea because it is harder to get the formatting right on the import translation and it is harder to edit since the other software package must be started to do the editing.

Adding Emphasis

When using a graph or a table, you should emphasize the key parts so that your points are stronger. One way to add emphasis is to animate the graph or table elements so that they appear one-by-one instead of all at one time. This allows you to discuss each element or data series individually and keep the audience focus on the message you are delivering. Using animation effects is much better than trying to point different elements out using a pointer device such as a laser pointer. You can also use drawing tools such as arrows and boxes to highlight a portion of the table or graph. You can use a strong contrasting colour for the drawing element to visually draw the audience's eyes to that part of the graph or table. Most presentation software packages also have a callout box drawing tool. This tool places a line pointing at a certain spot on the graph and then links that line to a box that contains text to explain the significance of the area being pointed to. I use this in one graph to replace a legend.

REFERENCES

- Kalton, Graham: *Introduction to Survey Sampling.* Beverly Hills, CA: Sage, 1983.
- Kanti Bagchi: *Research Methodology in Social Sciences: A Practical Guide*, Abhijeet Pub, 2007.
- Narender K. Chadha: *Research Methods for Sports Scientists*, Friends, 2001.

7

Management and Scaling

SMALL-SCALE PROJECT MANAGEMENT

Small-scale project management is the specific type of project management of small-scale projects. These projects are characterised by factors such as short duration; low person hours; small team; size of the budget and the balance between the time committed to delivering the project itself and the time committed to managing the project. They are otherwise unique, time delineated and require the delivery of a final output in the same way as large-scale projects.

Small-scale projects are by far the most common form of project enacted by institutions and large scale organisations who may utilise small projects in order to accomplish a range of small order tasks. For SME's and micro-businesses, especially in the creative industries, the running of small projects may be an essential component of their core business. Individuals and groups regularly utilise small-scale projects as a means to delivering a range of outcomes from organising a village fete to building a garden shed.

The balance between 'process' over 'output' is a key factor for consideration when looking at the effectiveness of applying project management methodologies to smaller projects. Other factors commonly associated with large-scale project management, for example time, cost and quality, still apply and broadly there are two approaches that can be taken:

- The adoption of a scaled-down version of PRINCE2 offers a flexible and reflexive approach to small-scale project management and limits the management burden while still enhancing the process. This methodology enables the project manager to utilise 'lean project planning' as a conceptual tool that can be configured to meet the requirements of small-scale projects in a variety of environments.

- AGILE is a risk driven approach that relies on a iterative cycle of review and evaluation. It limits the 'management overhead' to that which is useful for the project. The process allows for creative excursions and aims to deliver value outputs over shorter time-scales. The high level of flexibility in this approach is well suited to creative and experimental project environments.

Quality Management

The 'management overhead' describes the ratio between the effort required to document or manage a process and the eventual outcome of a project. With large-scale project methodologies the quality management is an important part of a project's process and aims to provide for continual improvement and a project output that meets the requirements of the end user. On small-scale projects it is not always possible to utilise standard quality management approaches due to limitations of time, budget and resources. The is still however a need to be creative and innovative while maintaining quality standards that, especially in the creative industries, maybe difficult to define or evaluate, and may defy simple categorisation. It is important to recognise that quality is an innate characteristic that we instinctively recognise. We know quality when we see it but find 'it' hard to say what it is in advance. Insight, intuition and creativity are indicators of quality that on a small-scale project are perhaps better evaluated on an instinctive level i.e. "is it good enough". Any lightweight, lean or small-scale project management methodology must scale back process management and documentation to an optimum level. A level which does not overburden the project with unnecessary administration and does not commit scarce resources to a quality management approach that constricts the ability to be creative and innovate. A simple evaluation based on an elaboration of the question "is it good enough" may well suffice for the purpose of many small-scale projects.

Creativity, Innovation and Implementation

"Innovation equals creativity plus implementation", where Creativity is a balance of "imagination and analysis", and implementation is a process of idea selection, development and commercialisation. This suggests there is a requirement for a two phase solution for the implementation of small-scale projects. The first phase being one of problem definition, analysis, and critical thinking; followed by a second action or implementation phase where the prime activity is the application of skills and knowledge to implement the creative idea. The breaking down of the process of innovation into two fundamental stages offers the possibility for thinking about small-scale projects as a two stage process. That of innovation and innovation implementation.

Scaling PRINCE2

The use of flexibile conceptual framework with integrated elements of the PRINCE2 methodology allows for the planning of small-scale projects to be structured a 'Work Breakdown Schedule' utilising the general headings:

- What is to be produced
- When is it to be produced
- By whom will it be produced
- How is quality to be specified and measured
- A statement on technical resources
- Stage Descriptions (minimum of 2) – following natural breakpoints, critical components, milestones, checkpoints, reviews etc....
    - o Creative and planning phase – leading to PID
    - o Action or implementation phase – subdivided as appropriate

This approach provides an effective and flexible framework for documenting a small-scale project utilising a PID which includes a Project Plan at its heart. This model offers a lightweight approach to documenting the project that is eminently scalable and does not add an unnecessary management burden to a small-scale project process. Consequently the framework offers a set of tools that will enhance quality and mirrors the two phases associated with innovation and innovation implementation. It therefore seems ideal for managing small-scale projects in the creative industries and can be easily adapted to suit industry specific work-flows and terminology.

Managing Project Risk

A simple risk assessment tool should be integral to the planning process and team members can be encouraged to use the risk assessment as a tool of critical enquiry that will help them identify risk factors and opportunities as part of a continual, iterative cycle offering a small project an easy and effective way of documenting its progress in a reflexive manner. Any projects that have a degree of complexity in the implementation phase might need to further sub-divide this phase using milestones, or checkpoints that allow the team to see if it is on track and this process could be easily integrated into the risk assessment tool.

The adoption of a risk assessment tool will enable the project manager to deal with exceptions or changes to the project as they arise and enables a flexible approach to implementing the project. The key to a 'reflexive' approach to exception and change is the way in which 'tolerance' is applied to the project i.e. amount by which the Project Manager or Project Team may deviate from the project plan (in relation to time, cost and quality) without the need to refer up to the chain of command or initiate codified exception or change protocols.

Risk assessment can easily be combined with an exception planning procedure to manage tolerance to changes in a project. The use of 'triggers' to initiate exception management procedures in order to deal with issues such as scope creep; changes in aims and objectives; changes in constraints; and changes in risk. Such a tool offers a method for interrogating the project brief during the implementation phase and should be utilised as part of the planning and review process. The use of a numerical factor gives a simple scale that triggers a response in accordance with previously agreed criteria.

Thus the Project Manager is able to make judgements about change and can be given a degree of autonomy taking into account their level of experience.

Adopting an AGILE approach

The Agile Manifesto: *"Individuals and interactions over processes and tools; creative solutions over comprehensive documentation; team working and collaboration over didactic formal organisation; responding to change over following a plan".*

Agile project management is risk & value driven i.e. an agile project plan need only address risks in relation to the projects values. The approach formulated by DeCarlo offers the following values as key to a 'sufficient methodology' for a projects success:

- People Values: people first, honest communication, work life balance, have the courage to take risks.
- Process Values: ongoing client collaboration, fast failures by tackling risks early, high visibility and accountability.
- Business Values: clarity of purpose, focus on results not tracking, early delivery of business value.

There is a focus on learning in Agile project management methodologies that utilises iterative reflection as an organisational tool. Agile is about learning in real environments rather than by modelling and simulation. This is achieved by breaking the project into "time boxes" or stages sometimes referred to as "sprints". At the end of each 'time box" the project team review and evaluate using a risk tool asking what have we learnt from this stage and what will we now change. The PID after a review might change fundamentally according to what has been learnt. Risk tools promote group discussion and reflection and are iterative across project life cycles or time boxes. A simple risk assessment may not suffice with an Agile approach however as it only captures the negative or "jeopardy risks" excluding the "opportunity risks". On creative or experimental projects the "opportunity risks" are of great importance since they may bring value to the project that had not been initially conceptualised.

At the completion of each iteration the project team might be required to utilise a simple tool such as a SWOT analysis as a risk register which captures both positive and negative risk attributes. After prioritising this list the top three on the positive and negative categories on the risk register then become the actions for the next "time box". Risks can be dealt with following a simple mantra of "avoid/transfer/mitigate/enhance". In this way 'risk becomes the a structuring tool that keeps the project Agile.

LEVEL OF MEASUREMENT

The "levels of measurement", or scales of measure are expressions that typically refer to the theory of scale types developed by the psychologist Stanley Smith Stevens. Stevens proposed his theory in a 1946 *Science* article titled "On the theory of scales of measurement". In that article, Stevens claimed that all measurement in science was conducted using four different types of scales that he called "nominal", "ordinal", "interval" and "ratio".

Nominal Scale

At the nominal scale, i.e., for a nominal category, one uses labels; for example, rocks can be generally categorized as igneous, sedimentary and metamorphic. For this scale, some valid operations are equivalence and set membership. Nominal measures offer names or labels for certain characteristics.

Variables assessed on a nominal scale are called categorical variables. Stevens (1946, p. 679) must have known that claiming nominal scales to measure obviously non-quantitative things would have attracted criticism, so he invoked his theory of measurement to justify nominal scales as measurement: "...the use of numerals as names for classes is an example of the assignment of numerals according to rule. The rule is: Do not assign the same numeral to different classes or different numerals to the same class. Beyond that, anything goes with the nominal scale."

The central tendency of a nominal attribute is given by its mode; neither the mean nor the median can be defined. We can use a simple example of a nominal category: first names. Looking at nearby people, we might find one or more of them named Aamir. Aamir is their label; and the set of all first names is a nominal scale. We can only check whether two people have the same name (equivalence) or whether a given name is in on a certain list of names (set membership), but it is impossible to say which name is greater or less than another (comparison) or to measure the difference between two names. Given a set of people, we can describe the set by its most common name (the mode), but cannot provide an "average name" or even the "middle name" among all the names. However, if we decide to sort our names alphabetically (or to sort them by length; or by how many times they appear in the US Census), we will begin to turn this nominal scale into an ordinal scale.

Ordinal Scale

Rank-ordering data simply puts the data on an ordinal scale. Ordinal measurements describe order, but not relative size or degree of difference between the items measured. In this scale type, the numbers assigned to objects or events represent the rank order (1st, 2nd, 3rd, etc.) of the entities assessed. A Likert Scale is a type of ordinal scale and may also use names with an order such as: "bad", "medium", and "good"; or "very satisfied", "satisfied", "neutral", "unsatisfied", "very unsatisfied." An example of an ordinal scale is the result of a horse race, which says only which horses arrived first, second, or third but include no information about race times. Another is the Mohs scale of mineral hardness, which characterizes the hardness of various minerals through the ability of a harder material to scratch a softer one, saying nothing about the actual hardness of any of them. Yet another example is military ranks; they have an order, but no well-defined numerical difference between ranks. When using an ordinal scale, the central tendency of a group of items can be described by using the group's mode (or most common item) or its median (the middle-ranked item), but the mean (or average) cannot be defined.

In 1946, Stevens observed that psychological measurement usually operates on ordinal scales, and that ordinary statistics like means and standard deviations do not have valid interpretations. Nevertheless, such statistics can often be used to generate fruitful information, with the caveat that caution should be taken in drawing conclusion from such statistical data.

Psychometricians like to theorise that psychometric tests produce interval scale measures of cognitive abilities but there is little prima facie evidence to suggest that such attributes are anything more than ordinal for most psychological data. In particular, IQ scores reflect an ordinal scale, in which all scores are only meaningful for comparison, rather than an interval scale, in which a given number of IQ "points" corresponds to a unit of intelligence. Thus it is an error to write that an IQ of 160 is just as different from an IQ of 130 as an IQ of 100 is different from an IQ of 70. In mathematical order theory, an ordinal scale defines a total preorder of objects (in essence, a way of sorting all the objects, in which some may be tied). The scale values themselves (such as labels like "great", "good", and "bad"; 1st, 2nd, and 3rd) have a total order, where they may be sorted into a single line with no ambiguities. If numbers are used to define the scale, they remain correct even if they are transformed by any monotonically increasing function. This property is known as the order isomorphism.

Interval Scale

Quantitative attributes are all measurable on interval scales, as any difference between the levels of an attribute can be multiplied by any real number to exceed or equal another difference. A highly familiar example of interval scale measurement is temperature with the Celsius scale. In this particular scale, the unit of measurement is 1/100 of the temperature difference between the freezing and boiling points of water under a pressure of 1 atmosphere. The "zero point" on an interval scale is arbitrary; and negative values can be used. The formal mathematical term is an affine space (in this case an affine line). Variables measured at the interval level are called "interval variables" or sometimes "scaled variables" as they have units of measurement. Ratios between numbers on the scale are not meaningful, so operations such as multiplication and division cannot be carried out directly. But ratios of differences can be expressed; for example, one difference can be twice another.

The central tendency of a variable measured at the interval level can be represented by its mode, its median, or its arithmetic mean. Statistical dispersion can be measured in most of the usual ways, which just involved differences or averaging, such as range, interquartile range, and standard deviation. Since one cannot divide, one cannot define measures that require a ratio, such as studentized range or coefficient of variation. More subtly, while one can define moments about the origin, only central moments are useful, since the choice of origin is arbitrary and not meaningful. One can define standardized moments, since ratios of differences are meaningful, but one cannot define coefficient of variation, since the mean is a moment about the origin, unlike the standard deviation, which is (the square root of) a central moment.

Ratio Measurement

Most measurement in the physical sciences and engineering is done on ratio scales. Mass, length, time, plane angle, energy and electric charge are examples of physical measures that are ratio scales. The scale type takes its name from the fact that measurement is the estimation of the ratio between a magnitude of a continuous quantity and a unit magnitude of the same kind (Michell, 1997, 1999). Informally, the distinguishing feature of a ratio scale is the possession of a non-arbitrary zero value. For example, the Kelvin temperature scale has a non-arbitrary zero point of absolute zero, which is denoted 0K and is equal to-273.15 degrees Celsius. This zero point is non arbitrary as the particles that compose matter at this temperature have zero kinetic energy. Examples of ratio scale measurement in the behavioural sciences are all but non-existent. Luce (2000) argues that an example of ratio scale measurement in psychology can be found in rank and sign dependent expected utility theory. All statistical measures can be used for a variable measured at the ratio level, as all necessary mathematical operations are defined. The central tendency of a variable measured at the ratio level can be represented by, in addition to its mode, its median, or its arithmetic mean, also its geometric mean or harmonic mean. In addition to the measures of statistical dispersion defined for interval variables, such as range and standard deviation, for ratio variables one can also define measures that require a ratio, such as studentized range or coefficient of variation.

Debate on Classification Scheme

There has been, and continues to be, debate about the merits of the classifications, particularly in the cases of the nominal and ordinal classifications (Michell, 1986). Thus, while

Stevens' classification is widely adopted, it is by no means universally accepted. Duncan (1986) observed that Stevens' classification *nominal measurement* is contrary to his own definition of *measurement*. Stevens (1975) said on his own definition of measurement that "the assignment can be any consistent rule. The only rule not allowed would be random assignment, for randomness amounts in effect to a nonrule". However, so-called nominal measurement involves arbitrary assignment, and the "permissible transformation" is any number for any other. This is one of the points made in Lord's (1953) satirical paper *On the Statistical Treatment of Football Numbers*.

Among those who accept the classification scheme, there is also some controversy in behavioural sciences over whether the mean is meaningful for ordinal measurement. In terms of measurement theory, it is not, because the arithmetic operations are not made on numbers that are measurements in units, and so the results of computations do not give numbers in units. However, many behavioural scientists use means for ordinal data anyway. This is often justified on the basis that ordinal scales in behavioural science are really somewhere between true ordinal and interval scales; although the interval difference between two ordinal ranks is not constant, it is often of the same order of magnitude. For example, applications of measurement models in educational contexts often indicate that total scores have a fairly linear relationship with measurements across a range of an assessment. Thus, some argue, that so long as the unknown interval difference between ordinal scale ranks is not too variable, interval scale statistics such as means can meaningfully be used on ordinal scale variables. Statistical analysis software such as PSPP require the user to select the appropriate measurement class for each variable. This ensures that subsequent user errors cannot inadvertently perform meaningless analyses (for example correlation analysis with a variable on a nominal level).

L. L. Thurstone made progress toward developing a justification for obtaining interval-level measurements based on the law of comparative judgment. Further progress was made by Georg Rasch (1960), who developed the probabilistic Rasch model that provides a theoretical basis and justification for obtaining interval-level measurements from counts of observations such as total scores on assessments. Another issue is derived from Nicholas R. Chrisman's article "Rethinking Levels of Measurement for Cartography", in which he introduces an expanded list of levels of measurement to account for various measurements that do not necessarily fit with the traditional notion of levels of measurement. Measurements bound to a range and repeat (like degrees in a circle, time, etc.), graded membership categories, and other types of measurement do not fit to Steven's original work, leading to the introduction of 6 new levels of measurement leading to: (1) Nominal, (2) Graded membership, (3) Ordinal, (4) Interval, (5) Log-Interval, (6) Extensive Ratio, (7) Cyclical Ratio, (8) Derived Ratio, (9) Counts and finally (10) Absolute. The extended levels of measurement are rarely used outside of academic geography.

Scale Types and Stevens' "Operational Theory of Measurement"

The theory of scale types is the intellectual handmaiden to Stevens' "operational theory of measurement", which was to become definitive within psychology and the behavioural sciences, despite Michell's characterization as its being quite at odds with Michell's understanding of measurement in the natural sciences (Michell, 1999). Essentially, the operational theory of measurement was a reaction to the conclusions of a committee established in 1932 by the British Association for the Advancement of Science to investigate the possibility of genuine scientific measurement in the psychological and behavioural sciences. This committee, which became known as the *Ferguson committee*, published a Final Report (Ferguson, et al., 1940, p. 245) in which Stevens' sone scale (Stevens & Davis, 1938) was an object of criticism: "...any law purporting to express a quantitative relation between sensation intensity and stimulus intensity is not merely false but is in fact meaningless unless and until a meaning can be given to the concept of addition as applied to sensation."

That is, if Stevens' *sone* scale was genuinely measuring the intensity of auditory sensations, then evidence for such sensations as being quantitative attributes must be produced. The evidence needed was the presence of *additive structure*- a concept comprehensively treated by the German mathematician Otto Hölder (Hölder, 1901). Given the physicist and measurement theorist Norman Robert Campbell dominated the Ferguson committee's deliberations, the committee concluded that measurement in the social sciences was impossible due to the lack of concatenation operations.

This conclusion was later rendered false by the discovery of the theory of conjoint measurement by Debreu (1960) and independently by Luce & Tukey (1964).

However, Stevens' reaction was not to conduct experiments to test for the presence of additive structure in sensations, but instead to render the conclusions of the Ferguson committee null and void by proposing a new theory of measurement: "Paraphrasing N.R. Campbell (Final Report), we may say that measurement, in the broadest sense, is defined as the assignment of numerals to objects and events according to rules *(Stevens, 1946, p.677).*"

Stevens was greatly influenced by the ideas of another Harvard academic, the Nobel laureate physicist Percy Bridgman (1927), whose doctrine of *operationism* Stevens used to define measurement. In Stevens' definition for example, it is the use of a tape measure that defines length (the object of measurement) as being measurable (and so by implication quantitative). Critics of operationism object that it confuses the relations between two objects or events for properties of one of those of objects or events.

The Canadian measurement theorist William Rozeboom (1966) was an early and trenchant critic of Stevens' theory of scale types. But it was not until much later with the work of mathematical psychologists Theodore Alper (1985, 1987), Louis Narens (1981a, b) and R. Duncan Luce (1986, 1987, 2001) did the concept of scale types receive the mathematical rigour that it lacked at its inception. As Luce (1997, p. 395) bluntly stated: "S.S. Stevens (1946, 1951, 1975) claimed that what counted was having an interval or ratio scale. Subsequent research has given meaning to this assertion, but given his attempts to invoke scale type ideas it is doubtful if he understood it himself...no measurement theorist I know accepts Stevens' broad definition of measurement...in our view, the only sensible meaning for 'rule' is empirically testable laws about the attribute.

MEASUREMENT SCALES

A topic which can create a great deal of confusion in social and educational research is that of types of scales used in measuring behaviour. It is critical because it relates to the types of statistics you can use to analyse your data. An easy way to have a paper rejected is to have used either an incorrect scale/statistic combination or to have used a low powered statistic on a high powered set of data.

Nominal

The lowest measurement level you can use, from a statistical point of view, is a nominal scale. A nominal scale, as the name implies, is simply some placing of data into categories, without any order or structure. A physical example of a nominal scale is the terms we use for colours. The underlying spectrum is ordered but the names are nominal. In research activities a YES/NO scale is nominal. It has no order and there is no distance between YES and NO.

and statistics

The statistics which can be used with nominal scales are in the non-parametric group. The most likely ones would be:

mode

crosstabulation-with chi-square

There are also highly sophisticated modelling techniques available for nominal data.

Ordinal

An ordinal scale is next up the list in terms of power of measurement.

The simplest ordinal scale is a ranking. When a market researcher asks you to rank 5 types of beer from most flavourful to least flavourful, he/she is asking you to create an ordinal scale of preference.

There is no objective distance between any two points on your subjective scale. For you the top beer may be far superior to the second preferred beer but, to another respondant with the same top and second beer, the distance may be subjectively small.

An ordinal scale only lets you interpret gross order and not the relative positional distances.

and statistics

Ordinal data would use non-parametric statistics. These would include:

Median and mode

rank order correlation

non-parametric analysis of variance

Modelling techniques can also be used with ordinal data.

Interval: The standard survey rating scale is an interval scale.

When you are asked to rate your satisfaction with a piece of software on a 7 point scale, from Dissatisfied to Satisfied, you are using an interval scale. It is an interval scale because it is assumed to have equidistant points between each of the scale elements. This means that we can interpret differences in the distance along the scale. We contrast this to an ordinal scale where we can only talk about differences in order, not differences in the degree of order. Interval scales are also scales which are defined by metrics such as logarithms. In these cases, the distances are note equal but they are strictly definable based on the metric used.

and statistics

Interval scale data would use parametric statistical techniques:

Mean and standard deviation

Correlation-r

Regression

Analysis of variance

Factor analysis

Plus a whole range of advanced multivariate and modelling techniques

Remember that you can use non-parametric techniques with interval and ratio data. But non-paramteric techniques are less powerful than the parametric ones.

Ratio: A ratio scale is the top level of measurement and is not often available in social research.

The factor which clearly defines a ratio scale is that it has a true zero point.

The simplest example of a ratio scale is the measurement of length (disregarding any philosophical points about defining how we can identify zero length).

The best way to contrast interval and ratio scales is to look at temperature. The Centigrade scale has a zero point but it is an arbitrary one. The Farenheit scale has its equivalent point at-32o. (Physicists would probably argue that Absolute Zero is the zero point for temperature but this is a theoretical concept.) So, even though temperture looks as if it would be a ratio scale it is an interval scale. Currently, we cannot talk about *no temperature*-and this would be needed if it were a ration scale.

and statistics

The same as for Interval data

ORDINAL SCALE

When items are classified according to whether they have more or less of a characteristic, the scale used is referred to as an ordinal scale (definition of ordinal scale). The main characteristic of the ordinal scale is that the categories have a logical or ordered relationship to each other.These types of scale permit the measurement of degrees of difference, but not the specific amount of difference. This scale is very common in marketing, satisfaction and attitudinal research. Any questions that ask the respondent to rate something are using ordinal scales. For example,

How would you rate the service of our wait-staff?

Excellent 0 Very good 0 Good 0 Fair 0 Poor 0

Although we would know that respondent X ("very good") thought the service to be better than respondent Y ("good"), we have no idea how much better nor can we even be sure that both respondents have the same understanding of what constitutes "good service" and therefore, whether they really differ in their opinion about its quality.

Likert scales are commonly used in attitudinal measurements. This type of scale uses a five-point scale ranging from strongly agree, agree, neither agree nor disagree, disagree, strongly disagree to rate people's attitudes. Variants of the Likert-scale exist that use any number of points between three and ten, however it is best to give at least four or five choices. Be sure to include all possible responses: sometimes respondents may not have an opinion or may not know the answer, and therefore you should include a "neutral" category or the possibility to check off "undecided/uncertain", "no opinion" or "don't know". Although some researchers treat them as an *interval scale*, we do not really know that the distances between answer alternatives are equal. Hence only the *mode* and *median* can be calculated, but not the *mean*. The *range* and percentile ranking can also be calculated.

INTERVAL SCALE

On interval measurement scales, one unit on the scale represents the same magnitude on the trait or characteristic being measured across the whole range of the scale. For example, if anxiety were measured on an interval scale, then a difference between a score of 10 and a score of 11 would represent the same difference in anxiety as would a difference between a score of 50 and a score of 51. Interval scales do not have a "true" zero point, however, and therefore it is not possible to make statements about how many times higher one score is than another. For the anxiety scale, it would not be valid to say that a person with a score of 30 was twice as anxious as a person with a score of 15. True interval measurement is somewhere between rare and nonexistent in the behavioural sciences. No interval-level scale of anxiety such as the one described in the example actually exists. A good example of an interval scale is the Fahrenheit scale for temperature. Equal differences on this scale represent equal differences in temperature, but a temperature of 30 degrees is not twice as warm as one of 15 degrees.

RATIO SCALE

When a scale consists not only of equidistant points but also has a meaningful zero point, then we refer to it as a *ratio scale*. If we ask respondents their ages, the difference between any two years would always be the same, and 'zero' signifies the absence of age or birth. Hence, a 100-year old person is indeed twice as old as a 50-year old one. Sales figures, quantities purchased and market share are all expressed on a ratio scale. Ratio scales should be used to gather quantitative information, and we see them perhaps most commonly when respondents are asked for their age, income, years of participation, etc. In order to respect the notion of equal distance between adjacent points on the scale, you must make each category the same size. Therefore, if your first category is \$0-\$19,999, your second category must be \$20,000-\$39,999. Obviously, categories should never overlap and categories should follow a logical order, most often increasing in size. Ratio scales are the most sophisticated of scales, since it incorporates all the characteristics of nominal (definition of *nominal scale*), ordinal (definition of *ordinal scale*) and interval scales (definition of *interval scale*). As a result, a large number of descriptive calculations are applicable.

SCALE (RATIO)

The scale ratio of some sort of model which represents an original proportionally is the ratio of a linear dimension of the model to the same dimension of the original. Examples include a 3-dimensional scale model of a building or the scale drawings of the elevations or plans of a building. In such cases the scale is dimensionless and exact throughout the model or drawing. The scale can be expressed in four ways: in words (a lexical scale), as a ratio, as a fraction and as a graphical (bar) scale. Thus on an architect's drawing we might read

'one centimetre to one metre' or 1:100 or 1/100

and a bar scale would also normally appear on the drawing.

In general a representation may involve more than one scale at the same time. For example a drawing showing a new road in elevation might use different horizontal and vertical scales. An elevation of a bridge might be annotated with arrows with a length proportional to a force loading, as in 1 cm to 1000 newtons: this is an example of a dimensional scale. A weather map at some scale may be annotated with wind arrows at a dimensional scale of 1 cm to 20 mph. A town plan may be constructed as an exact scale drawing but for larger areas a map projection is necessary and *no* projection can represent the

Earth's surface at a uniform scale: in general the scale of a projection depends on position and direction. The variation of scale may be considerable in *small* scale maps which may cover the globe. In *large* scale maps of small areas the variation of scale may be insignificant for most purposes but it is always present. The scale of a map projection must be interpreted as a nominal scale. (The usage *large* and *small* in relation to map scales relates to their expressions as fractions. The fraction 1/10,000 used for a local map is much *larger* than 1/100,000,000 used for a global map. There is no hard and fixed dividing line between small and large scales.)

Mathematical Note

In the general case of a differentiable bijection, the concept of scale can, to some extent, still be used, but it may depend on location and direction. It can be described by the Jacobian matrix. The modulus of the matrix times a unit vector is the scale in that direction. The non-linear case applies for example if a curved surface like part of the Earth's surface is mapped to a plane. In the case of an affine transformation the scale does not depend on location but it depends in general on direction. If the affine transformation can be decomposed into isometries and a transformation given by a diagonal matrix, we have directionally differential scaling and the diagonal elements (the eigenvalues) are the scale factors in two or three perpendicular directions.

STEVENS' RATIO SCALE

S. S. Stevens included "ratio scales" in his hierarchy of scales. "A ratio scale is an interval scale in which distances are stated with respect to a rational zero rather than with respect to, for example, the mean" (Nunnally, 1967, p.14). A rational zero is a location on an interval scale deliberately chosen for reasons other than the current data. The distinctive feature of a ratio scale is that it has a an origin defined by a dominating theory. Time measured from the "Big Bang" is on a ratio scale. Height is on a ratio scale when measured from sea-level, e.g., "one mountain is twice as high as another", but on an interval scale when measured from the mean of a sample of mountains.

When the "average" of a set of ratio scale numbers is intended to summarize their ratio, not interval, property, their ratio relationship with the scale's particular origin must be maintained. This is done by using the geometric, rather than the arithmetic, mean as the "average" for the ratios. To obtain the "average" of a set of ratio scale numbers, the logarithm of each number is calculated. The arithmetic mean of these logarithms is computed and this number is exponentiated to yield the geometric mean of the original ratio numbers.

Counts-A Special Case

"The numerosity of collections of objects [i.e., counts]... belongs to the class I have called ratio scales". Accordingly, in situations where it is important to maintain the notion that a count of 0 means "none at all", rather than "none extra", and a count 1 of means "only one object", rather than "one more to go with those we already have", then ratio scale arithmetic applies. To apply the usual interval statistics to such counts requires the logarithms of the counts to be obtained. This concept underlies one derivation of the Rasch model.

Rasch's Scale of Ratios

Georg Rasch's use of the term "Ratio Scale" differs from Stevens'. Rasch (1992, p. 69) specifies a scale of ratios, analogous to the Richter scale for earthquakes. As originally defined, zero on the Richter scale was intended to mean "no earth movement". Then scale values are defined such that an earthquake of "2" on the Richter scale is 10 times more severe than a "1". Richter-type scales are also called "logarithmic scales". Rasch also conceptualized degrees of difficulty and ability in ratio units when he wrote the multiplicative form of his model (p. 107):

$$t/(1-t) = z/d$$

But, whenever convenient, Rasch switched to an additive, i.e., interval, form by taking logarithms (p. 119):

$$\log_e(t/(1-t)) = \log_e(z)-\log_e(d)$$

In general, any interval scale can be transformed to a Stevens ratio scale by choosing an origin with some meaning. Further, any interval scale can be converted to a Rasch scale of ratios ("logarithmic scale") by choosing any origin and exponentiating. Consequently, the distinctions between these scale types have no mathematical importance.

GUTTMAN SCALE

In statistical surveys conducted by means of structured interviews or questionnaires, a subset of the survey items having binary (e.g., YES or NO) answers forms a Guttman scale (named after Louis Guttman) if they can be ranked in some order so that, for a rational respondent, the response pattern can be captured by a single index on that ordered scale. In other words, on a Guttman scale, items are arranged in an order so that an individual who agrees with a particular item also agrees with items of lower rank-order. For example, a series of items could be (1) "I am willing to be near ice cream"; (2) "I am willing to smell ice cream"; (3) "I am willing to eat ice cream"; and (4) "I love to eat ice cream". Agreement with any one item implies agreement with the lower-order items. This contrasts with topics studied using a Likert scale or a Thurstone scale.

The concept of Guttman scale likewise applies to series of items in other kinds of tests, such as achievement tests, that have binary outcomes. For example, a test of math achievement might order questions based on their difficulty and instruct the examinee to begin in the middle. The assumption is if the examinee can successfully answer items of that difficulty (e.g., summing two 3-digit numbers), s/he would be able to answer the earlier questions (e.g., summing two 2-digit numbers). Some achievement tests are organized in a Guttman scale to reduce the duration of the test.

By designing surveys and tests such that they contain Guttman scales, researchers can simplify the analysis of the outcome of surveys, and increase the robustness. Guttman scales also make it possible to detect and discard randomized answer patterns, as may be given by uncooperative respondents.

A hypothetical, perfect Guttman scale consists of a unidimensional set of items that are ranked in order of difficulty from least extreme to most extreme position. For example, a person scoring a "7" on a ten item Guttman scale, will agree with items 1-7 and disagree with items 8,9,10. An important property of Guttman's model is that a person's entire set of responses to all items can be predicted from their cumulative score because the model is deterministic.

A well known example of a Guttman scale is the Bogardus Social Distance Scale.

Another example is the original Beaufort wind force scale, assigning a single number to observed conditions of the sea surface ("Flat",..., "Small waves",..., "Sea heaps up and foam begins to streak",...), which was in fact a Guttman scale. The observation "Flat = YES" implies "Small waves = NO".

Deterministic Model

An important objective in Guttman scaling is to maximize the reproducibility of response patterns from a single score. A good Guttman scale should have a coefficient of reproducibility (the percentage of original responses that could be reproduced by knowing the scale scores used to summarize them) above .85. Another commonly used metric for assessing the quality of a Guttman scale, is Menzel's coefficient of scalability and the coefficient of homogeneity. To maximize unidimensionality, misfitting items are re-written or discarded.

Stochastic Models

Guttman's deterministic model is brought within a probabilistic framework in item response theory models, and especially Rasch measurement. The Rasch model requires a probabilistic Guttman structure when items have dichotomous responses (e.g. right/wrong). In the Rasch model, the Guttman response pattern is the most probable response pattern for a person when items are ordered from least difficult to most difficult (Andrich, 1985). In addition, the Polytomous Rasch model is premised on a deterministic *latent* Guttman response subspace, and this is the basis for integer scoring in the model (Andrich, 1978, 2005). Analysis of data using item response theory requires comparatively longer instruments and larger datasets to scale item and person locations and evaluate the fit of data to model. In practice, actual data from respondents do not closely match Guttman's deterministic model. Several probabilistic models of Guttman implicatory scales were developed by Krus (1977) and Krus and Bart (1974).

Applications

The Guttman scale is used mostly when researchers want to design short questionnaires with good discriminating ability.

The Guttman model works best for constructs that are hierarchical and highly structured such as social distance, organizational hierarchies, and evolutionary stages.

Unfolding Models

A class of unidimensional models that contrast with Guttman's model are unfolding models. These models also assume unidimensionality but posit that the probability of endorsing an item is proportional to the distance between the items standing on the unidimensional trait and the standing of the respondent. For example, items like "I think immigration should be reduced" on a scale measuring attitude towards immigration would be *unlikely* to be endorsed *both* by those favouring open policies *and also* by those favouring no immigration at all. Such an item might be endorsed by someone in the middle of the continuum. Some researchers feel that many attitude items fit this unfolding model while most psychometric techniques are based on correlation or factor analysis, and thus implicitly assume a linear relationship between the trait and the response probability. The effect of using these techniques would be to only include the most extreme items, leaving attitude instruments with little precision to measure the trait standing of individuals in the middle of the continuum.

SEMANTIC DIFFERENTIAL

Semantic differential is a type of a rating scale designed to measure the connotative meaning of objects, events, and concepts. The connotations are used to derive the attitude towards the given object, event or concept.

Osgood's semantic differential was designed to measure the connotative meaning of concepts. The respondent is asked to choose where his or her position lies, on a scale between two bipolar adjectives (for example: "Adequate-Inadequate", "Good-Evil" or "Valuable-Worthless"). Semantic differentials can be used to describe not only persons, but also the connotative meaning of abstract concepts—a capacity used extensively in affect control theory.

Theoretical underpinnings of Charles E. Osgood's semantic differential have roots in the medieval controversy between the nominalists and realists. Nominalists asserted that only real things are entities and that abstractions from these entities, called universals, are mere words. The realists held that universals have an independent objective existence either in a realm of their own or in the mind of God. Osgood's theoretical work also bears affinity to linguistics and general semantics and relates to Korzybski's structural differential.

The development of this instrument provides an interesting insight into the border area between linguistics and psychology. People have been describing each other since they developed the ability to speak. Most adjectives can also be used as personality descriptors. The occurrence of thousands of adjectives in English is an attestation of the subtleties in descriptions of persons and their behaviour available to speakers of English. Roget's Thesaurus is an early attempt to classify most adjectives into categories and was used within this context to reduce the number of adjectives to manageable subsets, suitable for factor analysis.

Osgood and his colleagues performed a factor analysis of large collections of semantic differential scales and found three recurring attitudes that people use to evaluate words and phrases: evaluation, potency, and activity. Evaluation loads highest on the adjective pair 'good-bad'. The 'strong-weak' adjective pair defines the potency factor. Adjective pair 'active-passive' defines the activity factor. These three dimensions of affective meaning were found to be cross-cultural universals in a study of dozens of cultures.

This factorial structure makes intuitive sense. When our ancestors encountered a person, the initial perception had to be whether that person represents a danger. Is the person good or bad? Next, is the person strong or weak? Our reactions to a person markedly differ if perceived as good and strong, good and weak, bad and weak, or bad and strong. Subsequently, we might extend our initial classification to include cases of persons who actively threaten us or represent only a potential danger, and so on. The evaluation, potency and activity factors thus encompass a detailed descriptive system of personality. Osgood's semantic differential measures these three factors. It contains sets of adjective pairs such as warm-cold, bright-dark, beautiful-ugly, sweet-bitter, fair-unfair, brave-cowardly, meaningful-meaningless. The studies of Osgood and his colleagues revealed that the evaluative factor accounted for most of the variance in scalings, and related this to the idea of attitudes.

The semantic differential is today one of the most widely used scales used in the measurement of attitudes. One of the reasons is the versatility of the items. The bipolar adjective pairs can be used for a wide variety of subjects, and as such the scale is nicknamed "the ever ready battery" of the attitude researcher.

STATISTICAL PROPERTIES

Five items, or 5 bipolar pairs of adjectives, have been proven to yield reliable findings, which highly correlate with alternative measures of the same attitude The biggest problem with this scale is that the properties of the level of measurement are unknown. The most statistically sound approach is to treat it as an ordinal scale, but it can be argued that the neutral response (i.e. the middle alternative on the scale) serves as an arbitrary zero point, and that the intervals between the scale values can be treated as equal, making it an interval scale.

A detailed presentation on the development of the semantic differential is provided in the monumental book, *Cross-Cultural Universals of Affective Meaning.* David R. Heise's *Surveying Cultures* provides a contemporary update with special attention to measurement issues when using computerized graphic rating scales.

NON-PARAMETRIC STATISTICS

In statistics, the term non-parametric statistics has at least two different meanings:

1. The first meaning of *non-parametric* covers techniques that do not rely on data belonging to any particular distribution. These include, among others:
   - o *distribution free* methods, which do not rely on assumptions that the data are drawn from a given probability distribution. As such it is the opposite of parametric statistics. It includes non-parametric statistical models, inference and statistical tests.
   - o *non-parametric statistics* (in the sense of a statistic over data, which is defined to be a function on a

sample that has no dependency on a parameter), whose interpretation does not depend on the population fitting any parametrized distributions. Statistics based on the ranks of observations are one example of such statistics and these play a central role in many non-parametric approaches.

2. The second meaning of *non-parametric* covers techniques that do not assume that the *structure* of a model is fixed. Typically, the model grows in size to accommodate the complexity of the data. In these techniques, individual variables *are* typically assumed to belong to parametric distributions, and assumptions about the types of connections among variables are also made. These techniques include, among others:
   - *non-parametric regression*, which refers to modelling where the structure of the relationship between variables is treated non-parametrically, but where nevertheless there may be parametric assumptions about the distribution of model residuals.
   - *non-parametric hierarchical Bayesian models*, such as models based on the Dirichlet process, which allow the number of latent variables to grow as necessary to fit the data, but where individual variables still follow parametric distributions and even the process controlling the rate of growth of latent variables follows a parametric distribution.

Applications and Purpose

Non-parametric methods are widely used for studying populations that take on a ranked order (such as movie reviews receiving one to four stars). The use of non-parametric methods may be necessary when data have a ranking but no clear numerical interpretation, such as when assessing preferences; in terms of levels of measurement, for data on an *ordinal scale.* As non-parametric methods make fewer assumptions, their applicability is much wider than the corresponding parametric methods. In particular, they may be applied in situations where less is known about the application in question. Also, due to the reliance on fewer assumptions, non-parametric methods are more robust.

Another justification for the use of non-parametric methods is simplicity. In certain cases, even when the use of parametric methods is justified, non-parametric methods may be easier to use. Due both to this simplicity and to their greater robustness, non-parametric methods are seen by some statisticians as leaving less room for improper use and misunderstanding. The wider applicability and increased robustness of non-parametric tests comes at a cost: in cases where a parametric test would be appropriate, non-parametric tests have less power. In other words, a larger sample size can be required to draw conclusions with the same degree of confidence.

Non-parametric Models

Non-parametric models differ from parametric models in that the model structure is not specified *a priori* but is instead determined from data. The term *non-parametric* is not meant to imply that such models completely lack parameters but that the number and nature of the parameters are flexible and not fixed in advance.

- A histogram is a simple nonparametric estimate of a probability distribution
- Kernel density estimation provides better estimates of the density than histograms.
- Nonparametric regression and semiparametric regression methods have been developed based on kernels, splines, and wavelets.
- Data envelopment analysis provides efficiency coefficients similar to those obtained by Multivariate Analysis without any distributional assumption.

Methods

Non-parametric (or distribution-free) inferential statistical methods are mathematical procedures for statistical hypothesis testing which, unlike parametric statistics, make no assumptions about the probability distributions of the variables being assessed. The most frequently used tests include

- Anderson–Darling test
- Statistical Bootstrap Methods
- Cochran's Q

- Cohen's kappa
- Friedman two-way analysis of variance by ranks
- Kaplan–Meier
- Kendall's tau
- Kendall's W
- Kolmogorov–Smirnov test
- Kruskal-Wallis one-way analysis of variance by ranks
- Kuiper's test
- Logrank Test
- Mann–Whitney U or Wilcoxon rank sum test
- median test
- Pitman's permutation test
- Rank products
- Siegel–Tukey test
- Spearman's rank correlation coefficient
- Wald–Wolfowitz runs test
- Wilcoxon signed-rank test.

NONPARAMETRIC TESTS

Occasionally, the assumptions of the t-tests are seriously violated. In particular, if the type of data you have is ordinal in nature and not at least interval. On such occasions an alternative approach is to use nonparametric tests. We are not going to place much emphasis on them in this unit as they are only occasionally used. But you should be aware of them and have some familiarity with them. Nonparametric tests are also referred to as distribution-free tests. These tests have the obvious advantage of not requiring the assumption of normality or the assumption of homogeneity of variance. They compare medians rather than means and, as a result, if the data have one or two outliers, their influence is negated.

Parametric tests are preferred because, in general, for the same number of observations, they are more likely to lead to the rejection of a false hull hypothesis. That is, they have more power. This greater power stems from the fact that if the data have been collected at an interval or ratio level, information is lost in the conversion to ranked data (i.e., merely ordering the data from the lowest to the highest value). The following table gives the non-parametric analogue for the paired sample t-test and the independent samples t-test. There is no obvious comparison for the one sample t-test. Chi-square is a one-sample test and there are alternatives to chi-square but we will not consider them further. Chi-square is already a non-parametric test. Pearson's correlation also has non-parametric alternative (Spearman's correlation) but we will not deal with it further either.

ANDREY KOLMOGOROV

Andrey Nikolaevich Kolmogorov (25 April 1903 – 20 October 198.) was a Soviet Russian mathematician, preeminent in the 20th century, who advanced various scientific fields, among them probability theory, topology, intuitionistic logic, turbulence, classical mechanics and computational complexity.

Biography

Kolmogorov was born at Tambov in 1903. His unwed mother died in childbirth and he was raised by his aunts in Tunoshna near Yaroslavl at the estate of his grandfather, a wealthy nobleman. His father, an agronomist by trade, was deported from Saint-Petersburg for participation in the revolutionary movement.

He disappeared and was presumed to have been killed in the Russian Civil War. Kolmogorov was educated in his aunt's village school, and his earliest literary efforts and mathematical papers were printed in the school newspaper. As an adolescent he designed perpetual motion machines, concealing their (necessary) defects so cleverly that his secondary-school teachers could not discover them. In 1910, his aunt adopted him and then they moved to Moscow, where he went to a gymnasium, graduating from it in 1920.

In 1920, Kolmogorov began to study at the Moscow State University and the Chemistry Technological Institute. Kolmogorov gained a reputation for his wide-ranging erudition. As an undergraduate, he participated in the seminars of the Russian historian S.V. Bachrushin, and he published his first research paper on the landholding practices in the Novgorod Republic in the fifteenth and sixteenth centuries. At the same time (1921–1922), Kolmogorov derived and proved several results in set theory and in the theory of Fourier series (trigonometrical series).

Maturity

In 1922 Kolmogorov constructed a Fourier series that diverges almost everywhere, gaining international recognition. Around this time he decided to devote his life to mathematics. In 1925 Kolmogorov graduated from Moscow State University, and began to study under the supervision of Nikolai Luzin. He made lifelong friends with Pavel Alexandrov who involved Kolmogorov in 1936 in an ugly political persecution of their common teacher, the so-called Luzin case or Luzin affair. Kolmogorov (together with A. Khinchin) became interested in probability theory. Also in 1925, he published his famous work in intuitionistic logic — *On the principle of the excluded middle*, where he proved that under a certain interpretation all statements of classical formal logic can be formulated as those of intuitionistic logic. In 1929 Kolmogorov earned his Doctor of Philosophy degree, Ph.D., at the Moscow State University.

In 1930, Kolmogorov went on his first long trip abroad, traveling to Göttingen and Munich, Germany, and then to Paris, France. His pioneering work *About the Analytical Methods of Probability Theory* was published (in German) in 1931. Also in 1931, he became a professor at Moscow University. In 1933, Kolmogorov published the book, *Foundations of the Theory of Probability*, laying the modern axiomatic foundations of probability theory and establishing his reputation as the world's leading living expert in this field. In 1935, Kolmogorov became the first chairman of probability theory at the Moscow State University. In 1939, he was elected a full member (academician) of the USSR Academy of Sciences. In a 1938 paper, Kolmogorov "established the basic theorems for smoothing and predicting stationary stochastic processes" — a paper that would have major military applications during the Cold War to come. Around the same years (1936) Kolmogorov contributed to the field of ecology and generalized the Lotka-Volterra model of predator-prey systems.

In his study of stochastic processes (random processes), especially Markov processes, Kolmogorov and the British mathematician Sydney Chapman independently developed the pivotal set of equations in the field, the Chapman–Kolmogorov equations.

Later on, Kolmogorov changed his research interests to the area of turbulence, where his publications beginning in 1941 had a significant influence on the field. In classical mechanics, he is best known for the Kolmogorov–Arnold–Moser theorem (first presented in 1954 at the International Congress of Mathematicians). In 1957 he solved Hilbert's thirteenth problem (a joint work with his student V. I. Arnold). He was a founder of algorithmic complexity theory, often referred to as Kolmogorov complexity theory, which he began to develop around this time.

Kolmogorov was married to Anna Dmitrievna Egorova in 1942. He pursued a vigorous teaching routine throughout his life, not only at the university level but also with younger children, as he was actively involved in developing a pedagogy for gifted children, in literature, and in music, as well as in mathematics. At the Moscow State University, Kolmogorov occupied different positions, including the heads of several departments: probability, statistics, and random processes; mathematical logic; and he also served as the Dean of the Moscow State University Faculty of Mechanics and Mathematics.

In 1971, Kolmogorov joined an oceanographic expedition aboard the research vessel Dmitri Mendeleev. He wrote a number of articles for the *Great Soviet Encyclopedia.* In his later years he devoted much of his effort to the mathematical and philosophical relationship between probability theory in abstract and applied areas.

Kolmogorov died in Moscow in 1987. A quotation, "Every mathematician believes he is ahead over all others. The reason why they don't say this in public, is because they are intelligent people" is attributed to him.

KOLMOGOROV–SMIRNOV TEST

In statistics, the Kolmogorov–Smirnov test (K–S test) is a nonparametric test for the equality of continuous, one-dimensional probability distributions that can be used to compare a sample with a reference probability distribution (one-sample K–S test), or to compare two samples (two-sample K–S test). The Kolmogorov–Smirnov statistic quantifies a distance between the empirical distribution function of the sample and the cumulative distribution function of the reference distribution, or between the empirical distribution functions of two samples. The null distribution of this statistic is calculated under the null hypothesis that the samples are drawn from the same distribution (in the two-sample case) or that the sample is drawn from the reference distribution (in the one-sample case). In each case, the distributions considered under the null hypothesis are continuous distributions but are otherwise unrestricted.

The two-sample KS test is one of the most useful and general nonparametric methods for comparing two samples, as it is sensitive to differences in both location and shape of the empirical cumulative distribution functions of the two samples.

The Kolmogorov–Smirnov test can be modified to serve as a goodness of fit test. In the special case of testing for normality of the distribution, samples are standardized and compared with a standard normal distribution. This is equivalent to setting the mean and variance of the reference distribution equal to the sample estimates, and it is known that using these to define the specific reference distribution changes the null distribution of the test statistic. Various studies have found that, even in this corrected form, the test is less powerful for testing normality than the Shapiro–Wilk test or Anderson–Darling test.

In a typical experiment, data collected in one situation (let's call this the control group) is compared to data collected in a different situation (let's call this the treatment group) with the aim of seeing if the first situation produces different results from the second situation. If the outcomes for the treatment situation are "the same" as outcomes in the control situation, we assume that treatment in fact causes no effect. Rarely are the outcomes of the two groups identical, so the question arises: How different must the outcomes be? Statistics aim to assign numbers to the test results; *P*-values report if the numbers differ significantly. Reject the null hypothesis if *P* is "small". The process of assigning numbers to results is not straightforward. There is no fairy god mother that can wave her magic wand and tell you if results are evidence for or against an effective treatment. One simple strategy you might have thought of is surely dead wrong: try lots of different statistics and pick the one that reports want you want. (Bill Gates will soon automate this process; coming soon: the "click here to try all tests" button.)

Let me explain why. Every statistical test makes "mistakes": tells you the treatment is effective when it isn't (type I error) or tells you the treatment is not effective when it is effective (type II error).

These mistakes are not user-errors, rather the statistical tool —properly used and applied to real data— simply lies some small fraction (say a few percent) of the time. Thus if you apply many different statistical tests you are very likely to get at least one wrong answer.

Statisticians, of course, try to make statistics that only rarely (say 5% of the time) lie. In doing this they tune their tests to be particularly good at detecting differences in common situations.

Used in those situations the tests may be the best possible tests. Used in different situations the tests may lie outrageously. For example, Student's *t*-test assumes that the situations produce "normal" data that differ only in that the average outcome in one situation is different from the average outcome in the other situation.

If you apply the *t*-test to non-normal data, you are probably increasing the risk of error. Now, in fact, the Central Limit Theorem shows that the *t*-test can avoid becoming unusually fallible when applied to non-normal datasets: If the control/ treatment datasets are sufficiently "large" the *t*-test does not lie outrageously even when applied to non-normal data.

Thus the *t*-test is called a "robust" test, since it continues to work well in situations different from those narrow situations for which it was created. This is important because users of statistical tests often do not know if their dataset meets the criteria intended by the creator of the statistical test.

There are then a few situations in which it is a mistake to trust the results of a *t*-test:

A. Situations in which the control and treatment groups do not differ in mean, but only in some other way. For example consider the datasets:

controlA={0.22,-0.87,-2.39,-1.79, 0.37,-1.54, 1.28,-0.31,-0.74, 1.72, 0.38,-0.17,-0.62,-1.10, 0.30, 0.15, 2.30, 0.19,-0.50,-0.09}

treatmentA={-5.13,-2.19,-2.43,-3.83, 0.50,-3.25, 4.32, 1.63, 5.18,-0.43, 7.11, 4.87,-3.10,-5.81, 3.76, 6.31, 2.58, 0.07, 5.76, 3.50}

Notice that both datasets are approximately balanced around zero; evidently the mean in both cases is "near" zero. However there is substantially more variation in the treatment group which ranges approximately from-6 to 6 whereas the control group ranges approximately from-2½ to 2½.

The datasets are different, but the *t*-test cannot see the difference.

B. Situations in which the treatment and control groups are smallish datasets (say 20 items each) that differ in mean, but substantial non-normal distribution masks the difference. For example, consider the datasets:

controlB={1.26, 0.34, 0.70, 1.75, 50.57, 1.55, 0.08, 0.42, 0.50, 3.20, 0.15, 0.49, 0.95, 0.24, 1.37, 0.17, 6.98, 0.10, 0.94, 0.38}

treatmentB= {2.37, 2.16, 14.82, 1.73, 41.04, 0.23, 1.32, 2.91, 39.41, 0.11, 27.44, 4.51, 0.51, 4.50, 0.18, 14.68, 4.66, 1.30, 2.06, 1.19}

These datasets were drawn from lognormal distributions that differ substantially in mean. The KS test detects this difference, the *t*-test does not. Of course, if the user knew that the data were non-normally distributed, s/he would know not to apply the *t*-test in the first place.

One of the advantages of the KS-test is that it leads to a graphical presentation of the data, which enables the user to detect normal distributions.

For larger datasets (say $N>40$), the Central Limit Theorem suggests that the *t*-test will produce valid results even in the face of non-normally distributed data. However, highly non-normal datasets can cause the *t*-test to produce fallible results, even for large N datasets. In the last example you will see a case where the *t*-test fails at $N=80$.

RANDOMNESS TESTS

The issue of randomness is an important philosophical and theoretical question. Many random number generators in use today generate what are called "random sequences" but they are actually the result of prescribed algorithms and so they are called pseudo-random number generators.

These generators do not always generate sequences which are sufficiently random and generate very repetitive patterns such as the infamous RANDU which fails many randomness tests dramatically including the Spectral Test. The use of an ill-conceived random number generator will result in invalid experiments, due to the lack of randomness.

Tests for randomness are not restricted to analysing the output of pseudo-random number generators, they can also be used to determine whether a set of data has a recognisable pattern to it. For example Wolfram used randomness tests on the output of Rule 30 to examine its potential for generating random numbers

Randomness tests (or tests of randomness), in data evaluation, are used to analyse the distribution pattern of a set of data.

In stochastic modelling, as in some computer simulations, the expected random input data can be verified to show that tests were performed using randomized data. In some cases, data reveals an obvious non-random pattern, as with so-called "runs in the data" (such as expecting random 0-9 but finding "4 3 2 1 0 4 3 2 1..." and rarely going above 4). If a selected set of data fails the tests, then parameters can be changed or other randomized data can be used which does pass the tests for randomness.

There are many practical measures of randomness for a binary sequence. These include measures based on statistical tests, transforms, and complexity or a mixture of these. The use of Hadamard transform to measure randomness was proposed by S. Kak and developed further by Phillips, Yuen, Hopkins, Beth and Dai, Mund, and Marsaglia and Zaman.

Several of these tests, which are of linear complexity, provide spectral measures of randomness. T. Beth and Z-D. Dai showed that Kolmogorov complexity and linear complexity are practically the same.

These practical tests make it possible to compare and contrast the randomness of strings. On probabilistic grounds, all strings, say of length 64, have the same randomness. However, two strings such as those given below:

string 1: 0101010101010101010101010101010101010101010101010101010101010101

string 2: 1100100001100001110111101110110011111010010000100101011110010110

appear to have different complexity. The first string admits a short linguistic description, namely "32 repetitions of '01'", which consists of 20 characters, and it can be efficiently constructed out of some basis sequences. The second one has no obvious simple description other than writing down the string itself, which has 64 characters, and it has no comparably efficient basis function representation. Using linear Hadamard spectral tests, the first of these sequences will be found to be of much less randomness than the second one, which agrees with intuition.

SIGN TEST

In statistics, the sign test can be used to test the hypothesis that there is "no difference in medians" between the continuous distributions of two random variables X and Y, in the situation when we can draw paired samples from X and Y.

It is a non-parametric test which makes very few assumptions about the nature of the distributions under test- this means that it has very general applicability but may lack the statistical power of other tests such as the paired-samples t-test.

Method

Let $p = \Pr(X > Y)$, and then test the null hypothesis H_0: $p = 0.50$. In other words, the null hypothesis states that given a random pair of measurements (x_i, y_i), then x_i and y_i are equally likely to be larger than the other.

To test the null hypothesis, independent pairs of sample data are collected from the populations $\{(x_1, y_1), (x_2, y_2), \ldots, (x_n, y_n)\}$. Pairs are omitted for which there is no difference so that there is a possibility of a reduced sample of m pairs.

Then let w be the number of pairs for which y_i " $x_i > 0$. Assuming that H_0 is true, then W follows a binomial distribution $W \sim b(m, 0.5)$. The "W" is for Frank Wilcoxon who developed the test, then later, the more powerful Wilcoxon signed-rank test.

Assumptions

Let $Z_i = Y_i - X_i$ for $i = 1, \dots, n$.

1. The differences Z_i are assumed to be independent.
2. Each Z_i comes from the same continuous population.
3. The values of X_i and Y_i represent are ordered (at least the ordinal scale), so the comparisons "greater than", "less than", and "equal to" are meaningful.

Significance Testing

Since the test statistic is expected to follow a binomial distribution, the standard binomial test is used to calculate significance.

The normal approximation to the binomial distribution can be used for large sample sizes, m>25.

The left-tail value is computed by Pr(W d" w), which is the p-value for the alternative H_1: $p < 0.50$. This alternative means that the X measurements tend to be higher.

The right-tail value is computed by Pr(W e" w), which is the p-value for the alternative H_1: $p > 0.50$. This alternative means that the Y measurements tend to be higher.

For a two-sided alternative H_1 the p-value is twice the smaller tail-value.

MEDIAN TEST

In statistics, Mood's median test is a special case of Pearson's chi-squared test. It is a nonparametric test that tests the null hypothesis that the medians of the populations from which two samples are drawn are identical.

The data in each sample are assigned to two groups, one consisting of data whose values are higher than the median value in the two groups combined, and the other consisting of data whose values are at the median or below. A Pearson's chi-squared test is then used to determine whether the observed frequencies in each group differ from expected frequencies derived from a distribution combining the two groups.

The test has low power (efficiency) for moderate to large sample sizes, and is largely regarded as obsolete. The Wilcoxon–Mann–Whitney U two-sample test should be considered instead. Siegel & Castellan (1988, p. 124) suggest that there is no alternative to the median test when one or more observations are "off the scale." The relevant difference between the two tests is that the median test only considers the position of each observation relative to the overall median, whereas the Wilcoxon–Mann–Whitney test takes the ranks of each observation into account. Thus the latter test is usually the more powerful of the two.

REFERENCES

- Gordon, R.: *Unidimensional Scaling of Social Variables: Concepts and Procedures.* New York: The Free Press, 1977.
- Jack Murrin, *Valuation: Measuring and Managing the Value of Companies,* New York, Wiley, 1994.
- Manas Dasgupta: *Research Methodology in Economics : Problems and Issues*, Deep and Deep, 2007.
- Denzin, N.: *The Research Act: A Theoretical Introduction to Sociological Methods.* Chicago: Aldine Press, 1967.
- Sandhya Neelam: *Research Methodology in Sociological Research*, Manglam Pub, Delhi, 2008.

8

Data Analysis

Analysis of data is a process of inspecting, cleaning, transforming, and modelling data with the goal of highlighting useful information, suggesting conclusions, and supporting decision making.

Data analysis has multiple facets and approaches, encompassing diverse techniques under a variety of names, in different business, science, and social science domains. Data mining is a particular data analysis technique that focuses on modelling and knowledge discovery for predictive rather than purely descriptive purposes.

Business intelligence covers data analysis that relies heavily on aggregation, focusing on business information. In statistical applications, some people divide data analysis into descriptive statistics, exploratory data analysis (EDA), and confirmatory data analysis (CDA).

EDA focuses on discovering new features in the data and CDA on confirming or falsifying existing hypotheses. Predictive analytics focuses on application of statistical or structural models for predictive forecasting or classification, while text analytics applies statistical, linguistic, and structural techniques to extract and classify information from textual sources, a species of unstructured data. All are varieties of data analysis.

Data integration is a precursor to data analysis, and data analysis is closely linked to data visualization and data dissemination. The term *data analysis* is sometimes used as a synonym for data modelling.

TYPE OF DATA

Data can be of several types

- Quantitative data is a number
  - o Often this is a continuous decimal number to a specified number of significant digits
  - o Sometimes it is a whole counting number
- Categorical data one of several categories
- Qualitative data is a pass/fail or the presence or lack of a characteristic

THE PROCESS OF DATA ANALYSIS

Data analysis is a process, within which several phases can be distinguished:

Data Cleaning

Data cleaning is an important procedure during which the data are inspected, and erroneous data are—if necessary, preferable, and possible—corrected. Data cleaning can be done during the stage of data entry. If this is done, it is important that no subjective decisions are made. The guiding principle provided by Adèr (ref) is: during subsequent manipulations of the data, information should always be cumulatively retrievable. In other words, it should always be possible to undo any data set alterations. Therefore, it is important not to throw information away at any stage in the data cleaning phase. All information should be saved (i.e., when altering variables, both the original values and the new values should be kept, either in a duplicate data set or under a different variable name), and all alterations to the data set should carefully and clearly documented, for instance in a syntax or a log.

Initial Data Analysis

The most important distinction between the initial data analysis phase and the main analysis phase, is that during initial data analysis one refrains from any analysis that are aimed at answering the original research question. The initial data analysis phase is guided by the following four questions:

Quality of Data

The quality of the data should be checked as early as

possible. Data quality can be assessed in several ways, using different types of analyses: frequency counts, descriptive statistics (mean, standard deviation, median), normality (skewness, kurtosis, frequency histograms, normal probability plots), associations (correlations, scatter plots).

Other initial data quality checks are:

- Checks on data cleaning: have decisions influenced the distribution of the variables? The distribution of the variables before data cleaning is compared to the distribution of the variables after data cleaning to see whether data cleaning has had unwanted effects on the data.
- Analysis of missing observations: are there many missing values, and are the values missing at random? The missing observations in the data are analysed to see whether more than 25% of the values are missing, whether they are missing at random (MAR), and whether some form of imputation is needed.
- Analysis of extreme observations: outlying observations in the data are analysed to see if they seem to disturb the distribution.
- Comparison and correction of differences in coding schemes: variables are compared with coding schemes of variables external to the data set, and possibly corrected if coding schemes are not comparable.

The choice of analyses to assess the data quality during the initial data analysis phase depends on the analyses that will be conducted in the main analysis phase.

Quality of Measurements

The quality of the measurement instruments should only be checked during the initial data analysis phase when this is not the focus or research question of the study. One should check whether structure of measurement instruments corresponds to structure reported in the literature.

There are two ways to assess measurement quality:

- Confirmatory factor analysis
- Analysis of homogeneity (internal consistency), which gives an indication of the reliability of a measurement

instrument. During this analysis, one inspects the variances of the items and the scales, the Cronbach's á of the scales, and the change in the Cronbach's alpha when an item would be deleted from a scale.

Initial Transformations

After assessing the quality of the data and of the measurements, one might decide to impute missing data, or to perform initial transformations of one or more variables, although this can also be done during the main analysis phase.

Possible transformations of variables are:

- Square root transformation (if the distribution differs moderately from normal)
- Log-transformation (if the distribution differs substantially from normal)
- Inverse transformation (if the distribution differs severely from normal)
- Make categorical (ordinal/dichotomous) (if the distribution differs severely from normal, and no transformations help)

One should check the success of the randomization procedure, for instance by checking whether background and substantive variables are equally distributed within and across groups.

If the study did not need and/or use a randomization procedure, one should check the success of the non-random sampling, for instance by checking whether all subgroups of the population of interest are represented in sample.

Other possible data distortions that should be checked are:

- dropout (this should be identified during the initial data analysis phase)
- Item nonresponse (whether this is random or not should be assessed during the initial data analysis phase)
- Treatment quality (using manipulation checks).

Characteristics of Data Sample

In any report or article, the structure of the sample must be accurately described. It is especially important to exactly determine the structure of the sample (and specifically the size of the subgroups) when subgroup analyses will be performed during the main analysis phase. The characteristics of the data sample can be assessed by looking at:

- Basic statistics of important variables
- Scatter plots
- Correlations
- Cross-tabulations

Final Stage of the Initial Data Analysis

During the final stage, the findings of the initial data analysis are documented, and necessary, preferable, and possible corrective actions are taken. Also, the original plan for the main data analyses can and should be specified in more detail and/or rewritten. In order to do this, several decisions about the main data analyses can and should be made:

- In the case of non-normals: should one transform variables; make variables categorical (ordinal/ dichotomous); adapt the analysis method?
- In the case of missing data: should one neglect or impute the missing data; which imputation technique should be used?
- In the case of outliers: should one use robust analysis techniques?
- In case items do not fit the scale: should one adapt the measurement instrument by omitting items, or rather ensure comparability with other (uses of the) measurement instrument(s)?
- In the case of (too) small subgroups: should one drop the hypothesis about inter-group differences, or use small sample techniques, like exact tests or bootstrapping?
- In case the randomization procedure seems to be defective: can and should one calculate propensity scores and include them as covariates in the main analyses?

Analyses

Several analyses can be used during the initial data analysis phase:

- Univariate statistics
- Bivariate associations (correlations)
- Graphical techniques (scatter plots)

It is important to take the measurement levels of the variables into account for the analyses, as special statistical techniques are available for each level:

- Nominal and ordinal variables
    - o Frequency counts (numbers and percentages)
    - o Associations
        - — circumambulations (crosstabulations)
        - — hierarchical loglinear analysis (restricted to a maximum of 8 variables)
        - — loglinear analysis (to identify relevant/ important variables and possible confounders)
    - o Exact tests or bootstrapping (in case subgroups are small)
    - o Computation of new variables
- Continuous variables
    - o Distribution
        - — Statistics (M, SD, variance, skewness, kurtosis)
        - — Stem-and-leaf displays
        - — Box plots

Main Data Analysis

In the main analysis phase analyses aimed at answering the research question are performed as well as any other relevant analysis needed to write the first draft of the research report.

Exploratory and Confirmatory Approaches

In the main analysis phase either an exploratory or confirmatory approach can be adopted. Usually the approach is decided before data is collected. In an exploratory analysis no clear hypothesis is stated before analysing the data, and the data is searched for models that describe the data well. In a confirmatory analysis clear hypotheses about the data are tested. Exploratory data analysis should be interpreted carefully. When testing multiple models at once there is a high chance on finding at least one of them to be significant, but this can be due to a type 1 error. It is important to always adjust the significance level when testing multiple models with, for example, a bonferroni correction. Also, one should not follow up an exploratory analysis with a confirmatory analysis in the same dataset.

An exploratory analysis is used to find ideas for a theory, but not to test that theory as well. When a model is found exploratory in a dataset, then following up that analysis with a comfirmatory analysis in the same dataset could simply mean that the results of the comfirmatory analysis are due to the same type 1 error that resulted in the exploratory model in the first place. The comfirmatory analysis therefore will not be more informative than the original exploratory analysis.

Stability of Results

It is important to obtain some indication about how generalizable the results are. While this is hard to check, one can look at the stability of the results. Are the results reliable and reproducible? There are two main ways of doing this:

- Cross-validation: By splitting the data in multiple parts we can check if analyses (like a fitted model) based on one part of the data generalize to another part of the data as well.
- Sensitivity analysis: A procedure to study the behaviour of a system or model when global parameters are (systematically) varied. One way to do this is with bootstrapping.

Statistical Methods

A lot of statistical methods have been used for statistical analyses. A very brief list of four of the more popular methods is:

- General linear model: A widely used model on which various statistical methods are based (e.g. t test, ANOVA, ANCOVA, MANOVA). Usable for assessing the effect of several predictors on one or more continuous dependent variables.
- Generalized linear model: An extension of the general linear model for discrete dependent variables.

- Structural equation modelling: Usable for assessing latent structures from measured manifest variables.
- Item response theory: Models for (mostly) assessing one latent variable from several binary measured variables (e.g. an exam).

Free Software for Data Analysis

- ROOT-C++ data analysis framework developed at CERN
- PAW-FORTRAN/C data analysis framework developed at CERN
- JHepWork-Java (multi-platform) data analysis framework developed at ANL
- KNIME-the Konstanz Information Miner, a user friendly and comprehensive data analytics framework.
- Data Applied-an online data mining and data visualization solution.
- R-a programming language and software environment for statistical computing and graphics.
- DevInfo-a database system endorsed by the United Nations Development Group for monitoring and analysing human development.
- Zeptoscope Basic-Interactive Java-based plotter developed at Nanomix.

Nuclear and Particle Physics

In nuclear and particle physics the data usually originate from the experimental apparatus via a data acquisition system. It is then processed, in a step usually called *data reduction*, to apply calibrations and to extract physically significant information. Data reduction is most often, especially in large particle physics experiments, an automatic, batch-mode operation carried out by software written ad-hoc. The resulting data *n-tuples* are then scrutinized by the physicists, using specialized software tools like ROOT or PAW, comparing the results of the experiment with theory.

The theoretical models are often difficult to compare directly with the results of the experiments, so they are used instead as input for Monte Carlo simulation software like Geant4, predict the response of the detector to a given theoretical event, producing simulated events which are then compared to experimental data.

MULTIVARIATE ANALYSIS

Multivariate analysis (MVA) is based on the statistical principle of multivariate statistics, which involves observation and analysis of more than one statistical variable at a time. In design and analysis, the technique is used to perform trade studies across multiple dimensions while taking into account the effects of all variables on the responses of interest.

Uses for multivariate analysis include:

- Design for capability (also known as capability-based design)
- Inverse design, where any variable can be treated as an independent variable
- Analysis of Alternatives (AoA), the selection of concepts to fulfill a customer need
- Analysis of concepts with respect to changing scenarios
- Identification of critical design drivers and correlations across hierarchical levels.

Multivariate analysis can be complicated by the desire to include physics-based analysis to calculate the effects of variables for a hierarchical "system-of-systems." Often, studies that wish to use multivariate analysis are stalled by the dimensionality of the problem. These concerns are often eased through the use of surrogate models, highly accurate approximations of the physics-based code. Since surrogate models take the form of an equation, they can be evaluated very quickly. This becomes an enabler for large-scale MVA studies: while a Monte Carlo simulation across the design space is difficult with physics-based codes, it becomes trivial when evaluating surrogate models, which often take the form of response surface equations.

Factor Analysis

Overview: Factor analysis is used to uncover the latent structure (dimensions) of a set of variables. It reduces attribute space from a larger number of variables to a smaller number of factors. Factor analysis originated a century ago with Charles

Spearman's attempts to show that a wide variety of mental tests could be explained by a single underlying intelligence factor.

Applications:

- To reduce a large number of variables to a smaller number of factors for data modelling
- To validate a scale or index by demonstrating that its constituent items load on the same factor, and to drop proposed scale items which cross-load on more than one factor.
- To select a subset of variables from a larger set, based on which original variables have the highest correlations with the principal component factors.
- To create a set of factors to be treated as uncorrelated variables as one approach to handling multi-collinearity in such procedures as multiple regression

Factor analysis is part of the general linear model (GLM) family of procedures and makes many of the same assumptions as multiple regression

MULTIVARIATE STATISTICS

Multivariate statistics is a form of statistics encompassing the simultaneous observation and analysis of more than one statistical variable. The application of multivariate statistics is multivariate analysis. Methods of bivariate statistics, for example simple linear regression and correlation, are special cases of multivariate statistics in which two variables are involved. Multivariate statistics concerns understanding the different aims and background of each of the different forms of multivariate analysis, and how they relate to each other. The practical implementation of multivariate statistics to a particular problem may involve several types of univariate and multivariate analysis in order to understand the relationships between variables and their relevance to the actual problem being studied.

In addition, multivariate statistics is concerned with multivariate probability distributions, in terms of both:

- how these can be used to represent the distributions of observed data;

- how they can be used as part of statistical inference, particularly where several different quantities are of interest to the same analysis.

Types of Analysis

There are many different models, each with its own type of analysis:

1. Multivariate analysis of variance (MANOVA) extends the analysis of variance to cover cases where there is more than one dependent variable to be analysed simultaneously: see also MANCOVA.
2. Multivariate regression analysis attempts to determine a formula that can describe how elements in a vector of variables respond simultaneously to changes in others. For linear relations, regression analyses here are based on forms of the general linear model.
3. Principal components analysis (PCA) creates a new set of orthogonal variables that contain the same information as the original set. It rotates the axes of variation to give a new set of orthogonal axes, ordered so that they summarize decreasing proportions of the variation.
4. Factor analysis is similar to PCA but allows the user to extract a specified number of synthetic variables, fewer than the original set, leaving the remaining unexplained variation as error. The extracted variables are known as latent variables or factors; each one may be supposed to account for covariation in a group of observed variables.
5. Canonical correlation analysis finds linear relationships among two sets of variables; it is the generalised (i.e. canonical) version of bivariate correlation.
6. Redundancy analysis is similar to canonical correlation analysis but allows the user to derive a specified number of synthetic variables from one set of (independent) variables that explain as much variance as possible in another (independent) set. It is a multivariate analogue of regression.

7. Correspondence analysis (CA), or reciprocal averaging, finds (like PCA) a set of synthetic variables that summarise the original set. The underlying model assumes chi-squared dissimilarities among records (cases). There is also canonical (or "constrained") correspondence analysis (CCA) for summarising the joint variation in two sets of variables (like canonical correlation analysis).
8. Multidimensional scaling comprises various algorithms to determine a set of synthetic variables that best represent the pairwise distances between records. The original method is principal coordinates analysis (based on PCA).
9. Discriminant analysis, or canonical variate analysis, attempts to establish whether a set of variables can be used to distinguish between two or more groups of cases.
10. Linear discriminant analysis (LDA) computes a linear predictor from two sets of normally distributed data to allow for classification of new observations.
11. Clustering systems assign objects into groups (called clusters) so that objects (cases) from the same cluster are more similar to each other than objects from different clusters.
12. Recursive partitioning creates a decision tree that attempts to correctly classify members of the population based on a dichotomous dependent variable.
13. Artificial neural networks extend regression and clustering methods to non-linear multivariate models.

Important Probability Distributions

There is a set of probability distributions used in multivariate analyses that play a similar role to the corresponding set of distributions that are used in univariate analysis when the normal distribution is appropriate to a dataset. These multivariate distributions are:

- Multivariate normal distribution
- Wishart distribution
- Multivariate Student-t distribution.

The Inverse-Wishart distribution is important in Bayesian inference, for example in Bayesian multivariate linear regression. Additionally, Hotelling's T-squared distribution is a univariate distribution, generalising Student's t-distribution, that is used in multivariate hypothesis testing.

Software & Tools

There are an enormous number of software packages and other tools for multivariate analysis, including:

- Calc
- MiniTab
- R
- SAS (software)
- sciPy for Python
- SPSS
- Stata
- STATISTICA
- TMVA-Toolkit for Multivariate Data Analysis in ROOT
- The Unscrambler.

REGRESSION ANALYSIS

In statistics, regression analysis includes any techniques for modelling and analysing several variables, when the focus is on the relationship between a dependent variable and one or more independent variables. More specifically, regression analysis helps one understand how the typical value of the dependent variable changes when any one of the independent variables is varied, while the other independent variables are held fixed.

Most commonly, regression analysis estimates the conditional expectation of the dependent variable given the independent variables — that is, the average value of the dependent variable when the independent variables are held fixed. Less commonly, the focus is on a quantile, or other location parameter of the conditional distribution of the dependent variable given the independent variables. In all cases, the estimation target is a function of the independent variables called the regression function. In regression analysis, it is also of interest to characterize the variation of the dependent variable around the regression function, which can be described by a probability distribution.

Regression analysis is widely used for prediction and forecasting, where its use has substantial overlap with the field of machine learning. Regression analysis is also used to understand which among the independent variables are related to the dependent variable, and to explore the forms of these relationships. In restricted circumstances, regression analysis can be used to infer causal relationships between the independent and dependent variables.

A large body of techniques for carrying out regression analysis has been developed. Familiar methods such as linear regression and ordinary least squares regression are parametric, in that the regression function is defined in terms of a finite number of unknown parameters that are estimated from the data. Nonparametric regression refers to techniques that allow the regression function to lie in a specified set of functions, which may be infinite-dimensional.

The performance of regression analysis methods in practice depends on the form of the data generating process, and how it relates to the regression approach being used. Since the true form of the data-generating process is in general not known, regression analysis often depends to some extent on making assumptions about this process. These assumptions are sometimes (but not always) testable if a large amount of data is available. Regression models for prediction are often useful even when the assumptions are moderately violated, although they may not perform optimally. However, in many applications, especially with small effects or questions of causality based on observational data, regression methods give misleading results.

The earliest form of regression was the method of least squares, which was published by Legendre in 1805, and by Gauss in 1809. Legendre and Gauss both applied the method to the problem of determining, from astronomical observations, the orbits of bodies about the Sun. Gauss published a further development of the theory of least squares in 1821, including a version of the Gauss–Markov theorem.

The term "regression" was coined by Francis Galton in the nineteenth century to describe a biological phenomenon. The phenomenon was that the heights of descendants of tall ancestors tend to regress down towards a normal average (a phenomenon also known as regression toward the mean). For Galton, regression had only this biological meaning, but his work was later extended by Udny Yule and Karl Pearson to a more general statistical context. In the work of Yule and Pearson, the joint distribution of the response and explanatory variables is assumed to be Gaussian. This assumption was weakened by R.A. Fisher in his works of 1922 and 1925. Fisher assumed that the conditional distribution of the response variable is Gaussian, but the joint distribution need not be. In this respect, Fisher's assumption is closer to Gauss's formulation of 1821.

Regression methods continue to be an area of active research. In recent decades, new methods have been developed for robust regression, regression involving correlated responses such as time series and growth curves, regression in which the predictor or response variables are curves, images, graphs, or other complex data objects, regression methods accommodating various types of missing data, nonparametric regression, Bayesian methods for regression, regression in which the predictor variables are measured with error, regression with more predictor variables than observations, and causal inference with regression.

Statistical Assumptions

When the number of measurements, N, is larger than the number of unknown parameters, k, and the measurement errors $\mathring{a}_i$ are normally distributed then *the excess of information* contained in (N-k) measurements is used to make statistical predictions about the unknown parameters. This excess of information is referred to as the degrees of freedom of the regression.

Underlying Assumptions

Classical assumptions for regression analysis include:

- The sample is representative of the population for the inference prediction.
- The error is a random variable with a mean of zero conditional on the explanatory variables.

- The independent variables are measured with no error. (Note: If this is not so, modelling may be done instead using errors-in-variables model techniques).
- The predictors are linearly independent, i.e. it is not possible to express any predictor as a linear combination of the others.
- The errors are uncorrelated, that is, the variance-covariance matrix of the errors is diagonal and each non-zero element is the variance of the error.
- The variance of the error is constant across observations (homoscedasticity). (Note: If not, weighted least squares or other methods might instead be used).

These are sufficient conditions for the least-squares estimator to possess desirable properties, in particular, these assumptions imply that the parameter estimates will be unbiased, consistent, and efficient in the class of linear unbiased estimators.

It is important to note that actual data rarely satisfies the assumptions. That is, the method is used even though the assumptions are not true.

Variation from the assumptions can sometimes be used as a measure of how far the model is from being useful. Many of these assumptions may be relaxed in more advanced treatments. Reports of statistical analyses usually include analyses of tests on the sample data and methodology for the fit and usefulness of the model.

Assumptions include the geometrical support of the variables (Cressie, 1996). Independent and dependent variables often refer to values measured at point locations. There may be spatial trends and spatial autocorrelation in the variables that violates statistical assumptions of regression. Geographic weighted regression is one technique to deal with such data (Fotheringham et al., 2002). Also, variables may include values aggregated by areas. With aggregated data the Modifiable Areal Unit Problem can cause extreme variation in regression parameters (Fotheringham and Wong, 1991). When analysing data aggregated by political boundaries, postal codes or census areas results may be very different with a different choice of units.

Regression Diagnostics

Once a regression model has been constructed, it may be important to confirm the goodness of fit of the model and the statistical significance of the estimated parameters. Commonly used checks of goodness of fit include the R-squared, analyses of the pattern of residuals and hypothesis testing. Statistical significance can be checked by an F-test of the overall fit, followed by t-tests of individual parameters.

Interpretations of these diagnostic tests rest heavily on the model assumptions. Although examination of the residuals can be used to invalidate a model, the results of a t-test or F-test are sometimes more difficult to interpret if the model's assumptions are violated. For example, if the error term does not have a normal distribution, in small samples the estimated parameters will not follow normal distributions and complicate inference. With relatively large samples, however, a central limit theorem can be invoked such that hypothesis testing may proceed using asymptotic approximations.

Regression with "Limited Dependent" Variables

The phrase "limited dependent" is used in econometric statistics for categorical and constrained variables. The response variable may be non-continuous ("limited" to lie on some subset of the real line). For binary (zero or one) variables, if analysis proceeds with least-squares linear regression, the model is called the linear probability model. Nonlinear models for binary dependent variables include the probit and logit model. The multivariate probit model is a standard method of estimating a joint relationship between several binary dependent variables and some independent variables. For categorical variables with more than two values there is the multinomial logit. For ordinal variables with more than two values, there are the ordered logit and ordered probit models. Censored regression models may be used when the dependent variable is only sometimes observed, and Heckman correction type models may be used when the sample is not randomly selected from the population of interest. An alternative to such procedures is linear regression based on polychoric correlation (or polyserial correlations) between the categorical variables. Such procedures differ in the assumptions made about the distribution of the variables in the population. If the variable is positive with low values and represents the repetition of the occurrence of an event, then count models like the Poisson regression or the negative binomial model may be used.

Interpolation and Extrapolation

Regression models predict a value of the *Y* variable given known values of the *X* variables. Prediction *within* the range of values in the dataset used for model-fitting is known informally as interpolation. Prediction *outside* this range of the data is known as extrapolation. Performing extrapolation relies strongly on the regression assumptions. The further the extrapolation goes outside the data, the more room there is for the model to fail due to differences between the assumptions and the sample data or the true values. For example, regression model failing the homoskedasticity assumption will make bigger mistakes the further out the extrapolation is. It is generally advised that when performing extrapolation, one should accompany the estimated value of the dependent variable with a prediction interval that represents the uncertainty. Such intervals tend to expand rapidly as the values of the independent variable(s) moved outside the range covered by the observed data.

For such reasons and others, some tend to say that it might be unwise to undertake extrapolation. However, this does not cover the full set of modelling errors that may be being made: in particular, the assumption of a particular form for the relation between *Y* and *X*. A properly conducted regression analysis will include an assessment of how well the assumed form is matched by the observed data, but it can only do so within the range of values of the independent variables actually available. This means that any extrapolation is particularly reliant on the assumptions being made about the structural form of the regression relationship. Best-practice advice here is that a linear-in-variables and linear-in-parameters relationship should not be chosen simply for computational convenience, but that all available knowledge should be deployed in constructing a regression model. If this knowledge includes the fact that the dependent variable cannot go outside a certain range of values, this can be made use of in selecting the model — even if the observed dataset has no values particularly near such bounds. The implications of this step of choosing an appropriate functional form for the regression can be great when extrapolation is considered. At a minimum, it can ensure that any extrapolation arising from a fitted model is "realistic" (or in accord with what is known).

Other Methods

Although the parameters of a regression model are usually estimated using the method of least squares, other methods which have been used include:

- Bayesian methods, e.g. Bayesian linear regression
- Least absolute deviations, which is more robust in the presence of outliers, leading to quantile regression
- Nonparametric regression, requires a large number of observations and is computationally intensive
- Distance metric learning, which is learned by the search of a meaningful distance metric in a given input space.

Software

All major statistical software packages perform least squares regression analysis and inference. Simple linear regression and multiple regression using least squares can be done in some spreadsheet applications and on some calculators. While many statistical software packages can perform various types of nonparametric and robust regression, these methods are less standardized; different software packages implement different methods, and a method with a given name may be implemented differently in different packages. Specialized regression software has been developed for use in fields such as survey analysis and neuroimaging.

MULTIPLE REGRESSION ANALYSIS

Multiple regression analysis is a powerful technique used for predicting the unknown value of a variable from the known value of two or more variables-also called the predictors. More precisely, multiple regression analysis helps us to predict the value of Y for given values of X_1, X_2, ..., X_k. For example the yield of rice per acre depends upon quality of seed, fertility of soil, fertilizer used, temperature, rainfall. If one is interested to study the joint affect of all these variables on rice yield, one can use this technique. An additional advantage of this technique is it also enables us to study the individual influence of these variables on yield.

By multiple regression, we mean models with just one dependent and two or more independent (exploratory) variables. The variable whose value is to be predicted is known as the dependent variable and the ones whose known values are used for prediction are known independent (exploratory) variables.

The Multiple Regression Model

In general, the multiple regression equation of Y on X_1, X_2, ..., X_k is given by:

$$Y = b_0 + b_1 X_1 + b_2 X_2 + \ldots\ldots\ldots\ldots\ldots\ldots + b_k X_k$$

Interpreting Regression Coefficients

Here b_0 is the intercept and b_1, b_2, b_3, ..., b_k are analogous to the slope in linear regression equation and are also called regression coefficients. They can be interpreted the same way as slope. Thus if $b_i = 2.5$, it would indicates that Y will increase by 2.5 units if X_i increased by 1 unit.

The appropriateness of the multiple regression model as a whole can be tested by the F-test in the ANOVA table. A significant F indicates a linear relationship between Y and at least one of the X's.

Once a multiple regression equation has been constructed, one can check how good it is (in terms of predictive ability) by examining the coefficient of determination (R^2). R^2 always lies between 0 and 1.

R^2-coefficient of determination

All software provides it whenever regression procedure is run. The closer R^2 is to 1, the better is the model and its prediction.

A related question is whether the independent variables individually influence the dependent variable significantly. Statistically, it is equivalent to testing the null hypothesis that the relevant regression coefficient is zero. This can be done using t-test. If the t-test of a regression coefficient is significant, it indicates that the variable is in question influences Y significantly while controlling for other independent explanatory variables.

Multiple regression technique does not test whether data are linear. On the contrary, it proceeds by assuming that the relationship between the Y and each of X_i's is linear. Hence as a rule, it is prudent to always look at the scatter plots of (Y, X_i), $i = 1, 2, \ldots, k$. If any plot suggests non linearity, one may use a suitable transformation to attain linearity.

Another important assumption is non existence of multicollinearity-the independent variables are not related among themselves. At a very basic level, this can be tested by computing the correlation coefficient between each pair of independent variables.

Other assumptions include those of homoscedasticity and normality.

Multiple regression analysis is used when one is interested in predicting a continuous dependent variable from a number of independent variables. If dependent variable is dichotomous, then logistic regression should be used.

DISCRIMINANT FUNCTION ANALYSIS

The main purpose of a discriminant function analysis is to predict group membership based on a linear combination of the interval variables. The procedure begins with a set of observations where both group membership and the values of the interval variables are known. The end result of the procedure is a model that allows prediction of group membership when only the interval variables are known. A second purpose of discriminant function analysis is an understanding of the data set, as a careful examination of the prediction model that results from the procedure can give insight into the relationship between group membership and the variables used to predict group membership.

For example, a graduate admissions committee might divide a set of past graduate students into two groups: students who finished the program in five years or less and those who did not. Discriminant function analysis could be used to predict successful completion of the graduate program based on GRE score and undergraduate grade point average. Examination of the prediction model might provide insights into how each predictor individually and in combination predicted completion or non-completion of a graduate program.

Another example might predict whether patients recovered from a coma or not based on combinations of demographic and treatment variables. The predictor variables might include age, sex, general health, time between incident and arrival at hospital, various interventions, etc. In this case the creation of the prediction model would allow a medical practitioner to assess the chance of recovery based on observed variables. The prediction model might also give insight into how the variables interact in predicting recovery.

The Simplest Case

The simplest case of discriminant function analysis is the prediction of dichotomous group membership based on a single variable. An example of the simplest case is the prediction of successful completion of a graduate program based on the GRE verbal score. In this case, since the prediction model includes only a single variable, it gives little insight into how variables interact with each other in prediction. Thus prediction of group membership will be the major focus of the next section of this chapter.

With respect to the data file and purpose of analysis, this simplest case is identical to the case of linear regression with dichotomous dependent variables. Data of this type may be represented in any number of different forms: scatterplots, tables of means and standard deviations, and overlapping frequency polygons. Because overlapping frequency polygons have such an intuitive appeal, they will be used to describe how discriminant function analysis works.

Prediction Accuracy

A single interval variable might discriminate between groups in an almost perfect fashion, not at all, or somewhere in between. For example, if one wished to differentiate adult males and females, one could collect information on how many bras the person owned, score on the last statistics test, and height. In the case of the number of bras, the discrimination would be very good, but not perfect (some women don't own any bras, some men do). In the case of the score on the last statistics test, little discrimination would be possible because males and females generally score about the same. In the case of height, some discrimination between adult males and females would be possible, but it would be far from perfect.

In general, the larger the difference between the means of the two groups relative to the within groups variability, the better the discrimination between the groups. The following program allows the student to explore data sets with different degrees of discrimination ability.

Modelling the Data

Discriminant function analysis is based on modelling the interval variable for each group with a normal curve. The mean of each group is used an estimate of mu for that group. Sigma for each group can be estimated by using weighted mean of the within group variances or using the standard deviation of that group. In the case of the weighted mean the variances are weighted by sample size and can be calculated either as the denominator for a nested t-test or as the square root of the Mean Squares Within Groups in an ANOVA, providing identical estimates. When using the weighted mean of the variances, one must assume that the generating function for each group produces numbers that in the long run have the same variability.

In the simple case of dichotomous groups and a single predictor variable, it really does not make a great deal of difference in the complexity of the model if the variability of each groups is assumed to be equal or not. This is not true, however, when more groups and more predictor variables are added to the model. For that reason, the assumption of equality of within group variance is almost universal in discriminant function analysis.

The following program allows the student to explore the relationship between different generating functions (poor, medium, or good discrimination; equal or unequal variances), sample size, and resulting model based on the sample. The student should verify that larger sample sizes provide resulting models that are more similar to the generating model. The student should also explore the effect of violations of the equality of variance assumptions on the resulting model.

Probabilities of Group Membership

The normal curve models of the predictor variables for each group and can be used to provide probability estimates of a particular score given membership in a particular group. In discriminant function analysis, the area in the tails under a normal curve model for a given group between points equally distant from mu is the probability of either point given that group. This probability is symbolized as P(D/G) on SPSS output.

For example, suppose that the normal curve model for a given group has a value of 13 for mu and 2 for sigma. The probability of a score of 16 would be the area in the tails of this normal curve between 10 and 16. The value of 10 was selected as the low score because 16 is three units above the mean (16-13 = 3) and 10 is three sigma units below the mean (13-3 = 10). This is all much easier visualized than stated.

Prior Probabilities

Prior probabilities are the likelihood of belonging to a particular group given no information about the person is available. In the classical testing literature prior probabilities are called *base rates*. Prior probabilities influence our decisions about group membership. Prior probabilities will be symbolized as P(G). For example, $P(G_1)$ is the prior probability of a score belonging to group 1. Consider the case of prediction of completion of graduate school using GRE verbal scores. Suppose that 99% of the students who started the graduate program successfully completed the program (it was a really easy program). Even if a student scored considerably lower than the mean of the successful group, program completion would most likely be predicted because almost everyone finishes. Likewise, in a graduate program where less than 10% of beginning students complete the program, the likelihood of completion will be fairly low no matter how high the GRE verbal score.

FACTOR ANALYSIS

Factor analysis is a statistical method used to describe variability among observed variables in terms of a potentially lower number of unobserved variables called factors. In other words, it is possible, for example, that variations in three or four observed variables mainly reflect the variations in fewer such unobserved variables. Factor analysis searches for such joint variations in response to unobserved latent variables. The observed variables are modeled as linear combinations of the potential factors, plus "error" terms.

The information gained about the interdependencies between observed variables can be used later to reduce the set of variables in a dataset. Factor analysis originated in psychometrics, and is used in behavioural sciences, social sciences, marketing, product management, operations research, and other applied sciences that deal with large quantities of data.

Factor analysis is related to principal component analysis (PCA), but the two are not identical. Because PCA performs a variance-maximizing rotation of the variable space, it takes into account all variability in the variables. In contrast, factor analysis estimates how much of the variability is due to common factors ("communality"). The two methods become essentially equivalent if the error terms in the factor analysis model can be assumed to all have the same variance.

Statistical Model

The following example is a fictionalized simplification for expository purposes, and should not be taken as being realistic. Suppose a psychologist proposes a theory that there are two kinds of intelligence, "verbal intelligence" and "mathematical intelligence", neither of which is directly observed. Evidence for the theory is sought in the examination scores from each of 10 different academic fields of 1000 students. If each student is chosen randomly from a large population, then each student's 10 scores are random variables. The psychologist's theory may say that for each of the 10 academic fields, the score averaged over the group of all students who share some common pair of values for verbal and mathematical "intelligences" is some constant times their level of verbal intelligence plus another constant times their level of mathematical intelligence, i.e., it is a linear combination of those two "factors". The numbers for a particular subject, by which the two kinds of intelligence are multiplied to obtain the expected score, are posited by the theory to be the same for all intelligence level pairs, and are called "factor loadings" for this subject. For example, the theory may hold that the average student's aptitude in the field of amphibiology is

{10 × the student's verbal intelligence} + {6 × the student's mathematical intelligence}.

The numbers 10 and 6 are the factor loadings associated with amphibiology. Other academic subjects may have different factor loadings.

Two students having identical degrees of verbal intelligence and identical degrees of mathematical intelligence may have different aptitudes in amphibiology because individual aptitudes differ from average aptitudes. That difference is called the "error" — a statistical term that means the amount by which an individual differs from what is average for his or her levels of intelligence.

The observable data that go into factor analysis would be 10 scores of each of the 1000 students, a total of 10,000 numbers. The factor loadings and levels of the two kinds of intelligence of each student must be inferred from the data.

Practical Implementation

Exploratory factor analysis (EFA) is used to uncover the underlying structure of a relatively large set of variables. The researcher's *a priori* assumption is that any indicator may be associated with any factor. This is the most common form of factor analysis. There is no prior theory and one uses factor loadings to intuit the factor structure of the data.

Confirmatory factor analysis (CFA) seeks to determine if the number of factors and the loadings of measured (indicator) variables on them conform to what is expected on the basis of pre-established theory. Indicator variables are selected on the basis of prior theory and factor analysis is used to see if they load as predicted on the expected number of factors. The researcher's *a priori* assumption is that each factor (the number and labels of which may be specified *a priori*) is associated with a specified subset of indicator variables. A minimum requirement of confirmatory factor analysis is that one hypothesizes beforehand the number of factors in the model, but usually also the researcher will posit expectations about which variables will load on which factors. The researcher seeks to determine, for instance, if measures created to represent a latent variable really belong together.

Types of Factoring

Principal component analysis (PCA): The most common form of factor analysis, PCA seeks a linear combination of variables such that the maximum variance is extracted from the variables. It then removes this variance and seeks a second linear combination which explains the maximum proportion of the remaining variance, and so on. This is called the principal axis method and results in orthogonal (uncorrelated) factors. Canonical factor analysis, also called Rao's canonical factoring, is a different method of computing the same model as PCA, which uses the principal axis method. CFA seeks factors which have the highest canonical correlation with the observed variables. CFA is unaffected by arbitrary rescaling of the data.

Common factor analysis, also called principal factor analysis (PFA) or principal axis factoring (PAF), seeks the least number of factors which can account for the common variance (correlation) of a set of variables. Image factoring: based on the correlation matrix of predicted variables rather than actual variables, where each variable is predicted from the others using multiple regression.

Alpha factoring: based on maximizing the reliability of factors, assuming variables are randomly sampled from a universe of variables. All other methods assume cases to be sampled and variables fixed.

Factor regression model: a combinatorial model of factor model and regression model; or alternatively, it can be viewed as the hybrid factor model, whose factors are partially known.

Terminology

Factor loadings: The factor loadings, also called component loadings in PCA, are the correlation coefficients between the variables (rows) and factors (columns). Analogous to Pearson's r, the squared factor loading is the percent of variance in that indicator variable explained by the factor. To get the percent of variance in all the variables accounted for by each factor, add the sum of the squared factor loadings for that factor (column) and divide by the number of variables. (Note the number of variables equals the sum of their variances as the variance of a standardized variable is 1.) This is the same as dividing the factor's eigenvalue by the number of variables.

Interpreting factor loadings: By one rule of thumb in confirmatory factor analysis, loadings should be.7 or higher to confirm that independent variables identified a priori are represented by a particular factor, on the rationale that the .7 level corresponds to about half of the variance in the indicator being explained by the factor. However, the .7 standard is a high one and real-life data may well not meet this criterion, which is why some researchers, particularly for exploratory purposes, will use a lower level such as .4 for the central factor and .25 for other factors call loadings above .6 "high" and those below .4 "low". In any event, factor loadings must be interpreted in the light of theory, not by arbitrary cutoff levels.

In oblique rotation, one gets both a pattern matrix and a structure matrix. The structure matrix is simply the factor loading matrix as in orthogonal rotation, representing the variance in a measured variable explained by a factor on both a unique and common contributions basis. The pattern matrix, in contrast, contains coefficients which just represent unique contributions. The more factors, the lower the pattern coefficients as a rule since there will be more common contributions to variance explained. For oblique rotation, the researcher looks at both the structure and pattern coefficients when attributing a label to a factor.

Communality: The sum of the squared factor loadings for all factors for a given variable (row) is the variance in that variable accounted for by all the factors, and this is called the communality. The communality measures the percent of variance in a given variable explained by all the factors jointly and may be interpreted as the reliability of the indicator.

Spurious solutions: If the communality exceeds 1.0, there is a spurious solution, which may reflect too small a sample or the researcher has too many or too few factors.

Uniqueness of a variable: That is, uniqueness is the variability of a variable minus its communality.

Eigenvalues:/Characteristic roots: The eigenvalue for a given factor measures the variance in all the variables which is accounted for by that factor. The ratio of eigenvalues is the ratio of explanatory importance of the factors with respect to the variables. If a factor has a low eigenvalue, then it is contributing little to the explanation of variances in the variables and may be ignored as redundant with more important factors. Eigenvalues measure the amount of variation in the total sample accounted for by each factor.

Extraction sums of squared loadings: Initial eigenvalues and eigenvalues after extraction (listed by SPSS as "Extraction Sums of Squared Loadings") are the same for PCA extraction, but for other extraction methods, eigenvalues after extraction will be lower than their initial counterparts. SPSS also prints "Rotation Sums of Squared Loadings" and even for PCA, these eigenvalues will differ from initial and extraction eigenvalues, though their total will be the same.

Factor scores (also called component scores in PCA): are the scores of each case (row) on each factor (column). To compute the factor score for a given case for a given factor, one takes the case's standardized score on each variable, multiplies by the corresponding factor loading of the variable for the given factor, and sums these products. Computing factor scores allows one to look for factor outliers. Also, factor scores may be used as variables in subsequent modelling.

Criteria for Determining the Number of Factors

Using one or more of the methods below, the researcher determines an appropriate range of solutions to investigate. Methods may not agree. For instance, the Kaiser criterion may suggest five factors and the scree test may suggest two, so the researcher may request 3-, 4-, and 5-factor solutions discuss each in terms of their relation to external data and theory.

Comprehensibility: A purely subjective criterion would be to retain those factors whose meaning is comprehensible to the researcher. This is not recommended.

Kaiser criterion: The Kaiser rule is to drop all components with eigenvalues under 1.0 – this being the eigenvalue equal to the information accounted for by an average single item. The Kaiser criterion is the default in SPSS and most statistical software but is not recommended when used as the sole cut-off criterion for estimating the number of factors as it tends to overextract factors.

Variance explained criteria: Some researchers simply use the rule of keeping enough factors to account for 90% (sometimes 80%) of the variation. Where the researcher's goal emphasizes parsimony (explaining variance with as few factors as possible), the criterion could be as low as 50%

Scree plot: The Cattell scree test plots the components as the X axis and the corresponding eigenvalues as the Y-axis. As one moves to the right, toward later components, the eigenvalues drop. When the drop ceases and the curve makes an elbow toward less steep decline, Cattell's scree test says to drop all further components after the one starting the elbow. This rule is sometimes criticised for being amenable to researcher-controlled "fudging". That is, as picking the "elbow" can be subjective because the curve has multiple elbows or is a smooth curve, the researcher may be tempted to set the cut-off at the number of factors desired by his or her research agenda.

Horn's Parallel Analysis (PA): A Monte-Carlo based simulation method that compares the observed eigenvalues with those obtained from uncorrelated normal variables. A factor or component is retained if the associated eigenvalue is bigger than the 95th of the distribution of eigenvalues derived from the random data. PA is one of the most recommendable rules for determining the number of components to retain, but only few programs include this option.

Before dropping a factor below one's cut-off, however, the researcher should check its correlation with the dependent variable. A very small factor can have a large correlation with the dependent variable, in which case it should not be dropped.

Rotation Methods

Rotation serves to make the output more understandable and is usually necessary to facilitate the interpretation of factors. Varimax rotation is an orthogonal rotation of the factor axes to maximize the variance of the squared loadings of a factor (column) on all the variables (rows) in a factor matrix, which has the effect of differentiating the original variables by extracted factor. Each factor will tend to have either large or small loadings of any particular variable. A varimax solution yields results which make it as easy as possible to identify each variable with a single factor. This is the most common rotation option.

Quartimax rotation is an orthogonal alternative which minimizes the number of factors needed to explain each variable. This type of rotation often generates a general factor on which most variables are loaded to a high or medium degree. Such a factor structure is usually not helpful to the research purpose.

Equimax rotation is a compromise between Varimax and Quartimax criteria. Direct oblimin rotation is the standard method when one wishes a non-orthogonal (oblique) solution – that is, one in which the factors are allowed to be correlated. This will result in higher eigenvalues but diminished interpretability of the factors. Promax rotation is an alternative non-orthogonal (oblique) rotation method which is computationally faster than the direct oblimin method and therefore is sometimes used for very large datasets.

FACTOR ANALYSIS IN PSYCHOMETRICS

Charles Spearman pioneered the use of factor analysis in the field of psychology and is sometimes credited with the invention of factor analysis. He discovered that school children's scores on a wide variety of seemingly unrelated subjects were positively correlated, which led him to postulate that a general mental ability, or *g*, underlies and shapes human cognitive performance. His postulate now enjoys broad support in the field of intelligence research, where it is known as the *g* theory.

Raymond Cattell expanded on Spearman's idea of a two-factor theory of intelligence after performing his own tests and factor analysis. He used a multi-factor theory to explain intelligence. Cattell's theory addressed alternate factors in intellectual development, including motivation and psychology. Cattell also developed several mathematical methods for adjusting psychometric graphs, such as his "scree" test and similarity coefficients. His research led to the development of his theory of fluid and crystallized intelligence, as well as his 16 Personality Factors theory of personality. Cattell was a strong advocate of factor analysis and psychometrics. He believed that all theory should be derived from research, which supports the continued use of empirical observation and objective testing to study human intelligence.

Applications in Psychology

Factor analysis is used to identify "factors" that explain a variety of results on different tests. For example, intelligence research found that people who get a high score on a test of verbal ability are also good on other tests that require verbal abilities. Researchers explained this by using factor analysis to isolate one factor, often called crystallized intelligence or verbal intelligence, that represents the degree to which someone is able to solve problems involving verbal skills.

Factor analysis in psychology is most often associated with intelligence research. However, it also has been used to find factors in a broad range of domains such as personality, attitudes, beliefs, etc. It is linked to psychometrics, as it can assess the validity of an instrument by finding if the instrument indeed measures the postulated factors.

Advantages

- Reduction of number of variables, by combining two or more variables into a single factor. For example, performance at running, ball throwing, batting, jumping and weight lifting could be combined into a single factor such as general athletic ability. Usually, in an item by people matrix, factors are selected by grouping related items. In the Q factor analysis technique, the matrix is transposed and factors are created by grouping related people: For example, liberals, libertarians, conservatives and socialists, could form separate groups.
- Identification of groups of inter-related variables, to see how they are related to each other. For example, Carroll used factor analysis to build his Three Stratum Theory. He found that a factor called "broad visual perception" relates to how good an individual is at visual tasks. He also found a "broad auditory perception" factor, relating to auditory task capability. Furthermore, he found a global factor, called "g" or general intelligence, that relates to both "broad visual perception" and "broad auditory perception". This means someone with a high

"g" is likely to have both a high "visual perception" capability and a high "auditory perception" capability, and that "g" therefore explains a good part of why someone is good or bad in both of those domains.

Disadvantages

- "...each orientation is equally acceptable mathematically. But different factorial theories proved to differ as much in terms of the orientations of factorial axes for a given solution as in terms of anything else, so that model fitting did not prove to be useful in distinguishing among theories." (Sternberg, 1977). This means all rotations represent different underlying processes, but all rotations are equally valid outcomes of standard factor analysis optimization. Therefore, it is impossible to pick the proper rotation using factor analysis alone.
- Factor analysis can be only as good as the data allows. In psychology, where researchers often have to rely on less valid and reliable measures such as self-reports, this can be problematic.
- Interpreting factor analysis is based on using a "heuristic", which is a solution that is "convenient even if not absolutely true" (Richard B. Darlington). More than one interpretation can be made of the same data factored the same way, and factor analysis cannot identify causality.

Factor Analysis in Marketing

The basic steps are:

- Identify the salient attributes consumers use to evaluate products in this category.
- Use quantitative :ıarketing research techniques (such as surveys) to collect data from a sample of potential customers concerning their ratings of all the product attributes.
- Input the data into a statistical program and run the factor analysis procedure. The computer will yield a set of underlying attributes (or factors).
- Use these factors to construct perceptual maps and other product positioning devices.

Information Collection

The data collection stage is usually done by marketing research professionals. Survey questions ask the respondent to rate a product sample or descriptions of product concepts on a range of attributes. Anywhere from five to twenty attributes are chosen. They could include things like: ease of use, weight, accuracy, durability, colourfulness, price, or size. The attributes chosen will vary depending on the product being studied. The same question is asked about all the products in the study. The data for multiple products is coded and input into a statistical program such as R, PSPP, SAS, Stata, STATISTICA, JMP and SYSTAT.

Analysis

The analysis will isolate the underlying factors that explain the data. Factor analysis is an interdependence technique. The complete set of interdependent relationships is examined. There is no specification of dependent variables, independent variables, or causality. Factor analysis assumes that all the rating data on different attributes can be reduced down to a few important dimensions. This reduction is possible because the attributes are related. The rating given to any one attribute is partially the result of the influence of other attributes. The statistical algorithm deconstructs the rating (called a raw score) into its various components, and reconstructs the partial scores into underlying factor scores. The degree of correlation between the initial raw score and the final factor score is called a *factor loading*. There are two approaches to factor analysis: "principal component analysis" (the total variance in the data is considered); and "common factor analysis" (the common variance is considered).

Note that principal component analysis and common factor analysis differ in terms of their conceptual underpinnings. The factors produced by principal component analysis are conceptualized as being linear combinations of the variables whereas the factors produced by common factor analysis are conceptualized as being latent variables. Computationally, the only difference is that the diagonal of the relationships matrix is replaced with communalities (the variance accounted for by more than one variable) in common factor analysis. This has the result of making the factor scores indeterminate and differ depending on the method of computation. Meanwhile, factor scores produced by principal component analysis are not dependent on the method of computation. Although there have been heated debates over the merits of the two methods, a number of leading statisticians have concluded that in practice there is little difference (Velicer and Jackson, 1990) which makes sense since the computations are quite similar despite the differing conceptual bases, especially for datasets where communalities are high and/or there are many variables, reducing the influence of the diagonal of the relationship matrix on the final result (Gorsuch, 1983).

The use of principal components in a semantic space can vary somewhat because the components may only "predict" but not "map" to the vector space. This produces a statistical principal component use where the most salient words or themes represent the preferred basis.

Advantages

- Both objective and subjective attributes can be used provided the subjective attributes can be converted into scores
- Factor Analysis can be used to identify hidden dimensions or constructs which may not be apparent from direct analysis
- It is easy and inexpensive to do

Disadvantages

- Usefulness depends on the researchers' ability to collect a sufficient set of product attributes. If important attributes are missed the value of the procedure is reduced.
- If sets of observed variables are highly similar to each other and distinct from other items, factor analysis will assign a single factor to them. This may make it harder to identify factors that capture more interesting relationships.
- Naming the factors may require background knowledge or theory because multiple attributes can be highly correlated for no apparent reason.

Factor Analysis in Physical Sciences

Factor analysis has also been widely used in physical sciences such as geochemistry, ecology, and hydrochemistry. In groundwater quality management, it is important to relate the spatial distribution of different chemical parameters to different possible sources, which have different chemical signatures. For example, a sulfide mine is likely to be associated with high levels of acidity, dissolved sulfates and transition metals. These signatures can be identified as factors through R-mode factor analysis, and the location of possible sources can be suggested by contouring the factor scores. In geochemistry, different factors can correspond to different mineral associations, and thus to mineralisation.

Factor analysis can be used for summarizing high-density oligonucleotide DNA microarrays data at probe level for Affymetrix GeneChips. In this case, the latent variable corresponds to the RNA concentration in a sample. Factor analysis has been implemented in several statistical analysis programs since the 1980s: SAS, BMDP and SPSS. It is also implemented in the *R* programming language with the *factanal* function. Rotations are implemented in the *GPArotation* R package.

COMPUTATIONAL APPROACH

Computationally, discriminant function analysis is very similar to analysis of variance (ANOVA). Let us consider a simple example. Suppose we measure height in a random sample of 50 males and 50 females. Females are, on the average, not as tall as males, and this difference will be reflected in the difference in means (for the variable *Height*). Therefore, variable height allows us to discriminate between males and females with a better than chance probability: if a person is tall, then he is likely to be a male, if a person is short, then she is likely to be a female.

We can generalize this reasoning to groups and variables that are less "trivial." For example, suppose we have two groups of high school graduates: Those who choose to attend college after graduation and those who do not. We could have measured students' stated intention to continue on to college one year prior to graduation. If the means for the two groups (those who actually went to college and those who did not) are different, then we can say that intention to attend college as stated one year prior to graduation allows us to discriminate between those who are and are not college bound (and this information may be used by career counselors to provide the appropriate guidance to the respective students).

To summarize the discussion so far, the basic idea underlying discriminant function analysis is to determine whether groups differ with regard to the mean of a variable, and then to use that variable to predict group membership (e.g., of new cases).

Analysis of Variance. Stated in this manner, the discriminant function problem can be rephrased as a one-way analysis of variance (ANOVA) problem. Specifically, one can ask whether or not two or more groups are *significantly different* from each other with respect to the mean of a particular variable. To learn more about how one can test for the statistical significance of differences between means in different groups you may want to read the Overview section to ANOVA/ MANOVA. However, it should be clear that, if the means for a variable are significantly different in different groups, then we can say that this variable discriminates between the groups.

In the case of a single variable, the final significance test of whether or not a variable discriminates between groups is the F test. As described in Elementary Concepts and ANOVA/ MANOVA, F is essentially computed as the ratio of the between-groups variance in the data over the pooled (average) within-group variance. If the between-group variance is significantly larger then there must be significant differences between means.

Multiple Variables. Usually, one includes several variables in a study in order to see which one(s) contribute to the discrimination between groups. In that case, we have a matrix of total variances and covariances; likewise, we have a matrix of pooled within-group variances and covariances. We can compare those two matrices via multivariate F tests in order to determined whether or not there are any significant differences (with regard to all variables) between groups. This procedure is identical to multivariate analysis of variance or MANOVA. As in MANOVA, one could first perform the multivariate test, and, if statistically significant, proceed to see which of the variables have significantly different means across the groups. Thus, even though the computations with multiple variables are more complex, the principal reasoning still applies, namely, that we are looking for variables that discriminate between groups, as evident in observed mean differences.

Stepwise Discriminant Analysis

Probably the most common application of discriminant function analysis is to include many measures in the study, in order to determine the ones that discriminate between groups. For example, an educational researcher interested in predicting high school graduates' choices for further education would probably include as many measures of personality, achievement motivation, academic performance, etc. as possible in order to learn which one(s) offer the best prediction.

Model. Put another way, we want to build a "model" of how we can best predict to which group a case belongs. In the following discussion we will use the term "in the model" in order to refer to variables that are included in the prediction of group membership, and we will refer to variables as being "not in the model" if they are not included.

Forward stepwise analysis. In stepwise discriminant function analysis, a model of discrimination is built step-by-step. Specifically, at each step all variables are reviewed and evaluated to determine which one will contribute most to the discrimination between groups. That variable will then be included in the model, and the process starts again.

Backward stepwise analysis. One can also step backwards; in that case all variables are included in the model and then, at each step, the variable that contributes least to the prediction of group membership is eliminated. Thus, as the result of a successful discriminant function analysis, one would only keep the "important" variables in the model, that is, those variables that contribute the most to the discrimination between groups.

F to enter, F to remove. The stepwise procedure is "guided" by the respective F to enter and F to remove values. The F value for a variable indicates its statistical significance in the discrimination between groups, that is, it is a measure of the extent to which a variable makes a unique contribution to the prediction of group membership. If you are familiar with stepwise multiple regression procedures, then you may interpret the *F* to enter/remove values in the same way as in stepwise regression.

Capitalizing on chance. A common misinterpretation of the results of stepwise discriminant analysis is to take statistical significance levels at face value. By nature, the stepwise procedures will capitalize on chance because they "pick and choose" the variables to be included in the model so as to yield maximum discrimination. Thus, when using the stepwise approach the researcher should be aware that the significance levels do not reflect the true *alpha* error rate, that is, the probability of erroneously rejecting H_0 (the null hypothesis that there is no discrimination between groups).

INTERPRETING A TWO-GROUP DISCRIMINANT FUNCTION

In the two-group case, discriminant function analysis can also be thought of as (and is analogous to) multiple regression. If we code the two groups in the analysis as *1* and *2*, and use that variable as the dependent variable in a multiple regression analysis, then we would get results that are analogous to those we would obtain via *Discriminant Analysis*. In general, in the two-group case we fit a linear equation of the type:

$$\text{Group} = a + b_1{*}x_1 + b_2{*}x_2 + \ldots + b_m{*}x_m$$

where a is a constant and b_1 through b_m are regression coefficients. The interpretation of the results of a two-group problem is straightforward and closely follows the logic of multiple regression: Those variables with the largest (standardized) regression coefficients are the ones that contribute most to the prediction of group membership.

DISCRIMINANT FUNCTIONS FOR MULTIPLE GROUPS

When there are more than two groups, then we can estimate more than one discriminant function like the one presented above. For example, when there are three groups, we could estimate (1) a function for discriminating between group 1 and groups 2 and 3 combined, and (2) another function for discriminating between group 2 and group 3. For example, we could have one function that discriminates between those high school graduates that go to college and those who do not (but rather get a job or go to a professional or trade school), and a second function to discriminate between those graduates that go to a professional or trade school versus those who get a job. The *b* coefficients in those discriminant functions could then be interpreted as before.

Canonical analysis. When actually performing a multiple group discriminant analysis, we do not have to specify how to combine groups so as to form different discriminant functions. Rather, you can automatically determine some optimal combination of variables so that the first function provides the most overall discrimination between groups, the second provides second most, and so on. Moreover, the functions will be independent or *orthogonal*, that is, their contributions to the discrimination between groups will not overlap. Computationally, you will perform a canonical correlation analysis that will determine the successive functions and canonical *roots* (the term root refers to the eigenvalues that are associated with the respective canonical function). The maximum number of functions will be equal to the number of groups minus one, or the number of variables in the analysis, whichever is smaller.

Interpreting the discriminant functions. As before, we will get *b* (and standardized *beta*) coefficients for each variable in each discriminant (now also called *canonical*) function, and they can be interpreted as usual: the larger the standardized coefficient, the greater is the contribution of the respective variable to the discrimination between groups. However, these coefficients do not tell us between which of the groups the respective functions discriminate. We can identify the nature of the discrimination for each discriminant (canonical) function by looking at the means for the functions across groups. We can also visualize how the two functions discriminate between groups by plotting the individual scores for the two discriminant functions.

Factor structure matrix. Another way to determine which variables "mark" or define a particular discriminant function is to look at the factor structure. The factor structure coefficients are the correlations between the variables in the model and the discriminant functions; if you are familiar with factor analysis you may think of these correlations as factor *loadings* of the variables on each discriminant function.

Some authors have argued that these structure coefficients should be used when interpreting the substantive "meaning" of discriminant functions. The reasons given by those authors are that (1) supposedly the structure coefficients are more stable, and (2) they allow for the interpretation of factors (discriminant functions) in the manner that is analogous to factor analysis. However, subsequent Monte Carlo research has shown that the discriminant function coefficients and the structure coefficients are about equally unstable, unless the n is fairly large (e.g., if there are 20 times more cases than there are variables). The most important thing to remember is that the discriminant function coefficients denote the unique (partial) contribution of each variable to the discriminant function(s), while the structure coefficients denote the simple correlations between the variables and the function(s). If one wants to assign substantive "meaningful" labels to the discriminant functions (akin to the interpretation of factors in factor analysis), then the structure coefficients should be used (interpreted); if one wants to learn what is each variable's unique contribution to the discriminant function, use the discriminant function coefficients (weights).

Significance of discriminant functions. One can test the number of roots that add *significantly* to the discrimination between group. Only those found to be statistically significant should be used for interpretation; non-significant functions (roots) should be ignored.

Summary. To summarize, when interpreting multiple discriminant functions, which arise from analyses with more than two groups and more than one variable, one would first test the different functions for statistical significance, and only consider the significant functions for further examination. Next, we would look at the standardized *b* coefficients for each variable for each significant function. The larger the standardized *b* coefficient, the larger is the respective variable's unique contribution to the discrimination specified by the respective discriminant function. In order to derive substantive "meaningful" labels for the discriminant functions, one can also examine the factor structure matrix with the correlations between the variables and the discriminant functions. Finally, we would look at the means for the significant discriminant functions in order to determine between which groups the respective functions seem to discriminate.

Assumptions

As mentioned earlier, discriminant function analysis is computationally very similar to MANOVA, and all assumptions for *MANOVA* mentioned in ANOVA/MANOVA apply. In fact, you may use the wide range of diagnostics and statistical tests of assumption that are available to examine your data for the discriminant analysis.

Normal distribution. It is assumed that the data (for the variables) represent a sample from a multivariate normal distribution. You can examine whether or not variables are normally distributed with histograms of frequency distributions. However, note that violations of the normality assumption are usually not "fatal," meaning, that the resultant significance tests etc. are still "trustworthy." You may use specific tests for normality in addition to graphs.

Homogeneity of variances/covariances. It is assumed that the variance/covariance matrices of variables are homogeneous across groups. Again, minor deviations are not that important; however, before accepting final conclusions for an important study it is probably a good idea to review the within-groups variances and correlation matrices. In particular a scatterplot matrix can be produced and can be very useful for this purpose. When in doubt, try re-running the analyses excluding one or two groups that are of less interest. If the overall results (interpretations) hold up, you probably do not have a problem. You may also use the numerous tests available to examine whether or not this assumption is violated in your data. However, as mentioned in *ANOVA / MANOVA*, the multivariate Box *M* test for homogeneity of variances/covariances is particularly sensitive to deviations from multivariate normality, and should not be taken too "seriously."

Correlations between means and variances. The major "real" threat to the validity of significance tests occurs when the means for variables across groups are correlated with the variances (or standard deviations). Intuitively, if there is large variability in a group with particularly high means on some variables, then those high means are not reliable. However, the overall significance tests are based on pooled variances, that is, the average variance across all groups. Thus, the significance tests of the relatively larger means (with the large variances) would be based on the relatively smaller pooled variances, resulting erroneously in statistical significance. In practice, this pattern may occur if one group in the study contains a few extreme outliers, who have a large impact on the means, and also increase the variability. To guard against this problem, inspect the descriptive statistics, that is, the means and standard deviations or variances for such a correlation.

The matrix ill-conditioning problem. Another assumption of discriminant function analysis is that the variables that are used to discriminate between groups are not completely redundant. As part of the computations involved in discriminant analysis, you will invert the variance/covariance matrix of the variables in the model. If any one of the variables is completely redundant with the other variables then the matrix is said to be *ill-conditioned*, and it cannot be inverted. For example, if a variable is the sum of three other variables that are also in the model, then the matrix is ill-conditioned.

Tolerance values. In order to guard against matrix ill-conditioning, constantly check the so-called tolerance value for each variable. This tolerance value is computed as *1 minus R-square* of the respective variable with all other variables included in the current model. Thus, it is the proportion of variance that is unique to the respective variable. You may also refer to Multiple Regression to learn more about multiple regression and the interpretation of the tolerance value. In general, when a variable is almost completely redundant (and, therefore, the matrix ill-conditioning problem is likely to occur), the tolerance value for that variable will approach 0.

Classification

Another major purpose to which discriminant analysis is applied is the issue of predictive classification of cases. Once a model has been finalized and the discriminant functions have been derived, how well can we *predict* to which group a particular case belongs?

A priori and *post hoc* predictions. Before going into the details of different estimation procedures, we would like to make sure that this difference is clear. Obviously, if we estimate, based on some data set, the discriminant functions that best discriminate between groups, and then use the *same* data to evaluate how accurate our prediction is, then we are very much capitalizing on chance. In general, one will *always* get a worse classification when predicting cases that were not used for the estimation of the discriminant function. Put another way, *post hoc* predictions are always better than *a priori* predictions. (The trouble with predicting the future *a priori* is that one does not know what will happen; it is much easier to find ways to predict what we already know has happened.) Therefore, one should never base one's confidence regarding the correct classification of future observations on the same data set from which the discriminant functions were derived; rather, if one wants to classify cases predictively, it is necessary to collect new data to "try out" (cross-validate) the utility of the discriminant functions.

Classification functions. These are not to be confused with the discriminant functions. The classification functions can be used to determine to which group each case most likely belongs. There are as many classification functions as there are groups. Each function allows us to compute *classification scores* for each case for each group, by applying the formula:

$$S_i = c_i + w_{i1}*x_1 + w_{i2}*x_2 + ... + w_{im}*x_m$$

In this formula, the subscript i denotes the respective group; the subscripts *1, 2, ..., m* denote the m variables; c_i is a constant for the i'th group, w_{ij} is the weight for the j'th variable in the computation of the classification score for the i'th group; x_j is the observed value for the respective case for the j'th variable. S_i is the resultant classification score.

We can use the classification functions to directly compute classification scores for some new observations.

Classification of cases. Once we have computed the classification scores for a case, it is easy to decide how to classify the case: in general we classify the case as belonging to the group for which it has the highest classification score. Thus, if we were to study high school students' post-graduation career/educational choices (e.g., attending college, attending a professional or trade school, or getting a job) based on several variables assessed one year prior to graduation, we could use the classification functions to predict what each student is most likely to do after graduation. However, we would also like to know the *probability* that the student will make the predicted choice. Those probabilities are called *posterior* probabilities, and can also be computed. However, to understand how those probabilities are derived, let us first consider the so-called *Mahalanobis* distances.

Mahalanobis distances. You may have read about these distances in other parts of the manual. In general, the Mahalanobis distance is a measure of distance between two points in the space defined by two or more correlated variables. For example, if there are two variables that are uncorrelated, then we could plot points (cases) in a standard two-dimensional scatterplot; the Mahalanobis distances between the points would then be identical to the Euclidean distance; that is, the distance as, for example, measured by a ruler. If there are three uncorrelated variables, we could also simply use a ruler (in a 3-D plot) to determine the distances between points. If there are more than 3 variables, we cannot represent the distances in a plot any more. Also, when the variables are correlated, then the axes in the plots can be thought of as being *non-orthogonal*; that is, they would not be positioned in right angles to each other. In those cases, the simple Euclidean distance is not an appropriate measure, while the Mahalanobis distance will adequately account for the correlations.

Mahalanobis distances and classification. For each group in our sample, we can determine the location of the point that represents the means for all variables in the multivariate space defined by the variables in the model. These points are called group *centroids*. For each case we can then compute the Mahalanobis distances (of the respective case) from each of the group centroids. Again, we would classify the case as belonging to the group to which it is closest, that is, where the Mahalanobis distance is smallest. Posterior classification probabilities. Using the Mahalanobis distances to do the classification, we can now derive probabilities. The probability that a case belongs to a particular group is basically proportional to the Mahalanobis distance from that group centroid (it is not exactly proportional because we assume a multivariate normal distribution around each centroid). Because we compute the location of each case from our prior knowledge of the values for that case on the variables in the model, these probabilities are called *posterior* probabilities. In summary, the posterior probability is the probability, based on our knowledge of the values of other variables, that the respective case belongs to a particular group. Some software packages will automatically compute those probabilities for all cases (or for selected cases only for cross-validation studies).

A priori classification probabilities. There is one additional factor that needs to be considered when classifying cases. Sometimes, we know ahead of time that there are more observations in one group than in any other; thus, the *a priori* probability that a case belongs to that group is higher. For example, if we know ahead of time that 60% of the graduates from our high school usually go to college (20% go to a professional school, and another 20% get a job), then we should adjust our prediction accordingly: *a priori*, and all other things being equal, it is more likely that a student will attend college that choose either of the other two options. You can specify different *a priori* probabilities, which will then be used to adjust the classification of cases (and the computation of posterior probabilities) accordingly.

In practice, the researcher needs to ask him or herself whether the unequal number of cases in different groups in the sample is a reflection of the true distribution in the population, or whether it is only the (random) result of the sampling procedure. In the former case, we would set the *a priori* probabilities to be proportional to the sizes of the groups in our sample, in the latter case we would specify the *a priori* probabilities as being equal in each group. The specification of different *a priori* probabilities can greatly affect the accuracy of the prediction.

Summary of the prediction. A common result that one looks at in order to determine how well the current classification functions predict group membership of cases is the *classification matrix*. The classification matrix shows the number of cases that were correctly classified (on the diagonal of the matrix) and those that were misclassified.

Another word of caution. To reiterate, *post hoc* predicting of what has happened in the past is not that difficult. It is not uncommon to obtain very good classification if one uses the same cases from which the classification functions were computed. In order to get an idea of how well the current classification functions "perform," one must classify (*a priori*) *different* cases, that is, cases that were not used to estimate the classification functions. You can include or exclude cases from the computations; thus, the classification matrix can be computed for "old" cases as well as "new" cases. Only the classification of new cases allows us to assess the predictive validity of the classification functions; the classification of old cases only provides a useful diagnostic tool to identify outliers or areas where the classification function seems to be less adequate.

LINEAR DISCRIMINANT ANALYSIS

Linear discriminant analysis (LDA) and the related Fisher's linear discriminant are methods used in statistics, pattern recognition and machine learning to find a linear combination of features which characterize or separate two or more classes of objects or events. The resulting combination may be used as a linear classifier, or, more commonly, for dimensionality reduction before later classification.

LDA is closely related to ANOVA (analysis of variance) and regression analysis, which also attempt to express one dependent variable as a linear combination of other features or measurements. In the other two methods however, the dependent variable is a numerical quantity, while for LDA it is a categorical variable (*i.e.* the class label). Logistic regression and probit regression are more similar to LDA, as they also explain a categorical variable. These other methods are preferable in applications where it is not reasonable to assume that the independent variables are normally distributed, which is a fundamental assumption of the LDA method.

LDA is also closely related to principal component analysis (PCA) and factor analysis in that both look for linear combinations of variables which best explain the data. LDA explicitly attempts to model the difference between the classes of data. PCA on the other hand does not take into account any difference in class, and factor analysis builds the feature combinations based on differences rather than similarities. Discriminant analysis is also different from factor analysis in that it is not an interdependence technique: a distinction between independent variables and dependent variables (also called criterion variables) must be made.

LDA works when the measurements made on independent variables for each observation are continuous quantities. When dealing with categorical independent variables, the equivalent technique is discriminant correspondence analysis.

Practical use

In practice, the class means and covariances are not known. They can, however, be estimated from the training set. Either the maximum likelihood estimate or the maximum a posteriori estimate may be used in place of the exact value in the above equations. Although the estimates of the covariance may be considered optimal in some sense, this does not mean that the resulting discriminant obtained by substituting these values is optimal in any sense, even if the assumption of normally distributed classes is correct.

Another complication in applying LDA and Fisher's discriminant to real data occurs when the number of observations of each sample does not exceed the number of samples. In this case, the covariance estimates do not have full rank, and so cannot be inverted. There are a number of ways to deal with this. One is to use a pseudo inverse instead of the usual matrix inverse in the above formulae. However, better numeric stability may be achieved by first projecting the problem onto the subspace spanned by $Ó_b$. Another strategy to deal with small sample size is to use a Shrinkage estimator of the covariance matrix, which can be expressed mathematically as

$$C_{new} = (1 - \lambda)\ C + \lambda I$$

where *I* is the identity matrix, and ë is the *shrinkage intensity* or *regularisation parameter*. This leads to the framework of regularized discriminant analysis or shrinkage discriminant analysis. Also, in many practical cases linear discriminants are not suitable. LDA and Fisher's discriminant can be extended for use in non-linear classification via the kernel trick. Here, the original observations are effectively mapped into a higher dimensional non-linear space. Linear classification in this non-linear space is then equivalent to non-linear classification in the original space. The most commonly used example of this is the kernel Fisher discriminant.

LDA can be generalized to multiple discriminant analysis, where c becomes a categorical variable with N possible states, instead of only two. Analogously, if the class-conditional densities are normal with shared covariances, the sufficient statistic for are the values of N projections, which are the subspace spanned by the N means, affine projected by the inverse covariance matrix.

These projections can be found by solving a generalized eigenvalue problem, where the numerator is the covariance matrix formed by treating the means as the samples, and the denominator is the shared covariance matrix.

Applications

In addition to the examples given below, LDA is applied in positioning and product management.

Bankruptcy Prediction

In bankruptcy prediction based on accounting ratios and other financial variables, linear discriminant analysis was the first statistical method applied to systematically explain which firms entered bankruptcy vs. survived. Despite limitations including known nonconformance of accounting ratios to the normal distribution assumptions of LDA, Edward Altman's 1968 model is still a leading model in practical applications.

Face Recognition

In computerised face recognition, each face is represented by a large number of pixel values. Linear discriminant analysis is primarily used here to reduce the number of features to a more manageable number before classification. Each of the new dimensions is a linear combination of pixel values, which form a template. The linear combinations obtained using Fisher's linear discriminant are called *Fisher faces*, while those obtained using the related principal component analysis are called *eigenfaces*.

Marketing

In marketing, discriminant analysis was once often used to determine the factors which distinguish different types of customers and/or products on the basis of surveys or other forms of collected data. Logistic regression or other methods are now more commonly used. The use of discriminant analysis in marketing can be described by the following steps:

1. Formulate the problem and gather data — Identify the salient attributes consumers use to evaluate products in this category — Use quantitative marketing research techniques (such as surveys) to collect data from a sample of potential customers concerning their ratings of all the product attributes. The data collection stage is usually done by marketing research professionals. Survey questions ask the respondent to rate a product from one to five (or 1 to 7, or 1 to 10) on a range of attributes chosen by the researcher. Anywhere from five to twenty attributes are chosen. They could include things like: ease of use, weight, accuracy, durability, colourfulness, price, or size. The attributes chosen will vary depending on the product being studied. The same question is asked about all the products in the study. The data for multiple products is codified and input into a statistical program such as R, SPSS or SAS. (This step is the same as in Factor analysis).
2. Estimate the Discriminant Function Coefficients and determine the statistical significance and validity — Choose the appropriate discriminant analysis method. The direct method involves estimating the discriminant function so that all the predictors are assessed simultaneously. The stepwise method enters the predictors sequentially. The two-group method should be used when the dependent variable has two categories or states. The multiple discriminant method is used when the dependent variable has three or more categorical states. Use Wilks's Lambda to test for

significance in SPSS or F stat in SAS. The most common method used to test validity is to split the sample into an estimation or analysis sample, and a validation or holdout sample. The estimation sample is used in constructing the discriminant function. The validation sample is used to construct a classification matrix which contains the number of correctly classified and incorrectly classified cases. The percentage of correctly classified cases is called the hit ratio.

3. Plot the results on a two dimensional map, define the dimensions, and interpret the results. The statistical program (or a related module) will map the results. The map will plot each product (usually in two dimensional space). The distance of products to each other indicate either how different they are. The dimensions must be labelled by the researcher. This requires subjective judgement and is often very challenging.

PRINCIPAL COMPONENTS AND FACTOR ANALYSIS

The main applications of factor analytic techniques are: (1) to *reduce* the number of variables and (2) to *detect structure* in the relationships between variables, that is to *classify variables*. Therefore, factor analysis is applied as a data reduction or structure detection method (the term *factor analysis* was first introduced by Thurstone, 1931). The topics listed below will describe the principles of factor analysis, and how it can be applied towards these two purposes. We will assume that you are familiar with the basic logic of statistical reasoning as described in Elementary Concepts. Moreover, we will also assume that you are familiar with the concepts of variance and correlation; if not, we advise that you read the Basic Statistics topic at this point.

There are many excellent books on factor analysis. For example, a hands-on how-to approach can be found in Stevens (1986); more detailed technical descriptions are provided in Cooley and Lohnes (1971); Harman (1976); Kim and Mueller, (1978a, 1978b); Lawley and Maxwell (1971); Lindeman, Merenda, and Gold (1980); Morrison (1967); or Mulaik (1972). The interpretation of secondary factors in hierarchical factor analysis, as an alternative to traditional oblique rotational strategies, is explained in detail by Wherry (1984). Confirmatory factor analysis. Structural Equation Modelling (SEPATH) allows you to test specific hypotheses about the factor structure for a set of variables, in one or several samples (e.g., you can compare factor structures across samples).

Correspondence analysis. Correspondence analysis is a descriptive/exploratory technique designed to analyse two-way and multi-way tables containing some measure of correspondence between the rows and columns. The results provide information which is similar in nature to those produced by factor analysis techniques, and they allow you to explore the structure of categorical variables included in the table.

BASIC IDEA OF FACTOR ANALYSIS AS A DATA REDUCTION METHOD

Suppose we conducted a (rather "silly") study in which we measure 100 people's height in inches and centimeters. Thus, we would have two variables that measure height. If in future studies, we want to research, for example, the effect of different nutritional food supplements on height, would we continue to use both measures? Probably not; height is one characteristic of a person, regardless of how it is measured.

Let's now extrapolate from this "silly" study to something that you might actually do as a researcher. Suppose we want to measure people's satisfaction with their lives. We design a satisfaction questionnaire with various items; among other things we ask our subjects how satisfied they are with their hobbies (item 1) and how intensely they are pursuing a hobby (item 2). Most likely, the responses to the two items are highly correlated with each other. (If you are not familiar with the correlation coefficient, we recommend that you read the description in Basic Statistics-Correlations) Given a high correlation between the two items, we can conclude that they are quite redundant.

Combining Two Variables into a Single Factor. You can summarize the correlation between two variables in a scatterplot. A regression line can then be fitted that represents the "best" summary of the linear relationship between the variables. If we could define a variable that would approximate the regression line in such a plot, then that variable would capture most of the "essence" of the two items. Subjects' single scores on that new factor, represented by the regression line, could then be used in future data analyses to represent that essence of the two items. In a sense we have reduced the two variables to one factor. Note that the new factor is actually a linear combination of the two variables.

Principal Components Analysis. The combining two correlated variables into one factor, illustrates the basic idea of factor analysis, or of principal components analysis to be precise (we will return to this later). If we extend the two-variable example to multiple variables, then the computations become more involved, but the basic principle of expressing two or more variables by a single factor remains the same.

Extracting Principal Components. We do not want to go into the details about the computational aspects of principal components analysis here, which can be found elsewhere (references were provided at the beginning of this section). However, basically, the extraction of principal components amounts to a *variance maximizing (varimax) rotation* of the original variable space. For example, in a scatterplot we can think of the regression line as the original *X* axis, rotated so that it approximates the regression line. This type of rotation is called *variance maximizing* because the criterion for (goal of) the rotation is to maximize the variance (variability) of the "new" variable (factor), while minimizing the variance around the new variable.

Generalizing to the Case of Multiple Variables. When there are more than two variables, we can think of them as defining a "space," just as two variables defined a plane. Thus, when we have three variables, we could plot a three-dimensional scatterplot, and, again we could fit a plane through the data.

Multiple orthogonal factors. After we have found the line on which the variance is maximal, there remains some variability around this line. In principal components analysis, after the first factor has been extracted, that is, after the first line has been drawn through the data, we continue and define another line that maximizes the remaining variability, and so on. In this manner, consecutive factors are extracted. Because each consecutive factor is defined to maximize the variability that is not captured by the preceding factor, consecutive factors are independent of each other. Put another way, consecutive factors are uncorrelated or *orthogonal* to each other.

How many Factors to Extract? Remember that, so far, we are considering principal components analysis as a data reduction method, that is, as a method for reducing the number of variables. The question then is, how many factors do we want to extract? Note that as we extract consecutive factors, they account for less and less variability. The decision of when to stop extracting factors basically depends on when there is only very little "random" variability left. The nature of this decision is arbitrary; however, various guidelines have been developed, and they are reviewed in *Reviewing the Results of a Principal Components Analysis* under *Eigenvalues and the Number-of-Factors Problem*.

Reviewing the Results of a Principal Components Analysis. Without further ado, let us now look at some of the standard results from a principal components analysis. To reiterate, we are extracting factors that account for less and less variance. To simplify matters, you usually start with the correlation matrix, where the variances of all variables are equal to 1.0. Therefore, the total variance in that matrix is equal to the number of variables.

For example, if we have 10 variables each with a variance of 1 then the total variability that can potentially be extracted is equal to 10 times 1. Suppose that in the satisfaction study introduced earlier we included 10 items to measure different aspects of satisfaction at home and at work.

Eigenvalues

In the second column (*Eigenvalue*) above, we find the variance on the new factors that were successively extracted. In the third column, these values are expressed as a percent of the total variance (in this example, 10). As we can see, factor 1 accounts for 61 percent of the variance, factor 2 for 18 percent, and so on. As expected, the sum of the eigenvalues is equal to the number of variables. The third column contains the cumulative variance extracted. The variances extracted by the factors are called the *eigenvalues*. This name derives from the computational issues involved.

Eigenvalues and the Number-of-Factors Problem

Now that we have a measure of how much variance each successive factor extracts, we can return to the question of how many factors to retain. As mentioned earlier, by its nature this is an arbitrary decision. However, there are some guidelines that are commonly used, and that, in practice, seem to yield the best results.

The Kaiser criterion. First, we can retain only factors with eigenvalues greater than 1. In essence this is like saying that, unless a factor extracts at least as much as the equivalent of one original variable, we drop it. This criterion was proposed by Kaiser (1960), and is probably the one most widely used. In using this criterion, we would retain 2 factors (principal components).

Which criterion to use. Both criteria have been studied. Theoretically, you can evaluate those criteria by generating random data based on a particular number of factors. You can then see whether the number of factors is accurately detected by those criteria. Using this general technique, the first method (*Kaiser criterion*) sometimes retains too many factors, while the second technique (scree test) sometimes retains too few; however, both do quite well under normal conditions, that is, when there are relatively few factors and many cases. In practice, an additional important aspect is the extent to which a solution is interpretable. Therefore, you usually examines several solutions with more or fewer factors, and chooses the one that makes the best "sense."

Principal Factors Analysis

Before we continue to examine the different aspects of the typical output from a principal components analysis, let us now introduce principal factors analysis. Let us return to our satisfaction questionnaire example to conceive of another "mental model" for factor analysis. We can think of subjects' responses as being dependent on two components. First, there are some underlying common factors, such as the "satisfaction-with-hobbies" factor we looked at before. Each item measures some part of this common aspect of satisfaction. Second, each item also captures a unique aspect of satisfaction that is not addressed by any other item.

Communalities. If this model is correct, then we should not expect that the factors will extract all variance from our items; rather, only that proportion that is due to the common factors and shared by several items. In the language of factor analysis, the proportion of variance of a particular item that is due to common factors (shared with other items) is called *communality*. Therefore, an additional task facing us when applying this model is to estimate the communalities for each variable, that is, the proportion of variance that each item has in common with other items. The proportion of variance that is unique to each item is then the respective item's total variance minus the communality. A common starting point is to use the squared multiple correlation of an item with all other items as an estimate of the communality. Some authors have suggested various iterative "post-solution improvements" to the initial multiple regression communality estimate; for example, the so-called MINRES method will try various modifications to the factor loadings with the goal to minimize the residual (unexplained) sums of squares.

Principal factors vs. principal components. The defining characteristic then that distinguishes between the two factor analytic models is that in principal components analysis we assume that *all* variability in an item should be used in the analysis, while in principal factors analysis we only use the variability in an item that it has in common with the other items. The pros and cons of each approach is beyond the scope of this introduction (refer to the general references provided in Principal components and Factor Analysis-Introductory Overview). In most cases, these two methods usually yield very similar results. However, principal components analysis is often preferred as a method for data reduction, while principal factors analysis is often preferred when the goal of the analysis is to detect structure.

REFERENCES

- Bajpai, R B : *Research Methodology : Data Presentation*, APH, 2007.
- Christopher Scott: *The World Fertility Survey: An Assessment.* Oxford: Oxford University Press, 1987.
- Karthikeyan, C. : *Behavioural Research Methodology*, Classical, 2004.

9

Operations Research

Operations research (also referred to as decision science, or management science) is an interdisciplinary mathematical science that focuses on the effective *use* of technology by organizations. In contrast, many other science & engineering disciplines focus on technology giving secondary considerations to its use.

Employing techniques from other mathematical sciences — such as mathematical modelling, statistical analysis, and mathematical optimization — operations research arrives at optimal or near-optimal solutions to complex decision-making problems. Because of its emphasis on human-technology interaction and because of its focus on practical applications, operations research has overlap with other disciplines, notably industrial engineering and operations management, and draws on psychology and organization science. Operations Research is often concerned with determining the maximum (of profit, performance, or yield) or minimum (of loss, risk, or cost) of some real-world objective. Originating in military efforts before World War II, its techniques have grown to concern problems in a variety of industries.

Operational research (OR) encompasses a wide range of problem-solving techniques and methods applied in the pursuit of improved decision-making and efficiency. Some of the tools used by operational researchers are statistics, optimization, probability theory, queuing theory, game theory, graph theory, decision analysis, mathematical modelling and simulation. Because of the computational nature of these fields, OR also has strong ties to computer science and analytics. Operational researchers faced with a new problem must determine which of these techniques are most appropriate given the nature of the system, the goals for improvement, and constraints on time and computing power.

Work in operational research and management science may be characterized as one of three categories:

- Fundamental or foundational work takes place in three mathematical disciplines: probability theory, mathematical optimization, and dynamical systems theory.
- Modelling work is concerned with the construction of models, analysing them mathematically, implementing them on computers, solving them using software tools, and assessing their effectiveness with data. This level is mainly instrumental, and driven mainly by statistics and econometrics.
- Application work in operational research, like other engineering and economics' disciplines, attempts to use models to make a practical impact on real-world problems.

The major subdisciplines in modern operational research, as identified by the journal *Operations Research*, are:

- Computing and information technologies
- Decision analysis
- Environment, energy, and natural resources
- Financial engineering
- Manufacturing, service sciences, and supply chain management
- Marketing Engineering
- Policy modelling and public sector work
- Revenue management
- Simulation
- Stochastic models
- Transportation.

As a formal discipline, operational research originated in the efforts of military planners during World War II. In the decades after the war, the techniques began to be applied more widely to problems in business, industry and society. Since that time, operational research has expanded into a field widely used in industries ranging from petrochemicals to airlines, finance, logistics, and government, moving to a focus on the development of mathematical models that can be used to analyse and optimize complex systems, and has become an area of active academic and industrial research.

Historical Origins

In the World War II era, operational research was defined as "a scientific method of providing executive departments with a quantitative basis for decisions regarding the operations under their control." Other names for it included operational analysis (UK Ministry of Defence from 1962) and quantitative management.

Prior to the formal start of the field, early work in operational research was carried out by individuals such as Charles Babbage. His research into the cost of transportation and sorting of mail led to England's universal "Penny Post" in 1840, and studies into the dynamical behaviour of railway vehicles in defence of the GWR's broad gauge. Percy Bridgman brought operational research to bear on problems in physics in the 1920s and would later attempt to extend these to the social sciences. The modern field of operational research arose during World War II.

Modern operational research originated at the Bawdsey Research Station in the UK in 1937 and was the result of an initiative of the station's superintendent, A. P. Rowe. Rowe conceived the idea as a means to analyse and improve the working of the UK's early warning radar system, Chain Home (CH). Initially, he analysed the operating of the radar equipment and its communication networks, expanding later to include the operating personnel's behaviour. This revealed unappreciated limitations of the CH network and allowed remedial action to be taken.

Scientists in the United Kingdom including Patrick Blackett (later Lord Blackett OM PRS), Cecil Gordon, C. H. Waddington, Owen Wansbrough-Jones, Frank Yates, Jacob Bronowski and Freeman Dyson, and in the United States with George Dantzig looked for ways to make better decisions in such areas as logistics and training schedules. After the war it began to be applied to similar problems in industry.

Second World War

During the Second World War close to 1,000 men and women in Britain were engaged in operational research. About 200 operational research scientists worked for the British Army.

Patrick Blackett worked for several different organizations during the war. Early in the war while working for the Royal Aircraft Establishment (RAE) he set up a team known as the "Circus" which helped to reduce the number of anti-aircraft artillery rounds needed to shoot down an enemy aircraft from an average of over 20,000 at the start of the Battle of Britain to 4,000 in 1941.

In 1941 Blackett moved from the RAE to the Navy, after first working with RAF Coastal Command, in 1941 and then early in 1942 to the Admiralty. Blackett's team at Coastal Command's Operational Research Section (CC-ORS) included two future Nobel prize winners and many other people who went on to be preeminent in their fields. They undertook a number of crucial analyses that aided the war effort. Britain introduced the convoy system to reduce shipping losses, but while the principle of using warships to accompany merchant ships was generally accepted, it was unclear whether it was better for convoys to be small or large. Convoys travel at the speed of the slowest member, so small convoys can travel faster. It was also argued that small convoys would be harder for German U-boats to detect. On the other hand, large convoys could deploy more warships against an attacker. Blackett's staff showed that the losses suffered by convoys depended largely on the number of escort vessels present, rather than on the overall size of the convoy. Their conclusion, therefore, was that a few large convoys are more defensible than many small ones.

While performing an analysis of the methods used by RAF Coastal Command to hunt and destroy submarines, one of the analysts asked what colour the aircraft were. As most of them were from Bomber Command they were painted black for nighttime operations. At the suggestion of CC-ORS a test was run to see if that was the best colour to camouflage the aircraft for daytime operations in the grey North Atlantic skies. Tests showed that aircraft painted white were on average not spotted until they were 20% closer than those painted black. This change indicated that 30% more submarines would be attacked and sunk for the same number of sightings.

Other work by the CC-ORS indicated that on average if the trigger depth of aerial delivered depth charges (DCs) was changed from 100 feet to 25 feet, the kill ratios would go up. The reason was that if a U-boat saw an aircraft only shortly before it arrived over the target then at 100 feet the charges would do no damage (because the U-boat wouldn't have time to descend as far as 100 feet), and if it saw the aircraft a long way from the target it had time to alter course under water so the chances of it being within the 20 feet kill zone of the charges was small. It was more efficient to attack those submarines close to the surface when these targets' locations were better known than to attempt their destruction at greater depths when their positions could only be guessed. Before the change of settings from 100 feet to 25 feet, 1% of submerged U-boats were sunk and 14% damaged. After the change, 7% were sunk and 11% damaged. (If submarines were caught on the surface, even if attacked shortly after submerging, the numbers rose to 11% sunk and 15% damaged). Blackett observed "there can be few cases where such a great operational gain had been obtained by such a small and simple change of tactics".

Bomber Command's Operational Research Section (BC-ORS), analysed a report of a survey carried out by RAF Bomber Command. For the survey, Bomber Command inspected all bombers returning from bombing raids over Germany over a particular period. All damage inflicted by German air defences was noted and the recommendation was given that armour be added in the most heavily damaged areas. Their suggestion to remove some of the crew so that an aircraft loss would result in fewer personnel loss was rejected by RAF command. Blackett's team instead made the surprising and counter-intuitive recommendation that the armour be placed in the areas which were completely untouched by damage in the bombers which returned. They reasoned that the survey was biased, since it only included aircraft that returned to Britain. The untouched areas of returning aircraft were probably vital areas, which, if hit, would result in the loss of the aircraft. (Info to help verify some/most of the above paragraph is found in "Dirty Little Secrets of the Twentieth Century" authored by James F. Dunnigan on pages 215-217

When Germany organised its air defences into the Kammhuber Line, it was realised that if the RAF bombers were to fly in a bomber stream they could overwhelm the night fighters who flew in individual cells directed to their targets by ground controllers. It was then a matter of calculating the statistical loss from collisions against the statistical loss from night fighters to calculate how close the bombers should fly to minimise RAF losses.

The "exchange rate" ratio of output to input was a characteristic feature of operational research. By comparing the number of flying hours put in by Allied aircraft to the number of U-boat sightings in a given area, it was possible to redistribute aircraft to more productive patrol areas. Comparison of exchange rates established "effectiveness ratios" useful in planning. The ratio of 60 mines laid per ship sunk was common to several campaigns: German mines in British ports, British mines on German routes, and United States mines in Japanese routes.

Operational research doubled the on-target bomb rate of B-29s bombing Japan from the Marianas Islands by increasing the training ratio from 4 to 10 percent of flying hours; revealed that wolf-packs of three United States submarines were the most effective number to enable all members of the pack to engage targets discovered on their individual patrol stations; revealed that glossy enamel paint was more effective camouflage for night fighters than traditional dull camouflage paint finish, and the smooth paint finish increased airspeed by reducing skin friction.

On land, the operational research sections of the Army Operational Research Group (AORG) of the Ministry of Supply (MoS) were landed in Normandy in 1944, and they followed British forces in the advance across Europe. They analysed, among other topics, the effectiveness of artillery, aerial bombing, and anti-tank shooting.

After World War II

With expanded techniques and growing awareness of the field at the close of the war, operational research was no longer limited to only operational, but was extended to encompass equipment procurement, training, logistics and infrastructure.

Problems addressed with operational research:

- critical path analysis or project planning: identifying those processes in a complex project which affect the overall duration of the project
- floorplanning: designing the layout of equipment in a factory or components on a computer chip to reduce manufacturing time (therefore reducing cost)
- network optimization: for instance, setup of telecommunications networks to maintain quality of service during outages
- Allocation problems
- Facility location
- Assignment Problems:
    - o Assignment problem
    - o Generalized assignment problem
    - o Quadratic assignment problem
    - o Weapon target assignment problem
- Bayesian search theory : looking for a target
- optimal search
- routing, such as determining the routes of buses so that as few buses are needed as possible
- supply chain management: managing the flow of raw materials and products based on uncertain demand for the finished products
- efficient messaging and customer response tactics
- automation: automating or integrating robotic systems in human-driven operations processes
- globalization: globalizing operations processes in order to take advantage of cheaper materials, labor, land or other productivity inputs

- transportation: managing freight transportation and delivery systems (Examples: LTL Shipping, intermodal freight transport)
- scheduling:
    - o personnel staffing
    - o manufacturing steps
    - o project tasks
    - o network data traffic: these are known as queueing models or queueing systems.
    - o sports events and their television coverage
- blending of raw materials in oil refineries
- determining optimal prices, in many retail and B2B settings, within the disciplines of pricing science.

Operational research is also used extensively in government where evidence-based policy is used.

Management Science

In 1967 Stafford Beer characterized the field of management science as "the business use of operations research". However, in modern times the term management science may also be used to refer to the separate fields of organizational studies or corporate strategy. Like operational research itself, management science (MS), is an interdisciplinary branch of applied mathematics devoted to optimal decision planning, with strong links with economics, business, engineering, and other sciences. It uses various scientific research-based principles, strategies, and analytical methods including mathematical modelling, statistics and numerical algorithms to improve an organization's ability to enact rational and meaningful management decisions by arriving at optimal or near optimal solutions to complex decision problems. In short, management sciences help businesses to achieve their goals using the scientific methods of operational research.

The management scientist's mandate is to use rational, systematic, science-based techniques to inform and improve decisions of all kinds. Of course, the techniques of management science are not restricted to business applications but may be applied to military, medical, public administration, charitable groups, political groups or community groups.

Management science is concerned with developing and applying models and concepts that may prove useful in helping to illuminate management issues and solve managerial problems, as well as designing and developing new and better models of organizational excellence.

The application of these models within the corporate sector became known as Management science.

Techniques

Some of the fields that have considerable overlap with Management Science include:

- Data mining
- Decision analysis
- Engineering
- Forecasting
- Game theory
- Industrial engineering
- Logistics
- Mathematical modelling
- Mathematical optimization
- Probability and statistics
- Project management
- Simulation
- Social network/Transportation forecasting models
- Supply chain management
- Financial engineering.

Applications of Management Science

Applications of management science are abundant in industry as airlines, manufacturing companies, service organizations, military branches, and in government. The range of problems and issues to which management science has contributed insights and solutions is vast. It includes:

- scheduling airlines, including both planes and crew,
- deciding the appropriate place to site new facilities such as a warehouse, factory or fire station,
- managing the flow of water from reservoirs,

- identifying possible future development paths for parts of the telecommunications industry,
- establishing the information needs and appropriate systems to supply them within the health service, and
- identifying and understanding the strategies adopted by companies for their information systems

Management science is also concerned with so-called "soft-operational analysis", which concerns methods for strategic planning, strategic decision support, and Problem Structuring Methods (PSM). In dealing with these sorts of challenges mathematical modelling and simulation are not appropriate or will not suffice. Therefore, during the past 30 years, a number of non-quantified modelling methods have been developed. These include:

- stakeholder based approaches including metagame analysis and drama theory
- morphological analysis and various forms of influence diagrams.
- approaches using cognitive mapping
- the Strategic Choice Approach
- robustness analysis.

Societies and Journals

The International Federation of Operational Research Societies (IFORS) is an umbrella organization for operational research societies worldwide, representing approximately 50 national societies including those in the US, UK, France, Germany, Canada, Australia, New Zealand, Philippines, India, Japan and South Africa (ORSSA). The constituent members of IFORS form regional groups, such as that in Europe. Other important operational research organizations are Simulation Interoperability Standards Organization (SISO) and Interservice/Industry Training, Simulation and Education Conference (I/ITSEC)

In 2004 the US-based organization INFORMS began an initiative to market the OR profession better, including a website entitled *The Science of Better* which provides an introduction to OR and examples of successful applications of OR to industrial problems. This initiative has been adopted by the Operational

Research Society in the UK, including a website entitled *Learn about OR*,.

INFORMS publishes twelve scholarly journals about operations research, including the top two journals in their class, according to 2005 Journal Citation Reports. They are:

- *Decision Analysis*
- *Information Systems Research*
- *INFORMS Journal on Computing*
- *INFORMS Transactions on Education* (an open access journal)
- *Interfaces: An International Journal of the Institute for Operations Research and the Management Sciences*
- *Management Science: A Journal of the Institute for Operations Research and the Management Sciences*
- *Manufacturing & Service Operations Management*
- *Marketing Science*
- *Mathematics of Operations Research*
- *Operations Research: A Journal of the Institute for Operations Research and the Management Sciences*
- *Organization Science*
- *Transportation Science.*

Other journals:

- *4OR-A Quarterly Journal of Operations Research*: jointly published the Belgian, French and Italian Operations Research Societies (Springer);
- *Decision Sciences* published by Wiley-Blackwell on behalf of the Decision Sciences Institute
- *European Journal of Operational Research (EJOR)*: Founded in 1975 and is presently by far the largest operational research journal in the world, with its around 9,000 pages of published papers per year. In 2004, its total number of citations was the second largest amongst Operational Research and Management Science journals;
- *INFOR Journal*: published and sponsored by the Canadian Operational Research Society;

- *International Journal of Operations Research and Information Systems (IJORIS)": an official publication of the Information Resources Management Association, published quarterly by IGI Global;*
- *Journal of Defense Modelling and Simulation (JDMS): Applications, Methodology, Technology*: a quarterly journal devoted to advancing the science of modelling and simulation as it relates to the military and defense.
- *Journal of the Operational Research Society (JORS)*: an official journal of The OR Society; this is the oldest continuously published journal of OR in the world, published by Palgrave;
- *Journal of Simulation (JOS)*: an official journal of The OR Society, published by Palgrave;
- *Mathematical Methods of Operations Research (MMOR)*: the journal of the German and Dutch OR Societies, published by Springer;
- *Military Operations Research (MOR)*: published by the Military Operations Research Society;
- *Opsearch*: official journal of the Operational Research Society of India;
- *OR Insight*: a quarterly journal of The OR Society, published by Palgrave;
- *Production and Operations Management*, the official journal of the Production and Operations Management Society
- *TOP*: the official journal of the Spanish Society of Statistics and Operations Research.

REFERENCES

- Bryman, A.: *Quality and Quantity in Social Research*. London: Unwin Hyman, 1992.
- Neelam, Sandhya: *Research Methodology in Sociological Research*, Manglam Pub, Delhi, 2008.
- Cox, D.R.: *Theoretical Statistics*. London: Chapman & Hall, 1974.

10

Quantitative Research

In the social sciences, quantitative research refers to the systematic empirical investigation of social phenomena via statistical, mathematical or computational techniques. The objective of quantitative research is to develop and employ mathematical models, theories and/or hypotheses pertaining to phenomena. The process of measurement is central to quantitative research because it provides the fundamental connection between empirical observation and mathematical expression of quantitative relationships. Quantitative research is used widely in social sciences such as psychology, economics, sociology, and political science, and less frequently in anthropology and history. Research in mathematical sciences such as physics is also 'quantitative' by definition, though this use of the term differs in context. In the social sciences, the term relates to empirical methods, originating in both philosophical positivism and the history of statistics, which contrast qualitative research methods.

Qualitative methods produce information only on the particular cases studied, and any more general conclusions are only hypotheses. Quantitative methods can be used to verify, which of such hypotheses are true. A comprehensive analysis of 1274 articles published in the top two American sociology journals between 1935 and 2005 found that roughly two thirds of these articles used quantitative methods.

Quantitative research is generally made using scientific methods, which can include:

- The generation of models, theories and hypotheses

- The development of instruments and methods for measurement
- Experimental control and manipulation of variables
- Collection of empirical data
- Modelling and analysis of data
- Evaluation of results.

In the social sciences particularly, quantitative research is often contrasted with qualitative research which is the examination, analysis and interpretation of observations for the purpose of discovering underlying meanings and patterns of relationships, including classifications of types of phenomena and entities, in a manner that does not involve mathematical models. Approaches to quantitative psychology were first modelled on quantitative approaches in the physical sciences by Gustav Fechner in his work on psychophysics, which built on the work of Ernst Heinrich Weber. Although a distinction is commonly drawn between qualitative and quantitative aspects of scientific investigation, it has been argued that the two go hand in hand. For example, based on analysis of the history of science, Kuhn (1961, p. 162) concludes that "large amounts of qualitative work have usually been prerequisite to fruitful quantification in the physical sciences". Qualitative research is often used to gain a general sense of phenomena and to form theories that can be tested using further quantitative research. For instance, in the social sciences qualitative research methods are often used to gain better understanding of such things as intentionality (from the speech response of the researchee) and meaning (why did this person/group say something and what did it mean to them?)(Kieron Yeoman).

Although quantitative investigation of the world has existed since people first began to record events or objects that had been counted, the modern idea of quantitative processes have their roots in Auguste Comte's positivist framework.

Use of Statistics

Statistics is the most widely used branch of mathematics in quantitative research outside of the physical sciences, and also finds applications within the physical sciences, such as in statistical mechanics. Statistical methods are used extensively within fields such as economics, social sciences and biology. Quantitative research using statistical methods starts with the collection of data, based on the hypothesis or theory. Usually a big sample of data is collected-this would require verification, validation and recording before the analysis can take place. Software packages such as SPSS and R are typically used for this purpose.

Causal relationships are studied by manipulating factors thought to influence the phenomena of interest while controlling other variables relevant to the experimental outcomes. In the field of health, for example, researchers might measure and study the relationship between dietary intake and measurable physiological effects such as weight loss, controlling for other key variables such as exercise.

Quantitatively based opinion surveys are widely used in the media, with statistics such as the proportion of respondents in favour of a position commonly reported. In opinion surveys, respondents are asked a set of structured questions and their responses are tabulated. In the field of climate science, researchers compile and compare statistics such as temperature or atmospheric concentrations of carbon dioxide.

Empirical relationships and associations are also frequently studied by using some form of General linear model, non-linear model, or by using factor analysis. A fundamental principle in quantitative research is that correlation does not imply causation. This principle follows from the fact that it is always possible a spurious relationship exists for variables between which covariance is found in some degree. Associations may be examined between any combination of continuous and categorical variables using methods of statistics.

Measurement

Views regarding the role of measurement in quantitative research are somewhat divergent. Measurement is often regarded as being only a means by which observations are expressed numerically in order to investigate causal relations or associations. However, it has been argued that measurement often plays a more important role in quantitative research. For example, Kuhn argued that within quantitative research, the results that are shown can prove to be strange. This is because accepting a theory based on results of quantitative data could prove to be a natural phenomenon. He argued that such abnormalities are interesting when done during the process of obtaining data, as seen below:

When measurement departs from theory, it is likely to yield mere numbers, and their very neutrality makes them particularly sterile as a source of remedial suggestions. But numbers register the departure from theory with an authority and finesse that no qualitative technique can duplicate, and that departure is often enough to start a search (Kuhn, 1961).

In classical physics, the theory and definitions which underpin measurement are generally deterministic in nature. In contrast, probabilistic measurement models known as the Rasch model and Item response theory models are generally employed in the social sciences. Psychometrics is the field of study concerned with the theory and technique for measuring social and psychological attributes and phenomena. This field is central to much quantitative research that is undertaken within the social sciences.

Quantitative research may involve the use of *proxies* as stand-ins for other quantities that cannot be directly measured. Tree-ring width, for example, is considered a reliable proxy of ambient environmental conditions such as the warmth of growing seasons or amount of rainfall. Although scientists cannot directly measure the temperature of past years, tree-ring width and other climate proxies have been used to provide a semi-quantitative record of average temperature in the Northern Hemisphere back to 1000 A.D.

When used in this way, the proxy record (tree ring width, say) only reconstructs a certain amount of the variance of the original record. The proxy may be calibrated (for example, during the period of the instrumental record) to determine how much variation is captured, including whether both short and long term variation is revealed.

In the case of tree-ring width, different species in different places may show more or less sensitivity to, say, rainfall or temperature: when reconstructing a temperature record there is considerable skill in selecting proxies that are well correlated with the desired variable.

Relationship with Qualitative Methods

In most physical and biological sciences, the use of either quantitative or qualitative methods is uncontroversial, and each is used when appropriate. In the social sciences, particularly in sociology, social anthropology and psychology, the use of one or other type of method can be a matter of controversy and even ideology, with particular schools of thought within each discipline favouring one type of method and pouring scorn on to the other. The majority tendency throughout the history of social science, however, is to use eclectic approaches. Quantitative methods might be used with a global qualitative frame. Qualitative methods might be used to understand the meaning of the conclusions produced by quantitative methods. Using quantitative methods, it is possible to give precise and testable expression to qualitative ideas. This combination of quantitative and qualitative data gathering is often referred to as mixed-methods research.

DISTINCTIONS FROM QUANTITATIVE RESEARCH

First, in qualitative research, cases can be selected purposefully, according to whether or not they typify certain characteristics or contextual locations. Second, the researcher's role receives greater critical attention. This is because in qualitative research the possibility of the researcher taking a 'neutral' or transcendental position is seen as more problematic in practical and/or philosophical terms. Hence qualitative researchers are often exhorted to reflect on their role in the research process and make this clear in the analysis.

Third, while qualitative data analysis can take a wide variety of forms, it differs from quantitative research in its focus on language, signs and meaning. In addition, qualitative research approaches analysis holistically and contextually, rather than being reductionistic and isolationist. Nevertheless, systematic and transparent approaches to analysis are almost always regarded as essential for rigor. For example, many qualitative methods require researchers to carefully code data and discern and document themes consistently and reliably. Perhaps the most traditional division between the uses of qualitative and quantitative research in the social sciences is that qualitative methods are used for exploration (i.e., hypothesis-generating) or for explaining puzzling quantitative results. Quantitative methods, by contrast, are used to test hypotheses. This is because establishing content validity — do measures measure what a researcher thinks they measure? — is seen as one of the strengths of qualitative research. Some consider quantitative methods to provide more representative, reliable and precise measures through focused hypotheses, measurement tools and applied mathematics. By contrast, qualitative data is usually difficult to graph or display in mathematical terms.

Qualitative research is often used for policy and program evaluation research since it can answer certain important questions more efficiently and effectively than quantitative approaches. This is particularly the case for understanding how and why certain outcomes were achieved (not just what was achieved) but also for answering important questions about relevance, unintended effects and impact of programs such as: Were expectations reasonable? Did processes operate as expected? Were key players able to carry out their duties? Did the program cause any unintended effects?

Qualitative approaches have the advantage of allowing for more diversity in responses as well as the capacity to adapt to new developments or issues during the research process itself. While qualitative research can be expensive and time-consuming to conduct, many fields of research employ qualitative techniques that have been specifically developed to provide more succinct, cost-efficient and timely results. Rapid Rural Appraisal is one formalized example of these adaptations but there are many others.

Data Collection

Qualitative researchers may use different approaches in collecting data, such as the grounded theory practice, narratology, storytelling, classical ethnography, or shadowing. Qualitative methods are also loosely present in other methodological approaches, such as action research or actor-network theory. Forms of the data collected can include interviews and group discussions, observation and reflection field notes, various texts, pictures, and other materials. Qualitative research often categorizes data into patterns as the primary basis for organizing and reporting results. Qualitative researchers typically rely on the following methods for gathering information: *Participant Observation, Non-participant Observation, Field Notes, Reflexive Journals, Structured Interview, Semi-structured Interview, Unstructured Interview, and Analysis of documents and materials.*

The ways of participating and observing can vary widely from setting to setting. Participant observation is a strategy of reflexive learning, not a single method of observing In participant observation researchers typically become members of a culture, group, or setting, and adopt roles to conform to that setting.

In doing so, the aim is for the researcher to gain a closer insight into the culture's practices, motivations and emotions. It is argued that the researchers' ability to understand the experiences of the culture may be inhibited if they observe without participating. Some distinctive qualitative methods are the use of focus groups and key informant interviews.

The focus group technique involves a moderator facilitating a small group discussion between selected individuals on a particular topic. This is a particularly popular method in market research and testing new initiatives with users/workers.

One traditional and specialized form of qualitative research is called cognitive testing or pilot testing which is used in the development of quantitative survey items. Survey items are piloted on study participants to test the reliability and validity of the items. In the academic social sciences the most frequently used qualitative research approaches include the following:

1. Ethnographic Research, used for investigating cultures by collecting and describing data that is intended to help in the development of a theory. This method is also called "ethnomethodology" or "methodology of the people". An example of applied ethnographic research, is the study of a particular culture and their understanding of the role of a particular disease in their cultural framework.
2. Critical Social Research, used by a researcher to understand how people communicate and develop symbolic meanings.

3. Ethical Inquiry, an intellectual analysis of ethical problems. It includes the study of ethics as related to obligation, rights, duty, right and wrong, choice etc.
4. Foundational Research, examines the foundations for a science, analyses the beliefs and develops ways to specify how a knowledge base should change in light of new information.
5. Historical Research, allows one to discuss past and present events in the context of the present condition, and allows one to reflect and provide possible answers to current issues and problems. Historical research helps us in answering questions such as: Where have we come from, where are we, who are we now and where are we going?
6. Grounded Theory, is an inductive type of research, based or "grounded" in the observations or data from which it was developed; it uses a variety of data sources, including quantitative data, review of records, interviews, observation and surveys.
7. Phenomenology, describes the "subjective reality" of an event, as perceived by the study population; it is the study of a phenomenon.
8. Philosophical Research, is conducted by field experts within the boundaries of a specific field of study or profession, the best qualified individual in any field of study to use an intellectual analyses, in order to clarify definitions, identify ethics, or make a value judgment concerning an issue in their field of study.

QUALITATIVE MEASURES RESEARCH

Qualitative research is a vast and complex area of methodology that can easily take up whole textbooks on its own.

The purpose of this section is to introduce you to the idea of qualitative research (and how it is related to quantitative research) and give you some orientation to the major types of qualitative research data, approaches and methods.

There are a number of important questions you should consider before undertaking qualitative research:

Do you want to generate new theories or hypotheses? One of the major reasons for doing qualitative research is to become more experienced with the phenomenon you're interested in. Too often in applied social research (especially in economics and psychology) we have our graduate students jump from doing a literature review on a topic of interest to writing a research proposal complete with theories and hypotheses based on current thinking. What gets missed is the direct experience of the phenomenon. We should probably require of all students that before they mount a study they spend some time living with the phenomenon.

Before doing that multivariate analysis of gender-based differences in wages, go observe several work contexts and see how gender tends to be perceived and seems to affect wage allocations. Before looking at the effects of a new psychotropic drug for the mentally ill, go spend some time visiting several mental health treatment contexts to observe what goes on. If you do, you are likely to approach the existing literature on the topic with a fresh perspective born of your direct experience. You're likely to begin to formulate your own ideas about what causes what else to happen. This is where most of the more interesting and valuable new theories and hypotheses will originate. Of course, there's a need for balance here as in anything else. If this advice was followed literally, graduate school would be prolonged even more than is currently the case. We need to use qualitative research as the basis for direct experience, but we also need to know when and how to move on to formulate some tentative theories and hypotheses that can be explicitly tested.

Do you need to achieve a deep understanding of the issues? I believe that qualitative research has special value for investigating complex and sensitive issues. For example, if you are interested in how people view topics like God and religion, human sexuality, the death penalty, gun control, and so on, my guess is that you would be hard-pressed to develop a quantitative methodology that would do anything more than summarize a few key positions on these issues. While this does have its place (and its done all the time), if you really want to try to achieve a deep understanding of how people think about these topics, some type of in-depth interviewing is probably called for.

Are you willing to trade detail for generalizability? Qualitative research certainly excels at generating information that is very detailed. Of course, there are quantitative studies that are detailed also in that they involve collecting lots of numeric data. But in detailed quantitative research, the data themselves tend to both shape and limit the analysis. For example, if you collect a simple interval-level quantitative measure, the analyses you are likely to do with it are fairly delimited (e.g., descriptive statistics, use in correlation, regression or multivariate models, etc.). And, generalizing tends to be a fairly straightforward endeavour in most quantitative research. After all, when you collect the same variable from everyone in your sample, all you need to do to generalize to the sample as a whole is to compute some aggregate statistic like a mean or median.

Things are not so simple in most qualitative research. The data are more "raw" and are seldom pre-categorized. Consequently, you need to be prepared to organize all of that raw detail. And there are almost an infinite number of ways this could be accomplished. Even generalizing across a sample of interviews or written documents becomes a complex endeavour.

The detail in most qualitative research is both a blessing and a curse. On the positive side, it enables you to describe the phenomena of interest in great detail, in the original language of the research participants. In fact, some of the best "qualitative" research is often published in book form, often in a style that almost approaches a narrative story. One of my favourite writers (and, I daresay, one of the finest qualitative researchers) is Studs Terkel.

He has written intriguing accounts of the Great Depression (Hard Times), World War II (The Good War) and socioeconomic divisions in America (The Great Divide), among others. In each book he follows a similar qualitative methodology, identifying informants who directly experienced the phenomenon in question, interviewing them at length, and then editing the interviews heavily so that they "tell a story" that is different from what any individual interviewee might tell but addresses the question of interest. If you haven't read one of Studs' works yet, I highly recommend them.

On the negative side, when you have that kind of detail, it's hard to determine what the generalizable themes may be. In fact, many qualitative researchers don't even care about generalizing — they're content to generate rich descriptions of their phenomena.

That's why there is so much value in mixing qualitative research with quantitative. Quantitative research excels at summarizing large amounts of data and reaching generalizations based on statistical projections. Qualitative research excels at "telling the story" from the participant's viewpoint, providing the rich descriptive detail that sets quantitative results into their human context.

Is funding available for this research? I hate to be crass, but in most social research we do have to worry about how it will get paid for. There is little point in proposing any research that would be unable to be carried out for lack of funds. For qualitative research this is an often especially challenging issue. Because much qualitative research takes an enormous amount of time, is very labour intensive, and yields results that may not be as generalizable for policy-making or decision-making, many funding sources view it as a "frill" or as simply too expensive. There's a lot that you can (and shouldn't) do in proposing qualitative research that will often enhance its fundability. My pet peeve with qualitative research proposals is when the author says something along these lines (Of course, I'm paraphrasing here. No good qualitative researcher would come out and say something like this directly.):

This study uses an emergent, exploratory, inductive qualitative approach. Because the basis of such an approach is that one does not predetermine or delimit the directions the investigation might take, there is no way to propose specific budgetary or time estimates. Of course, this is just silly! There is always a way to estimate (especially when we view an estimate as simply an educated guess!). I've reviewed proposals that say almost this kind of thing and let me assure you that I and other reviewers don't judge the researcher's credibility as very high under these circumstances. As an alternative that doesn't hem you in or constrain the methodology, you might reword the same passage something like:

This study uses an emergent, exploratory, inductive qualitative approach. Because the basis of such an approach is that one does not predetermine or delimit the directions the investigation might take, it is especially important to detail the specific stages that this research will follow in addressing the research questions. [Inset detailed description of data collection, coding, analysis, etc. Especially note where there may be iterations of the phases.]. Because of the complexities involved in this type of research, the proposal is divided into several broad stages with funding and time estimates provided for each.

Notice that the first approach is almost an insult to the reviewer. In the second, the author acknowledges the unpredictability of qualitative research but does as reasonable a job as possible to anticipate the course of the study, its costs, and milestones. Certainly more fundable.

QUANTITATIVE APPROACHES INTO THE RESEARCH PROCESS

The case for separate paradigms is that qualitative and quantitative researchers hold different epistemological assumptions, belong to different research cultures and have different researcher biographies that work against convergence. Indeed qualitative researchers are embracing even greater reflexivity, for example taking account of the influence of the researcher in the research encounter, finding new ways of relating the voices of marginal groups to academic knowledge and researcher interpretation. On the quantitative front researchers are constantly urged by bodies such as the UK's Economic and Social Research Council to develop their skills base in order to keep up with developments elsewhere (notably the US); this may serve to maintain the barricades between qualitative and quantitative research through ever greater sophistication and complexity of statistical techniques.

While researchers rationalize their interpretive frameworks in terms of fundamental distinctions of ontology, epistemology and theory, they develop over time habits and dispositions as well as particular expertise and preferences for particular approaches and may lack the time and inclination to extend skills and interests in other directions and across the qualitative/

quantitative divide. Research practice is also shaped by the research environment—by the funds available for a research project and by the shortterm contracts of many researchers in the UK.

While research practices diverge, there is considerable pressure for convergence at this present time. Externally, there is increased demand for research to inform policy and for practical rather than scientific research, again a trend that may work against specialization in either qualitative or quantitative research.

The importance placed upon particular types of research evidence is subject to changes in political climates and persuasions. As Janet Finch argued in the 1980s, British government has long preferred quantitative evidence in contrast to more pluralistic methodological preferences of US governments in the same period.

Currently, there are external pressures, from national and EU funders, for researchers to inform policy and therefore to disseminate in lay language. There is a whole industry in Britain and the US, and increasingly Europe, devoted to evaluation of policy that utilizes qualitative as well as quantitative methods. In the US, the demand for qualitative research has been caught up in the wider politics of interest groups who have argued that the benefits of government programmes to the poor did not show up in much quantitative work. Many of these trends suggest greater rather than less convergence between approaches.

Both externally and internally, the pressures of research markets and the marketization of universities in the 1990s and twenty-first century are leading to the institutionalization of research training. The a rrival of a skills-based economy in which training has superseded notions of apprenticeship is as influential in research as elsewhere in the labour market. In Britain, in the past ten to fifteen years, we have seen a steady expansion in masters' degrees courses in research methods and in other courses dedicated to research training. Today's students on masters courses are typically introduced to both qualitative and quantitative methods, whereas in the past they were not exposed to such a wide range of methods.

Pressure from users and the enhanced diversity of skills influence the type of research that is done as well as the questions posed, and how they are addressed. They also affect how research is written up for different audiences or 'user' groups.

Researchers today are required to communicate in 'double speak': in the specialized languages that define their 'fields' (as opposed to disciplines) and in a generic, popular language that addresses 'research users'. Such emphasis upon dissemination may have the effect of increasing the importance of research which takes an action perspective, that is draws upon actors' perspectives both in the interpretation and in the presentation of the data. This is not to suggest, however, that quantitative research is being displaced.

However, responding to pressures from funders and the demand to disseminate and to do so in particular kinds of ways can result in epistemological issues vanishing from view in the way data analysis is discussed, while methodological issues may be reduced to skills training. Lack of space in the article format also can mean that methodological issues are relegated to footnotes, while in books they appear in appendices or end notes. These pressures have on the other hand helped to generate an increase in journals and books devoted to methodological issues.

Context of Justification

Our methods and their assumptions are revisited in a second context—what is known as the context of justification where the data are analysed and interpreted. As some would argue, in the context of justification the resulting data sets cannot be linked together unproblematically. For it is at this phase that ontological, epistemological and theoretical issues raise their heads in the encounter with data. In the cold light of data analysis we are forced to reflect on different kinds of 'truth' or 'validity' and to take account of the fact that our different types of data are constituted by the assumptions and methods that elicit them.

Thus we cannot unproblematically assume that data from different methods will corroborate one another as is implied in the strategy of triangulation—that is where the choice of methods is intended to investigate a *single* social phenomenon from different vantage points. Data collected from different methods cannot be simply added together to produce a unitary or rounded reality. When we combine methods, there are a number of possible outcomes; corroboration of results is only one of at least four possibilities:

Corroboration: The 'same results' are derived from both qualitative and quantitative methods.

Elaboration: The qualitative data analysis exemplifies how the quantitative findings apply in particular cases.

Complementarity: The qualitative and quantitative results differ but *together* they generate insights.

Contradiction: Where qualitative data and quantitative findings conflict.

In other words, when researchers work with different types of data within the same research project, the way they use these data will vary according to the *phase* of the research in which the researcher brings the different data sets into play.

Bryman distinguishes between the ways in which qualitative and quantitative research are combined in terms of: (a) the *importance* given to qualitative and quantitative approaches in the research investigation and (b) the *time ordering* or sequencing of the approaches. However, as he suggests, such distinctions are not always possible in practice because they rely on being able to identify the dominance of one approach.

REFERENCES

- Brannen, J.: *Mixing Methods: Qualitative and Quantitative Research.* London: Avebury, 1992.
- Bryman, A.: *Quality and Quantity in Social Research.* London: Unwin Hyman, 1992.
- Corder, G.W. & Foreman, D.I.: *Nonparametric Statistics for Non-Statisticians: A Step-by-Step Approach*, Wiley, 1977.
- Karthikeyan, C. : *Behavioural Research Methodology*, Classical, 2004.

Bibliography

Babbie, E.R.: *Survey Research Methods*. Belmont, CA: Wadsworth, 1973.

Bajpai, R B : *Research Methodology : Data Presentation*, APH, 2007.

Bhanwar Lal Garg: *An Introduction to Research Methodology*, RBSA Pub, 2002.

Brannen, J.: *Mixing Methods: Qualitative and Quantitative Research*. London: Avebury, 1992.

Bryman, A.: *Quality and Quantity in Social Research*. London: Unwin Hyman, 1992.

Burke, Frank M., *Valuation and Valuation Planning for Closely Held Businesses*, Englewood Cliffs, NJ, Prentice Hall, 1981.

Christopher Scott: *The World Fertility Survey: An Assessment*. Oxford: Oxford University Press, 1987.

Corder, G.W. & Foreman, D.I.: *Nonparametric Statistics for Non-Statisticians: A Step-by-Step Approach*, Wiley, 1977.

Dasgupta, Manas: *Research Methodology in Economics : Problems and Issues*, Deep and Deep, 2007.

Denzin, N.: *The Research Act: A Theoretical Introduction to Sociological Methods*. Chicago: Aldine Press, 1967.

Fowler, Floyd J., : *Survey Research Methods,* Newbury Park, CA: Sage, 1993.

Fox, J. & Tracy, P.: *Randomized Response: A Method for Sensitive Surveys*. Beverly Hills, CA: Sage, 1986.

Garg, Ajit Lal : *An Introduction to Research Methodology*, RBSA Pub, 2002.

Gordon, R.: *Unidimensional Scaling of Social Variables: Concepts and Procedures*. New York: The Free Press, 1977.

Guala, F.: *The Methodology of Experimental Economics,* New York, Cambridge University Press, 2005.

Gupta, Sudhir: *Workshop on Research Methodology*, Centrum Press, 2011.

Heise, David R.: *Surveying Cultures: Discovering Shared Conceptions and Sentiments.* Hoboken NJ: Wiley, 2010.

Jack Murrin, *Valuation: Measuring and Managing the Value of Companies,* New York, Wiley, 1994.

Jagmohan Diwan: *Fundamentals of Rural Sociology,* Cyber Tech Pub, Delhi, 2009.

Kalton, Graham: *Introduction to Survey Sampling.* Beverly Hills, CA: Sage, 1983.

Kanak Kanti Bagchi: *Research Methodology in Sociàl Sciences: A Practical Guide,* Abhijeet Pub, 2007.

Kapila Mittal: *Research Methodology in Social Sciences,* Vista International, 2006.

Karthikeyan, C. : *Behavioural Research Methodology,* Classical, 2004.

Karthikeyan, C. : *Behavioural Research Methodology,* Classical, 2004.

Maxwell, J. A.: *Qualitative Research Design: An Interactive Approach.* Thousand Oaks, CA: Sage Publishing, 1996.

McCaston, M. Katherine: *Tips for Collecting, Reviewing, and Analyzing Secondary Data.* Partnership & Household Livelihood Security Unit, 1998.

Mittal, Kapila: *Research Methodology in Social Sciences,* Vista International, 2006.

Mohamed Haneefa K:*Research on Library Computerisation,* Ess Ess Pub, 2006.

Mujawar, W.R. : *Research Methodology in Social Work,* Manglam Publications, 2010.

Narender K. Chadha: *Research Methods for Sports Scientists,* Friends, 2001.

Oommen, T.K. : *Knowledge and Society : Situating Sociology and Social Anthropology,* Oxford University Press, London, 2007.

Sandhya Neelam: *Research Methodology in Sociological Research,* Manglam Pub, Delhi, 2008.

Snider, J. G., and Osgood, C. E.: *Semantic Differential Technique: A Sourcebook.* Chicago: Aldine, 1969.

Sudhir Gupta: *Workshop on Research Methodology,* Centrum Press, 2011.

Trochim, W.: *The Research Methods Knowledge Base.* Ithaca, NY: Cornell Custom Publishing, 1999.

Ullman, D. G.: *Making Robust Decisions,* Trafford, 2006.

Index

□□□